The Merger of Knowledge with Power

Essays in Critical Science

THE MERGER OF KNOWLEDGE WITH POWER

Essays in Critical Science

J.R. Ravetz

Mansell Publishing Limited

London and New York

First published 1990 by
Mansell Publishing Limited, *A Cassell Imprint*
Artillery House, Artillery Row, London SW1P 1RT, England
125 East 23rd Street, Suite 300, New York 10010, USA

British Library Cataloguing in Publication Data

Ravetz, Jerome R. (Jerome Raymond), *1929–*
   The merger of knowledge with power.
   1. Philosophy of science. Theories
   I. Title
   501

   ISBN 0–7201–2021–7

Library of Congress Cataloging-in-Publication Data

Ravetz, Jerome R.
      The merger of knowledge with power: essays in critical science/
   J.R. Ravetz.
         p.   cm.
      Bibliography: p.
      Includes index.
      ISBN 0–7201–2021–7
      1. Science—Philosophy. I. Title.
   Q175.R297   1989   89–2650
   501–dc20   CIP

This book has been printed and bound in Great Britain. Typeset in Baskerville by
Colset (Private) Ltd., Singapore, and printed and bound by Biddles Ltd., Guildford on
Onslow Book Wove paper.

To Zia Sardar, friend and comrade,
for making this book possible,
and much besides.

Contents

Preface   ix

Introduction   1

1. WHERE WE'RE AT   5

The Problem   10
A Critical Awareness of Science   12
Risks and Their Regulation   31
Recombinant DNA Research: Whose Risks?   63
Hardware and Fantasy in Military Technology   81

2. HOW WE GOT HERE   95

What Was the Scientific Revolution?   100
Francis Bacon and the Reform of Philosophy   116
Criticisms of Science: From Past to Present   137
The Marxist Vision of J.D. Bernal   153

3. A NEW AWARENESS   175

Ideological Commitments in the Philosophy of Science   180
Quality in Consumerist Civilization: Ibn Khaldun Revisited   199
Gaia and the Philosophy of Science   211
Science, Ignorance and Fantasies   222

4. CONSTRUCTIVE APPROACHES   231

Qualified Quantities: Towards an Arithmetic of Real
     Experience (written jointly with S.O. Funtowicz)   235
Usable Knowledge, Usable Ignorance: Incomplete
     Science with Policy Implications   260

Contents

A New Social Contract for Science   284
Science: Orthodoxies, Critiques and Alternatives   301
Towards a Critical Science   312

EPILOGUE: Science and Charity   319

Index (compiled by Sara Firman)   322

Preface

These essays were mainly written during the long period that I taught the History and Philosophy of Science at the University of Leeds. Before then I did postgraduate research in mathematics at Trinity College, Cambridge, arriving there from Swarthmore College, USA, where I received my liberal education.

My sense of social responsibility for science goes back to my upbringing in a radical family in America. My awareness of the cosmological dimensions in criticisms of science was stimulated by my work in the early Campaign for Nuclear Disarmament, and then enriched by my studies and teaching in the history of science.

My major philosophical work, *Scientific Knowledge and Its Social Problems* (Oxford University Press, 1971), was devoted to laying the foundations for an understanding of the social activity of science in its 'industrialized' phase. I could not accept the traditional view of science as an accumulation of nuggets of truth, nor could I follow the prevalent philosophical concern for a 'logic' of science. Rather, basing myself on the experience of research of myself and friends, as well as on my knowledge of the way the world works, I characterized science as a special craft activity of creating and solving problems in the study of Nature. On this basis I could analyse the social dimensions of scientific work, in particular the problems of quality control and ethics. I could also show some of the characteristic difficulties in the way of applying science to problems of industry or social welfare. The ideas of 'criteria of adequacy', 'pitfall' and 'quality control of science', now in common use, can be traced to this book. In its concluding section I used the term 'critical science', explicitly on the analogy of the *philosophes* of the eighteenth century, and also warned against its pitfalls.

During the 1970s I moved away from academic research, and pursued two very different paths simultaneously: inner meditational experience, and active involvement in the social aspects of science. This latter was done through my position as Executive Secretary of the Council for Science and Society (London) (1973–76), and later as a member representing the public interest on the Genetic Manipulation Advisory Group. It was during my period at the Council that I met, and instantly formed a friendship, with Zia Sardar. On more than one occasion we considered collaborating on a book of criticism of science; but for myself the book could not really begin until I had a conception of a positive conclusion, and this was never forthcoming. Early in the 1980s I began work on a philosophical novel, called *Science among the People*, using a story about an ordinary middle-class neighbourhood as a vehicle for my dialectical philosophy of the knowledge and the practice of science.

My main research in the 1980s has been conducted in collaboration with S.O. Funtowicz, on quality control in scientific information, through the management of its uncertainties. We have devised a notational system for expressing the different sorts of uncertainty by which such information is affected; and this is based on a dialectical philosophy of scientific knowledge, including its quantitative basis. The system was developed through several research contracts; and a book, *Uncertainty and Quality in Science for Policy*, has been accepted by the publishers Kluwer.

Through all this time I have been writing essays on a variety of topics, most on request for a symposium, conference or Festschrift. A selection of these form the present book. Some are reprinted with few changes, while others have been nearly or completely rewritten. In general, the references have not been systematically updated, so they are not to be taken as guides to the literature at the present time.

The title of this book is a commentary on the vision of Francis Bacon, to whom we owe so much of the idealism that has motivated modern European science. His greatest work starts off with the statement that 'knowledge and power meet in one'; and he had long previously called for a 'marriage' of the rational and empirical approaches to science. Now in the later twentieth century there has indeed been a meeting of knowledge and power; but, contrary to the hopes of prophets of science down through the ages, it seems to be less of a marriage of equal partners than a merger of unequal corporations. The need for a critical presence around and within science has never been greater.

In one sense this book is obsolescent as it appears, for the changes in the social practice of science are accelerating; even the most recent essays here cannot provide a full perspective for what may soon be coming. But taken as a whole, they give a background of understanding; and my next philosophical task is to comprehend a future for science where there may be few constraints and many surprises.

Introduction

Within the last generation the public perception of science and technology has changed drastically. Although we still depend on 'science' (in this extended sense) for the operation and improvement of our material culture, few will still believe that science has the answer to all human problems. Indeed, we are now confronted by a set of problems, increasing in number and in intensity, which are the results of technological and industrial developments; and for which science, while a necessary element of their solution, will by no means be sufficient. Whereas before one could imagine science advancing boldly, steadily rolling back the frontier between knowledge and ignorance, now we must cope with our ignorance of the ramified effects of science-based processes. The 'hard facts' for which science is the paradigm example are, in these new problems, painfully conspicuous by their absence. Now we must collectively make some very hard decisions in the near future, lest our natural environment become degraded beyond repair; and for these, the best that science can provide will be rather uncertain and 'soft' data-inputs. We are living in an age where these perturbations of our environment are producing a sort of 'science-based ignorance'; and the greatest danger of all is that we should remain ignorant of our ignorance, and thereby live in an illusion of security from science.

The world of science itself has been correspondingly transformed. The old image of the rather other-worldly seeker after truth, who by his knowledge and integrity was automatically given credence for his pronouncements, has given way to a variety of different actors in conflicting roles. These include the scientist-worker and the scientist-entrepreneur, as well as the science-journalist and the citizen-scientist, themselves encountering the scientist-expert and the scientist-regulator. The teaching of science is now beginning to respond to these changed realities; although the core of science is still taught as immortal, impenetrable hard facts, there is an increasing awareness of the social dimension of science in its applications and problems. All this is encouraging for the development of an appropriate response of science to its new challenges. How well the world of traditional established science will respond to these new currents, and make its proper contribution to the solution of the problems created by its own successes, still remains to be seen. It may take a full generation of recruits whose common sense of science has been formed by a social and ecological consciousness before the traditional conceptions, valuable and valid in their own times but now outmoded, can be replaced. My work over these years has largely been devoted to assisting in the development of that new consciousness.

Thus the world of science faces a host of new problems, which were scarcely imaginable to the brave prophets of science, from Francis Bacon to those of the recent post-war period, such as J.D. Bernal. If there were a simple solution to them all, then this book would be a treatise rather than a collection of essays. My many-sided approach to the problems reflects their complexity; the absence of a definitive solution reflects the state of the world in which we live. Ever since the invention of nuclear weapons, we have faced the possibility of being destroyed by our science-based inventions. Now the same result may come from the ordinary operation of our science-based industry. If the solution does not lie within science, then how far beyond it must we go?

As a guide to the structure and contents of this book, I recall that there are two radically different conceptions of science. From the outside, as presented by most teachers and publicists, it is a set of answers, usually beyond criticism by an inexpert audience, and by their form giving no hint of the boundary between knowledge and ignorance that they represent. But from the inside, for those engaged in research, the accomplished answers are interesting only as tools for the solution of new questions. The real life of science is on that boundary between knowledge and ignorance that we call the research frontier. The art of doing exciting and innovative research is to know what sorts of questions to ask, i.e. where in the area of ignorance that lies beyond the last solved problem is there the possibility of a fruitful exploration. This living science is reflected in the quality of a great teacher, who not only presents what is known in a clear and compelling form, but who also manages to convey (even if only implicitly) the excitement of discovery, on problems solved and on those not yet solved. In this sense, a good question is worth a dozen good answers; for then curiosity is awakened, and anyone can imagine being the one to find the answer. That is the way that real comprehension and enthusiasm is generated, for what is learned then is truly the creation of the learner.

Here my discussions run through a fourfold approach, starting with a review of our present situation, through its roots, then advancing some new insights that are useful for our comprehension of science, and concluding with some positive steps. The style is suggestive rather than definitive; I exhibit a variety of ways of grasping a problem, corresponding to the variety of my experiences of attempting to understand it. The open questions are not listed formally as research exercises; for the complexity of the problems, so far as I understand them, precludes such a simple method. But since everything I say here is tentative and exploratory, reflecting the development and hopefully the continuing maturing of my ideas, the questioning character of my enterprise should be easily appreciated.

The collection of essays opens and closes with selections from my earlier book. To some extent this is to provide a record of the development of my ideas and insights; but also because I believe that what I wrote then is still useful for defining the work as a whole. In the epilogue I show again that for me the commitment to humanity must be at the core of the scientific endeavour, if it is to be worth pursuing at all.

1

WHERE WE'RE AT

The world of science is changing, and at an accelerating pace. In the Introduction to my *Scientific Knowledge and its Social Problems* (Oxford University Press, 1971), I emphasized this change, although then I could appreciate only some of its aspects. Then I spoke of 'industrialization', and of the problems of maintaining the health and vitality of science (as traditionally understood) under these new conditions. The motto I chose, still looking backwards, was 'science is not soap': the production of scientific knowledge requires very special conditions of morale and commitment if the quality of the product is to be maintained.

Since then, my outlook has broadened, and I have a better understanding of science as seen from the outside. If I were to choose a single brief motto to express the change in the status of science, it would be this contrast: In the old days, 'science' took the credit for penicillin, while 'society' got the blame for the Bomb. Now, every schoolchild knows who it was that saved the whales: not Science, but Greenpeace.

Although in many ways science represents the best in our civilization, and traditionally had been thought to be free of the taint of its worst aspects, still it has been decisively shaped by its cultural context. Now that modern European civilization has passed the half-millennium mark in its history of expansion and domination, it is easier for us to consider it as whole, including the natural science that conveys its essential character. I attempt this in the first essay in this section, 'A critical awareness of science'. This was produced for an occasion where, I believed, I was invited as someone who would challenge received views on the essential beneficence of science. This I attempted to do; and even though I have softened the text in places, it may still convey a strident, negative tone to some readers. If so, that is the result of my lack of literary skill; and I hope that the other essays will provide a balance.

If there is any single topic that expresses the new challenges to science, it is 'risks'. From pollution threats to industrial and natural disasters and new diseases, all these phenomena have a common element: uncertainty about their occurrence and about their harmful effects. The management of risks, mainly through regulation, thus becomes one of the central tasks of our high-technology society. There has been a strong tendency to treat it all as an applied science, whose accredited experts do everything possible for the protection of the public and deserve trust and gratitude on that account. That view has been vigorously contested; and now there is general agreement that values are inescapably involved in the assessment of risks, and politics in their management. Some have taken that position to extremes, arguing that it's all a matter of lifestyles to worry about nuclear power plants. Risks thereby present a challenge to the philosophy of science, to show how the more 'objective' elements of risk assessment are real, and the more 'subjective' elements are valid, in this paradigm case of the application of science to policy problems. For the essay on 'Risks and their regulation' I have amalgamated four earlier ones, which together provide a contrasting set of themes and approaches.

One of the classic controversies concerning risks in recent years was the debate, mainly conducted in the USA, over the possible hazards of recombinant DNA research. This was initiated by a unique act of statesmanship in a scientific community: a public warning that certain sorts of experiments were potentially hazardous, and the imposition of a voluntary moratorium until the risks were brought under control. The goodwill achieved by this action was dissipated within a short time, and a heated debate raged in 1976 and 1977, with almost all the researchers united against a varied collection of external critics and a few defectors. To some extent this was a characteristically American phenomenon, since the regulation of the research in the UK was accomplished on the customary consensual basis with a minimum of public strife. However, there were real issues at stake, at their core being the questions of what is the problem and who is to have control over its definition. Studying the DNA debate at that level can be instructive for understanding what may seem to be confused and unnecessarily contentious debates on other risks questions.

Although I do not wish lightly to discard the hard core of rationality and objectivity in any scientific endeavour, I do not wish to defend all that is done in the name of science against fundamental criticism. In my earlier book I analysed the problems of quality control, and showed how there is no lower limit to quality in productions called scientific, or indeed technological. It is easier to show shoddy work, or indeed vacuity, in this latter case, for the examples are more public and more easily comprehended. Defence procurement is notoriously prone to lapses of quality control; and the special character of nuclear weaponry (being designed to prevent its own use) makes its testing quite problematic. All these tendencies combined and culminated in the Strategic Defense Initiative (SDI), where critics finally raised the question of whether it was all an expensive fantasy. With the SDI as an incontrovertible example, I can study the extent to which the whole nuclear enterprise is fantasy, and consider the related question of why no one has previously seen through the emperor's bombs. If we are to understand the present social problems of science, we must divest ourselves of the delusion that it protects us against fantasy; and this case is the easiest to describe and analyse in full.

Through all these essays, I remark wherever necessary that our civilization, of which we are all members and which is the best one we have, depends on science in a multitude of ways. In these critical analyses of our present situation, I do not imply that science is evil or misconceived, or that we would be better off without it. Science, and our understanding of it, will certainly need to change, if science and indeed our civilization are to survive. My purpose here is to illustrate problems so that the change will be the result of forethought and debate, rather than a panic response to unexpected external events and pressures. This is a task for all who are concerned with science, among whom the professional scientists and their sponsors are a minority.

The Problem

The activity of modern natural science has transformed our knowledge and control of the world about us; but in the process it has also transformed itself; and it has created problems which natural science alone cannot solve. Modern society depends increasingly on industrial production based on the application of scientific results; but the production of these results has itself become a large and expensive industry; and the problems of managing that industry, and of controlling the effects of its products, are urgent and difficult. All this has happened so quickly within the past generation, that the new situation, and its implications, are only imperfectly understood. It opens up new possibilities for science and for human life, but it also presents new problems and dangers. For science itself, the analogies between the industrial production of material goods and that of scientific results have their uses, and also their hazards. As a product of a socially organized activity, scientific knowledge is very different from soap; and those who plan for science will neglect that difference at their peril. Also, the understanding and control of the effects of our science-based technology present problems for which neither the academic science of the past, nor the industrialized science of the present, possesses techniques or attitudes appropriate to their solution. The illusion that there is a natural science standing pure and separate from all involvement with society is disappearing rapidly; but it tends to be replaced by the vulgar reduction of science to a branch of commercial or military industry. Unless science itself is to be debased and corrupted, and its results used in a headlong rush to social and ecological catastrophe, there must be a renewed understanding of the very special sort of work, so delicate and so powerful, of scientific inquiry.

If we are to achieve the benefits of industrialized science, and avert its dangers, then both the common-sense understanding of science and the disciplined philosophy of science will need to be modified and enriched. As they exist now, both have come down from periods when the conditions of work in science, and the practical and ideological problems encountered by its proponents, were quite different from those of the present day. Science is no longer a marginal pursuit of little practical use carried on by a handful of enthusiasts; and it no longer needs to justify itself by a direct answer to the challenge of other fields of knowledge claiming exclusive access to truth. As the world of science has grown in size and in power, its deepest problems have changed from the epistemological to the social. Although the character of the knowledge embodied in a particular scientific result is largely independent of the social context of its first achievement, the increase and improvement of scientific knowledge is a very specialized and delicate social process, whose continued health and vitality under new conditions is by no means to be taken for granted. Moreover, science has grown to its present size and importance through its application to the solution of other sorts of problems, and these extensions react back on science and become part of it. For an understanding of this extended and enriched 'science', we must consider those sorts of disciplined inquiry whose goals include power as well as knowledge.

Extracted from J.R. Ravetz, *Scientific Knowledge and its Social Problems*, Oxford University Press, 1971.

A Critical Awareness of Science

When the perceptive person considers the state of science today, she or he may be forgiven for some bewilderment. The traditional dreams of scientific progress, for the improvement of the material and then the moral condition of mankind, seem to be in the process of realization as never before. But now they are mixed with nightmares, of widespread and increasing, perhaps irreversible degradation and destruction of the environment and humanity as well. When we consider particular issues and problems, such as pollution or economic development of the world's poor, it becomes increasingly difficult to disentangle the positive, beneficial aspects of science (including the technology in which it is practically realized) from the malignant. The task of framing a policy for science which is both benign for humanity and the environment, and also practical in political and technical terms, becomes ever more daunting.

If we are to avoid the sterile responses of rejecting either all of the achievements of science, or all of the criticisms, we must find some way to disentangle the good and evil (as we perceive them) in the phenomenon of science today. To this end I have produced an analysis into categories that are much more simple than I would normally employ. I consider the Good, the True, Society and Cosmology, in relation to the world's poor, and to the roots of our own world-view. It is unavoidably schematic, and many of my statements must be given without the qualifications that would normally lend softness and subtlety to them. However, if this essay is accepted as a sketch of a position to be articulated, and a challenge to complacency in our view of science, it can be worthwhile.

In my discussion, I shall first state the phenomena of the present paradoxical condition of science, then indicate the historic roots of our predicament, and conclude with a sketch of possible ways to a solution. Lest the analysis be too abstract, I also include a discussion of the phenomena from the perspective of that majority of the world's people who are poor.

I shall organize each phase of the discussion under four main headings. The first two are the perennial themes of the Good and the True. These express the basic human values in whose terms the worth of science is judged. The others are Society and Cosmology. These represent the context of scientific endeavour; they are broadly (though not exclusively) paired with the Good and the True for their main sorts of interaction with the world of science. I shall vary the order in which the four aspects are introduced in each section for the better presentation of the argument in each case.

I shall frequently observe how, in human affairs and even in the work of science, it is impossible to segregate off the 'negative' aspects of a phenomenon from the 'positive'. This characteristic may be called 'duality', 'complementarity', 'polarity' or 'dialectic'. I do not have a consistent theory or terminology for describing or analysing it. Gerald Holton (1974) has already discussed this patterning in connection with the progress and assessment of science; I stress its paradoxical and disturbing aspects rather more. It suggests the troubling conclusion that any of our actions are liable to be evil in part. How then are we to apply scientific rationality for human good? I have no answer to such a question; I can only say that at this point I must exhibit the polarity in all these phenomena, as a precondition for true understanding and good action.

The Positive Image

We may begin with a brief statement of the popular faith in science, as revealed by opinion polls. The main emphasis is on what can be apprehended: the improvement of the material conditions of life, through the reduction of drudgery and danger. Even the recognized hazards of pollution, and various possible global crises, do not yet balance the real benefits, in the comfort and security of life, consciously enjoyed by increasingly wide groups of people in recent decades. In our pragmatic world, such goods vouch for the truth of science as a system of factual knowledge. The traditional enemy of science, scriptural religion, is a great nuisance in some places (as in the less advanced parts of America) but no real threat. And although the ancient occult sciences had a frightening growth during the turbulent 1960s, they have by now at least stabilized, still out on the fringe. The hegemony of official, institutionalized natural science and its applications is unchallenged. And the exciting progress of science still gives hopes of new discoveries and powers. The response to the new challenges of environment pollution and resources scarcity, though troubled by an unaccustomed degree of political involvement and debate, shows that science can successfully modify its work and its style to make a continuing contribution to human welfare. Even the recent protest movements, populist in style with occasional Luddite or Arcadian themes, are only a cry for an improved application of the modern scientific principle of government, the achievement of a greater welfare for a greater number. And, at the very deepest level of culture, the cosmology in which our science operates, where material effects are commensurate with their impersonal causes, may well rescue from the 'occult' those yet unexplained phenomena (such as dowsing and acupuncture) where reliable public repetition ensures their genuineness.

This is, then, an optimistic picture for the present state and immediate future of science. Anyone who wishes to remain reassured may stop there, confident that any impending problems are only local difficulties. Any other opinion is only a matter of judgement. But the picture would be incomplete without the other side.

The Problems

The Phenomena

There is an abundance of piecemeal criticisms of science, and reservations about some aspects of its state. I will introduce the discussion of the pheno-mena by quoting from one revealing commentary which was not (apparently) even intended as a criticism. Since it was made by Professor Harvey Brooks of Harvard University, a truly wise man of the world of science, it is all the more revealing. Although he is explicitly referring to technology, we can safely include 'science' in the judgement.

> The central fact about modern technology is that its powers for both good and evil increase as it evolves. . . . Living with technology is like climbing a mountain along a knife-edge which narrows as it nears the summit. With each step we mount higher, but the precipices on either side are steeper and the valley floor farther below. As long as we can keep our footing, we approach our goal, but the risks of a misstep constantly mount. Furthermore, we cannot simply back up, or even cease to move forward. We are irrevocably committed to the peak. (Brooks 1973, *Zygon*, Vol. 8, No. 1, 35)

One could not ask for a more frank and self-aware confession of the Faustian drive of our modern scientific enterprise. We can agree that our technology-based world, underpinned by modern science, is in a state fairly described as 'brilliant but precarious'. Perhaps there is no way to preserve its present bene-fits except by putting them increasingly at risk, through progress of the sort imagined by Professor Brooks. If this is so, that is a truly paradoxical situation. Let us explore the structure of that paradox.

Problems: The Good

To ourselves and our immediate ancestors, the vastly increased material prosperity and the consequent political and social amelioration are products of the applications of science. Those who, in one way or another, preach the virtues of austerity or poverty encounter the brute fact of our affluence and the apparently universal desire to maintain and increase it. It therefore comes as a disquieting surprise that so many present and impending ills seem to derive from that same science-based technology. Moreover, it is not at all certain that further application of the same approach will cure these troubles. Some, such as ionizing radiation, diffused asbestos fibres, or a disturbed atmosphere, may well be beyond our means of control.

Furthermore, some applications of science present increasing threats to the stability and survival of our civilization: with nuclear energy the question is not whether but when uncontrolled proliferation of weapons will occur; with microprocessors, the economic redundancy of humans on a mass scale conjures up visions of unprecedented social readjustment or maladjustment. We notice here that science, acting through a technology responding to military demands and market opportunities, *makes* the problem. Its solution will involve some techniques, but essentially lies in the sphere of politics and values. Thus the faith of the Enlightenment is stood on its head.

The Baconian vision of a philanthropic science now become clouded and compromised. Restoration of confidence will not be accomplished by exhortation or rhetoric. Nor will it do to try to keep the name of 'science' clean, as by the logic that gives science credit for penicillin and blames society for the Bomb. There is certainly no clear way through, from our inherited ideology of science as a source of the Good.

Problems: The True

For centuries it has been the proud boast of spokesmen for science that by their way, and no other, could real knowledge be attained. This ideology has supported the established doctrinaire style of the teaching of science, where every problem has one and only one solution. So long as the development of science seemed a simple progress, either the discovery of new laws or the correction of (retrospectively) obvious errors, this view was plausible. But now perceptions of change within theoretical science, and a new awareness of the ways science is actually deployed in the solution of practical problems, have eroded the old confidence.

Within science, we cannot any longer believe that the application of scientific method will protect scientists from adopting or maintaining false beliefs, nor that these innovators subsequently proved correct were more rigorous or methodical than their critics. The progress of science, while still accepted as real on a large scale, becomes more problematical in its details.

When challenges are thrown up by discovery of malfunctions in our environment, the weakness of our science as a practical tool is exposed. We usually discover our ignorance concerning both the data and the mechanism of their production. And the conclusions of natural science, in these matters that affect our survival, are far from the ideal of Galileo: neither certainly true nor necessary, and depending essentially on human judgements. The category of 'trans-science' problems, capable of a scientific statement but requiring a political solution, describes our predicament well. And the need to regulate technology and hazardous scientific research redresses the long-standing imbalance of intellectual prestige between technical expertise and human wisdom.

Problems: Society

The promise of science deriving from the Enlightenment was not merely for material benefits, but for the cultural progress attendant on the diffusion of the scientific spirit. Science was then seen as an affair of 'savants' or philosophers, whose primary loyalty was to the truth and to humanity. The faith in the civilizing powers of the ethos of science then survived nearly to this day. But once we depict science as largely composed of research-workers, who are 'puzzle-solving within paradigms' that are set by their leaders or by external agencies, the political and social significance of the endeavour is transformed. Somehow it has proved possible for scientific communities to make a concordat with repressive regimes, securing a limited area of autonomy, in return for co-operation and acquiescence where desired. It then ceases to be a puzzle that scientists can be recruited for military or commercial ventures of dubious morality; or that the norms of behaviour of pure research are so easily modified in the interests of employers or governments.

In the name of 'science', large bureaucracies have developed, most notably in the military sphere. However isolated these may be from ordinary academic communities, they require the acquiescence of the apparently uninvolved academic teachers and researchers for their continued operation and influence. Nuclear weapons of mass annihilation, now endowed with a survival instinct of their own, provide a clear example here.

Also, the 'democracy' of scientific work and scientific knowledge is now revealed as somewhat abstract. There is unequal access to élite institutions; there is the political influencing of priorities and standards in all but exceedingly pure research; there is a heritage of job discrimination against minorities in science as elsewhere; and there are the strong survivals of prejudiced attitudes in many fields legitimated as scientific (consider the significance of the enforcement of the supine rather than the squatting position for childbirth).

The result of all this is that the lessons that science can give to society are muted; the traditional assumption of the moral superiority of scientists is no longer automatically tenable. Then, when the applications of science create such hazards for the whole world, any attempted scientific solution is easily discounted as part of the problem.

Problems: Cosmology

Since cosmological assumptions are unquestioned and unquestionable in the teaching and practice of any science, it is difficult to detect them, still less to probe their adequacy. But there are cases on the borders of the hitherto successful reductionist sciences of nature, where cosmology operates fairly explicitly, if not as a logical entailment then at least as a stylistic pressure. Thus the obsolete atomistic ideal of 'genuine' science still informs research in behavioural disciplines, promoting an 'objectivity' in methods that is believed to render insight unnecessary, and resulting in vacuity on a very large scale. The result is a pretence of knowledge and power where there is none, and confusion and impotence worse confounded.

The reductionist dogmas in fields dealing with humans in health and disease, as nutrition and medicine, still impede the development of broader conceptions of problems and solutions. To appreciate the state of medicine in this respect, one need only consider the neglect of physiotherapy, itself not an 'alternative' system but only one that sees the whole body belonging to a human being. Or there is the continued purveying of addictive mood-influencing drugs on physicians' prescription (which we might call 'ethical dope'), since the emotional roots of distress and illness are intractible to medical science. The refusal to recognize the role of social and psychological factors in health has its institutional and economic roots also; but these are given plausibility by the 'scientific' flavour of the dominant picture of the human body as a piece of plumbing.

The main article of faith in the present world-view of science is the denial of any intelligence or consciousness operating here in the world, other than that which can be localized to the brains of ourselves or of very closely related species. Hence the Darwinian theory of evolution, which while it explains everything predicts nothing and seems structurally incapable of falsification, is accepted as the only conceivable rational explanation of how the unimaginably rich and subtle order of nature has come to be. In this view, the defining criterion for quality of an organism, a type or (by natural extension) a culture, is material survival, achieved through successful propagation. Applied to the civilization of which it is an expression, it yields up a paradox: our survival, as particular societies, as a civilization, indeed as a species, has been problematic for nearly two generations now; and most increments of scientific knowledge make us, on balance, less likely rather than more likely to survive. The positive argument for dimensions of reality beyond those allowed by Descartes has been relegated to cranks and cleries; but this *reductio ad extinctionem* of our reductionist cosmology in its own terms may illustrate the depth of the new dilemma of the modern scientific world-view.

The Perspective of the Poor

Their Experience of Science

To speak of the 'poor' has an old-fashioned, condescending tone, unsuitable for this era of anti-colonialism and development. But the easy optimism of the post-war period about the transfer of our science and technology is gone; and it is now clear that because of social and political factors, the poor will be with us for a long time. In considering the human meaning of science, we must therefore consider their plight. In doing so we must either think dialectically or else perpetrate nonsense.

'The poor' is an overly general term, since there is a continuum of misery, from the homeless of the United States through those south of the border, down to the teeming millions of the flood-plains of Bangladesh. Some poor countries seem to pull themselves up, others remain in abysmal poverty. But for most countries it is recognized that poverty is not a simple, 'natural' imbalance between mouths to feed and land for growing food. Hardly any country is lacking in an affluent upper-class; few famines are caused by empty warehouses. The world's poor nations now function as the slums for the world's rich: the places where no one believes in them as home. Old-style tribalism or landlordism is replaced by agribusiness and runaway industries. Again in most cases, a rotten, oppressive *Gemeinschaft* gives way to a *Gesellschaft* that offers advancement for some at the price of total misery for many. No matter how poor a peasant is, it is always worth someone's while (be it landlord, merchant, bureaucrat or spouse), to exploit them (in the last case, her) economically, politically or however.

Hence we see the general stagnation (admittedly worsened by the ruinous interest payments after the decade of loan-pushing by the big banks) which requires such heroic or even gargantuan efforts to break. The various technical-fix fantasies inspired by European science over the decades, from enforced sterilization, through bureaucratized high-technology agriculture, or attempts to 'stamp out' disease germs regardless of their social milieu, can now be seen as the benevolent aspect of a process of scientific–cultural exploitation of the world's poor, whose commercial side is the exportation of dried cows' milk and cigarettes for the babies and mothers out there.

The Poor and the Scientifically True

The facts of science, which in their own culture seem individually so peculiarly irrelevant to human concerns, become implements of the worst sort of imperialism, that of consciousness. At every level, from the grading of prestige by the abstractness of one's field of research or study, through the shaping of a syllabus around scholastic rather than practical concerns, to the enforcement of a harsh, flat, alien style of thought in problem-solving, the imported

Western science is quite other than 'universal' and 'democratic' in the lives of those it touches. And those who are incapable of assimilating it are then doubly victimized: as Illich has shown, they are then officially deemed inferior for having failed to better themselves through obtaining certificates of a skilled brain.

To be sure, the use of knowledge as an instrument of social differentiation and ideological control goes back long before modern science. Indeed, the ostensibly public character of our science has enabled it to function repeatedly as an instrument of liberation from the tyranny of official esoteric knowledge in 'traditional' societies. But if we are to be open to reality, rather than try to pat it into shape, we must accommodate this dialectical interpenetration of the nice and the nasty. This is nowhere more necessary than among the poor, who might even be defined as those for whom the contradictions of material life are not tucked away out of sight.

The Poor and Science-Based Society

In their social and political lives, the world's poor have been similarly exposed to the raw contradictions of our scientific way. The political benefits of modernization have been reserved mainly for an urban élite. The machinery of constitutional and even democratic or socialist government is displayed to the appropriate European mass media periodically, but the cynicism of the show is scarcely concealed. At its worst, chieftains using jet airplanes rather than spears, or gangsters with epaulettes and aid funds, run 'kleptocracies', peculiarly debased mixtures of tribal and capitalist societies, or bureau-cratized tyrannies of one sort or another. It is not for us to be condescending, since their stagnation and underdevelopment is the obverse of our 'overdevel-opment', whereby we must extract their cash crops and minerals to feed our wants and fashions.

The failure of the post-war attempts to 'develop' the Third World econo-mically and socially in our image reflects the loss of impetus of the total system of European imperialism, after a half-millennium of expansion. 'We' cannot keep 'them' in our economic, social and cultural system; 'we' cannot even prevent 'them' from lurching into barbarism. The 'civilizing mission' of Europe, a source of much of the earlier idealism and drive of our cultural imperialism, is open to question. We must, then, lose the complacent confi-dence in the simple universality and superiority of our scientific world-view. Its own traditional criterion of truth, which is power, now tells against it in this all-important respect.

The Poor and the Goods of Science

We need not believe that the pre-conquest 'other' world was a pastoral idyll, in order to accept that the European impact was peculiarly traumatic. We destroyed their gods, either explicitly and deliberately, or by the imposition of a material and intellectual culture that emptied them of experiential meaning. To use an ecological analogy, European scientific civilization has been (for the others) rather like a weed: encountering an order where life, death, good and evil passed through regular cycles of alteration, our ways intruded (with people, guns, doctrines, diseases and drugs), and flourished wherever there was an instability, soon choking out the culture that belonged to that special place. Now it is settled there, ineradicably so, but producing strange and frequently inharmonious hybrids of life-styles and cosmologies. Therein lies a principal cause of the continuing poverty, stagnation and corruption of colonial life, in the social, economic and cultural dimensions. In such a context, apparently impractical and unrealistic criteria for economic life, such as those derived by E.F. Schumacher from the teachings of the Buddha, now become rather less fantastic than the perspectives of Americanizing the life-styles of all the world's billions.

The World's Poor and the European Scientific Cosmology

So long as we insist that religion is an affair of the intellect (believing the impossible, called 'faith'), somewhat aided by sentiment, and we rigorously exclude the possibility that the transcendent dimensions can be experienced palpably and ordinarily, we will remain baffled by other cultures. And, whether by accident or by the actions of our ancestors, the demarcation between the world's rich and poor runs close to that of cultures. To justify our own cosmology, we have denigrated the others, and those who live in them. This spiritual destruction will eventually be blamed by the victims on 'science', since the metaphysics of our science still dares not enrich itself beyond Descartes' dualism of a totally dead material world complemented by disembodied, desiccated rational souls. But we should not be swayed by culture-guilt into believing that every 'traditional' survival is superior to the more 'Western' rival; that would be to react, ignoring the polarity of such phenomena. Can we but say that the cosmological question is among the most urgent, and as yet the least attended, of all those on our agenda?

The Roots of Our Predicament

The Dialectic of History

Radical thinkers, intoxicated with their concepts, believe that all can be transformed on the turn of an idea. Conservative actors, settled in the constraints of inherited custom, sense that nothing can really change except of itself. The tension between the shallowness of the one and the complacency of the other, has motivated social philosophy in Europe for centuries. Only if we give up attachment to some simplistic Good as realized either in a fantasy future or in a fictional past, can we comprehend what history can tell us of ourselves.

The roots of our predicament will not be so simply enumerated; they extend back through centuries of contradictory phenomena of the sort we have just exhibited for the present moment of time. Each contradiction has its own cycle of development, during which the balance of apparent costs and benefits shifts drastically (what Illich calls 'the watershed') and perhaps suddenly. This sort of history can help us to understand the abrupt reversal of evaluation that has occurred in connection with Science in recent years.

The European Cosmology

Let us take the deepest root of all that defines European culture and consciousness; and let us not be dismayed if the glory of our civilization may also contain the seeds of its eventual decay. Identifying the essential common element in classical Greek philosophy and mature Hebrew religion can be a game without end (or even without rules). But if we cast around for themes, we see a significant cluster. There is a quite strongly marked drive for the *explicit*, as in the philosophical probings or the moral code respectively; with it is a need for an *absolute* foundation of knowledge of the True or of the Good that is independent of the will of ourselves or even that of a personal deity; and finally there is a personal identification with any position as the *exclusive* solution of its problem. These stylistic features of the two sorts of thought go with a general reduction of the degree of higher psychic functions that are believed to be enjoyed by the various beings of the external world, both visible and invisible. This is particularly striking when compared with neighbouring cultures of the time. To us, 'animism' and its relatives in 'superstition' and 'irrationality' have the full force of the uncleanliness associated with a taboo. In such a world as ours, the human person is then alienated from his total environment, and is self-conscious and necessarily self-justifying. Such a person is capable of the heights of individual achievement, but also of depths of immersion in loneliness and the meaninglessness of existence.

All possible variations in the degree of expression of these traits have occurred in the evolution of Europe; but we need only compare our sensibility to that of other familiar great cultures, be they Muslim, Indian, Chinese, even Japanese, to say nothing of non-literate societies, to appreciate their plausibility as a composite identifying portrait. We can see that a particularly exaggerated version of this cosmology took hold in Europe in the seventeenth century. The 'scientific revolution' was a sudden hardening of the sensibility of the educated classes, which fostered the rapid development of particular sorts of sciences involving a disenchanted mathematics applied to a dehumanized world of nature. This desperately flat metaphysical basis defined the style and content of the European natural science that soon moved beyond the level of its predecessors at an accelerating pace, eventually yielding the triumphs of knowledge and power that we all know.

The cosmological root of modern European science, its tendency to the reduced, explicit and exclusive style for objects and arguments, lies very deep in our culture. Opposed sensibilities lie equally deep: Pythagorean, alchemical and romantic themes recur through time, and they have been more important than is recognized, for the origins of our ideals of technical mastery as well as for our poetry. The scientists of the Renaissance were generally as much imbued with alchemy and magic as the poets. This tradition in natural philosophy lasted into the seventeenth century and produced some of the early works of great science; the scientific revolutionaries shared more with that tradition than they cared to admit. But these themes have, up to now, generally been maintained as a suppressed 'darker' side of our modern educated European sensibility. The sorts of enhanced experience of reality, external as well as internal, that are commonplace in other cultures, seem to have occurred, or to have been acknowledged, only fitfully in Europe. Thus, *feng shui* survives well in China except where it is self-consciously modernizing, while here 'ley lines' are still recognized only by the eccentric few. Hence the 'counter-culture' of the 1960s, together with its descendants, can justly be considered to be an importation of an Eastern technology, in this case of the non-tangible realm.

Our Roots: The True

The European idea of the True, which defines our sciences, is thus one where reality consists of objects with hard edges. Our ordinary logic admits only 'yes *or* no', not 'yes *and* no', nor yet 'yes *nor* no'. With such components we have built amazing structures of rigorous and rigid thought, and yet more amazing material realizations of them. Such a logic is now known to be inappropriate for comprehending the outermost world that it has discovered, the physics of the very large and the very small. There, the other logics, similar to those of the pantheist or the mystic, seem necessary. But that discovery is still scarcely appreciated. For coping with the vast problems of our uncontrollable total environment, we still use the logical tools suited for straight-lines and abstract mass-points.

This conception of truth is singularly ill-suited to variety or change in knowledge: our basic categories force us to oscillate between dogmatism and scepticism. Our philosophy of knowledge (in science and outside) cannot cope with error, but either ignores it, or explains it away as an accident that could in principle be eliminated. Describing the sorts of relatively successful knowledge that we can achieve (in science as in technology), and its roots in the interplay of personal, social and natural and metaphysical elements, is a philosophical task that is barely begun or even conceived. I am now beginning to see a way through, not using the idea of *error* as much as that of *ignorance*. It is possible to sketch out a dialectical interpenetration of knowledge with ignorance, each implying the other in a way that is not merely good dialectics, but also very important for understanding the uncertainties that affect all our statements about the world.

Our Roots: The Good

Our idea of the Good is correspondingly harsh. Particularly since the Reformation and the Scientific Revolution, the awareness of the benefits of inward contemplation has wilted before the rewards of external action. Consequently, in the interpersonal realm, the quiet, intangible reaching-out describable as 'compassion' is too soft to be distinguished from passivity or indifference. Instead our benevolence appears as a compulsion to reform the object of our concern, preferable by actions of universal applicability and under the guidance of a scientifically established theoretical system.

The reality of the human suffering, material and spiritual, that evoked this response, is not in question. Any nostalgic looking backward towards the days before the impersonal Welfare principle needs to ignore the overwhelming mass of misery and degradation that resulted from leaving charity to the charitable. Nor it is sensible to lay responsibility on individuals or cultures, for those vast changes in sensibility and inward experience which incline us to one or another conception of the Good or the True. But we now have had sufficient experience of the frustrations of the Good conceived exclusively in the material and social planes, that we should see the limitations in our world-view and ourselves in their light. Again, seeing ourselves as the exaggerated 'masculine' pole of a dialectic can provide the right sort of humility and insight.

Our Roots: Society

A look at European society in the terms of the present crisis well illustrates the need for dialectical thinking. The alienation of our inner and personal selves, so obvious to those outside our culture, is a drastic impoverishment. But it is complemented by an enrichment: a widespread awareness of a social and ethical self, as possessing the right to independence and dignity. This, even more than crass material goods and evils, has been the corrosive solvent of other cultures, previously organized around customary acceptance of inequality based on accidents of tribe, family or gender.

This new secular self-consciousness is variously realized under titles such as 'democracy' or 'socialism'. With its enhancement of individual effort and acquisitiveness, it is deeply related to the social order we have inherited, and also provides a psychological and social context for our style of scientific enquiry. Its negative side is increasingly realized in communities with permanent social tensions and unrealizable popular expectations. Should our

technology fail to continue to buy acquiescence abroad and at home, individualism and anomie could degenerate into anarchy and chaos.

The Power of European Imperialist Science

All the foregoing generalizations could be a subject for the academic history of
ideas, were it not for the recent transformation of the scattered learned
sciences and empirical arts into an engine of unprecedented and scarcely
imaginable power, both for the production of new knowledge and for its
translation into tools. The consciousness of this power, which has made
modern Europe so qualitatively different in its material culture from any other
civilization ever, has produced the expectations and mass demands of the
material good life, which rulers must now either respect or else attempt to
crush with barbaric brutality. The very sudden transition to a future other
than that of increasing material plenty has not yet been grasped by those who
manage our nominally Welfare States. Its implications for politics and the
political role of science are just some more items on the agenda of those who
must try to steer us past the shoals that we and our ancestors have made.

In the long view, the power of our modern science has much of its human
significance in the cycle of domination by European society over the rest of the
world, that got under way in the fourteenth century and reached its summit in
1914. It is a myth of recent origin that science and scientists were not involved
in our imperialist conquest. The mathematical sciences in the sixteenth
century served exploration and war; similarly the 'field' sciences in subsequent
centuries. There was an intimate connection, personal and ideological,
between the English philosophical movement that eventually produced the
Royal Society, and the rape and plunder of Ireland in the Civil War period.
Thus our science has, in its global context, the same contradictory history as
the rest of our culture: destruction and development, oppression and liberation, all joined in one discordant ensemble.

The reaction to European science by other peoples will be similarly
inconstant and inconsistent: generally the tools are desired, but their cultural
entanglements are viewed with a mixture of admiration, envy, hate and fear.
The naivety of the good intentions of those of us who would export or impose
our own scientific ways have been sufficiently exposed. But the problem of
unscrambling the mess of our imperialistic scientific heritage has barely been
considered.

Ways to a Solution

The European Crisis

The problem of European science is thus a problem of the civilization of which
it is an integral and defining component. For Europe as a whole, this has been

a century in which much has gone wrong. The self-confidence of the middle-class European male as he surveyed the world in, say, 1900, is now lost for ever. One war of butchery led by incompetents; another of genocide started by a maniac; various empires breaking up in big and little chunks with no prospect of repair; the constant and permanent threat of total catastrophe should there be a misreading of a warning about nuclear weapons; a natural environment now reacting in unpredictable and non-linear ways; and most recently a realization that the material prosperity (and hence social stability) of the mid-century years depended on local and foreign circumstances that cannot be maintained. Although scientific discoveries continue to be made and applied, the sense of triumph in that progress is muted or altogether lost. The natural sciences now raise social and ethical problems at every turn, and the social sciences are sadly recognized as being as far as ever from being mature and effective foundations for enlightened social engineering.

To view this array of worries as 'a problem' and to seek a solution as if it involved only the construction of lines and circles, is itself a very strong commitment, not at all justified by the phenomena under review. Let us instead consider the various styles of response that present themselves.

The Academic Reactionary: The Absolute Value of Truth

For many scientists, the immediate world of routine teaching and research has not yet changed all that much; and from that perspective it is not easy to see why it should change at all. The academic scientist's fictional past is a compound of the innocence of science in the days before it yielded material power, and the affluence of science once its products could be put to use in the world. To protect his world, he invokes an idol of Objective Truth, making it sovereign over all other considerations (except perhaps the proven immediate hazards of research). Proponents of this view are unhappy victims of a narrow professional ideology of 'pure research', designed to resolve the contradiction that science requires constant external support and yet is unable to give a detailed accounting of the benefits rendered in return. Because they identify with a past that never was, I call them 'reactionaries', even though their general politics might sometimes be quite liberal or even radical in appearance.

Philosophers of science are increasingly admitting the complexity of the process whereby scientific knowledge is achieved, and are recognizing unsolved and insoluble problems of clarifying the structure and content of generally accepted scientific theories. Those who still believe that significant scientific facts can be collected like pebbles on a beach are adhering to a very fundamentalist faith. Further, the ever closer interpenetration of science and industry makes the claim of 'purity' hollow; and once there are external influences on the choice of problems (and hence of results) the 'objectivity' of science loses an important dimension. The distinction between the free acquisition of knowledge and its subsequent socially constrained application, is little more than the last refuge of a precarious minority vested interest.

The intellectual collapse of an ideology may take several decades or even generations to work its way through to common-sense understanding, even among the eminent. The delay will be particularly marked when there are special interests to protect, and no satisfactory alternative presents itself for that function. Hence we may expect many reiterations of the old faith, superficially modified by lip-service to 'social responsibility'. One salient point at which the unreality of such rhetoric becomes obvious, is the claim that scientific knowledge is essentially 'public'. There are sectors where this holds, but when we consider research and development (R & D) managed in either military or commercial institutions, or in many civil service settings, we see that 'repeatable' is by no means the same as 'public'. Proclaiming 'public knowledge' in order to conceal the importance of 'corporate know-how' serves to confuse debates on technology policies. There, the styles of politics, journalism and even detective work are frequently more appropriate for achievement of public scientific information, than those of traditional refereed academic research.

But even here there are dialectical contradictions. The autonomy obtained by the 'pure' scientist in his research or academic institution does fend off the worst sorts of blundering or malevolent interference in the process of enquiry. To have science serve 'the people' is a noble ideal, but in practice a bureaucracy stands between the two parties, and defines those tasks by which the service is to be done. Then all sorts of irrelevant and damaging pressures may be applied, for the perennial power-game of society does not depend on the 'ownership' relation for its motives and rewards. Hence political radicals may need to find shelter in universities behind scientific reactionaries, for the pursuit of their own work. If they are embarrassed thereby, that is a sign of the room for further maturing in their understanding.

The Policy-Science Conservative and the Achievement of the Good

A sort of science which is not peculiarly devoted to acquiring knowledge is now becoming recognized in principle by sociologists of science, although not yet by philosophers of science. Yet the importance of such science, which may be called 'applied', 'mission-orientated', or 'regulatory' or 'public-interest' (emphasizing one or other aspect) is great and steadily growing. The directors of this work will be found in government, in industrial labs, and (as individuals with a personal and exceptional outside role) in universities in Europe. In America, the 'service' tradition in state universities, the vast research businesses run by the great universities, and a general spirit of entrepreneurship have long ago blurred the distinction between 'basic' and 'mission-orientated' research.

In this sort of science, resources of manpower and equipment are deployed, sometimes on a massive scale, in response to problems set by some external goal, be it for military, commercial, political or social benefit. Those who promote and manage such enterprises must be sensitive to the desires of their clientele, lest they find themselves abandoned as obsolete and irrelevant. Of course they need not adhere slavishly to the client's conception of any given problem, no more than any professional abandons his expertise and self-interest when undertaking a brief. However, a reasonable facsimile of 'relevance' must be maintained by policy-science. Its task may be defined as the setting and solving of those technical problems which promise to resolve the practical problems brought by corporate clients.

In comparison with those academic scientists, eminent and humble, who find the outside world an unwelcome intrusion, the policy-scientists may appear as very aware and even radical. They maintain familiarity and perhaps a dialogue with critics of existing policies, and show no doubt that the various social responsibilities of scientists must be fully and publicly discharged. When I refer to them as 'conservative' I do not use the term in a pejorative sense, but only to call attention to an attitude or commitment. Generally, they do not welcome change either within the social system of science nor in its technical and political environment. But, like enlightened conservatives in any sphere, they attempt to comprehend it, to respect its cause and thereby to channel it away from dangerous courses.

However, such a conservative starts with the conviction that every problem can be managed, and in particular without cost to his professional status or ideology. Nor can he easily accept that an unpleasant problem is deeply rooted in a social system with which he strongly identifies. I have personally seen how difficult it is for individuals, however well motivated, to be simultaneously part of the problem and of the solution. Hence the powers of analysis, and even of perception, of such a person have their limits; paradoxically these tend to be more severe on matters closer to that person's professional competence and commitment.

The policy-scientists suffer from another disability; while they command (or influence) research funds that dwarf those of their academic colleagues, they do not control curricula for science teaching at any level. Hence their influence on the consciousness of younger scientists is indirect, and the false ideology of 'pure' science is still passed on with remarkably little direct challenge from inside the world of science.

The conclusion is that this group of scientists might indeed manage well, so long as the problems are manageable. But should we have a convergence of crises in and around science, then we should not be surprised to find an inadequacy of vision and resolution, even among those policy-scientists who had been aware of some separate components of the crisis. Also, should our society encounter the sorts of contradictions of basic values and cosmologies that already afflict the world's poor, then our particular dominant conception of the Good, material and social, and the policy-scientists who operate in its framework, might even become hindrances to their resolution.

The Isolated Social—Political Reformers of Science

The 1960s saw a dramatic increase in awareness that the social institution of science in any class-divided society must, in many important respects, be tailored to fit the requirements of its context. Young scientists who had been misled by the apparent objectivity of scientific knowledge, and perhaps by the personally liberal sentiments of some teachers, were shocked to discover the degree to which science, and themselves, were recruited to the service of a repressive social system. A vocal minority, in America and elsewhere, then dedicated themselves to the reform of science, under the slogan 'science for the people'. A similar discovery was made in China, and contributed to the campaigns of the Cultural Revolution, now described as the rule of the Gang of Four.

Since that turbulent decade, such social reformers have had a thin time. Their organizations in the West have dwindled, and China has swung away from the traditional left in social and political style. What still flourish in the West are special-issue campaigns, usually centred on some particular objectionable technology. Though many organizers and participants privately have radical opinions about government and bureaucracies in general, there has been little concerted attempt to concentrate criticism on the scientific—technical establishment as such. Even the movements for 'appropriate' or 'alternative' technologies, varying between populism and meditation for their bases, do not focus their public criticism on the social institutions which foster the 'high technology' that they wish to replace.

So a radical critique, in social—political terms, of the world of 'science' is left to a very few authors and editors. I personally believe that the enfeeblement of the critical spirit reflects the much reduced plausibility of any solution to the problem of 'science for the people', which is cast in traditional political terms. Since analyses of this sort need to provide solutions working at the social level, not just for mere individual people, the political reformers of science are now the victims of their own criteria of success, which are severe in themselves and perhaps also inappropriate. Once one loses faith in the unique and dominating influence of the abstraction called 'ownership', the path of radical reform leads away from its traditional European ideologies, such as socialism; but whither is not yet determined.

Radicalism for Science—from Red to Green

As the force of traditional socialism wanes, there emerge new forms of protest and their associated theories. As yet they are scattered, ranging from middle-class NIMBY campaigns (Not In My Back Yard), through the counter-science groups which collect and publicize environmental health statistics that contradict the official denials of danger, to the ecological activists (such as Greenpeace) who use commando-Gandhi tactics to publicize global scandals;

28

and over to the alternative health movements, be they feminist, oriental or spiritually inspired.

So far there is little direct confrontation with Science as such; perhaps for such people that symbol is as outworn and irrelevant as Religion. At the political level the engagement is with various sections of the political–technical establishment; in that context the lone scientist making his exciting discoveries is as obsolete as the knight-errant on horseback. At the theoretical level, the enemy is partly that establishment, partly our industrial society, and partly ourselves.

As with every confrontation, there is a dialogue. Politicians of all sorts experience partial conversions to Green thinking; and as campaigners gain power they experience the burdens of responsibility. In some fields, such as health, the sharing of insights seems genuine; younger doctors have less of the traditional scientistic phobia of any treatment that cannot be explained in atomistic terms. All these movements bring us fairly directly to the existential questions of what is the real quality, and hence the real meaning of life; and as the twentieth century comes to its close, it is increasingly clear that neither the knowledge nor the power of science could provide fully satisfactory answers.

Can a Cosmological Critique be Relevant?

To discuss alternative world-views seriously is nearly enough in itself to have one classed as an 'anti-science element'. To believe that paranormal phenomena exist, or that 'altered state of consciousness' has any significance, is to place onself well out on the eccentric fringe where, for instance, the *jus docendi* would not extend. Yet to insist that rationality, the values of civilization, the success of science, or some other good is essentially tied to the Cartesian reductionist cosmology is really to be somewhat parochial. It cannot be denied that in the other great civilizations where science has flourished, such as China, India or Islam, the socially constructed reality of educated common sense has been different from and richer than ours. Nor can we deny the chronology of our own great scientific revolution: advances in technology, and even the master-works of early modern science such as those of Gilbert, Kepler and Harvey, belonged to an older world-picture, and were achieved *before* the spread of the new metaphysics proclaimed by Descartes, Galileo and Gassendi.

Perhaps the particular contributions of modern Europe, its science/technology and its political democracy, have been related to its disenchanted cosmology. But perhaps its negative side, its aggressive and destructive actions towards other people and other species, are equally so related. Again, we do not try to determine whether 'good' or 'bad' is in some absolute excess; rather we study the contradictory tendencies as they have developed and nurtured, and then try to sense in which way a resolution may flow.

At this concluding point of my analysis, a rather elementary statement of the credo of the European scientific world-view might be more plausible, and useful, than at the beginning. Let us consider: 'The true facts and the good things are provided by the Science of a purely tangible world, and they are each simple and separate'. Attempts to control nature and to reform society by applications of this faith have become increasingly problematic and throw up phenomena that are paradoxical, contradictory, and increasingly difficult to control, at every step. This is the substance of the cosmological criticism of science today.

What Sorts of Problems, What Sorts of Solutions?

It is certainly difficult to avoid a schizoid feeling when one writes (or reads) about radical criticisms of science while located physically in a comfortable room in some affluent and secure European city. Perhaps meetings about the great problems of science could have an obligatory session in some thought-provoking location, such as Beirut, Belfast or Phnom Penh, not to mention Hiroshima. We could then be reminded that the summer of 1939 was an exceptionally fine one.

My own views on the various elements of the criticism of science as outlined here, are of little importance. If I did not think them worthy of reporting, I would have described something else; but if I believed the whole range of criticisms literally and one-sidedly, I would not have bothered to write at all. I hope that I have at least exhibited a range of problems, and indicated some elements of possible solutions. If there is any point which I feel prepared to defend now, it is the approach that appreciates and strives to encompass the apparent duality and contradiction in all these phenomena. In this I implicitly criticize and depart from the scientific style as laid down by Galileo and Descartes; how much of a change in metaphysics is entailed thereby has yet to be seen.

Adapted from a lecture by J.R. Ravetz entitled 'Critiques of science today', presented at a Nobel Symposium on Ethics for Science Policy', held at Stockholm in August 1978. A much abridged version was published in the proceedings of the symposium: *Ethics for Science Policy* (ed. T. Segerstedt), Pergamon, 1979, pp. 49–56.

Reference

Holton, G. *Thematic Origins of Scientific Thought*. Cambridge, MA: Harvard University Press.

Risks and Their Regulation

This essay is adapted from several short pieces that I wrote over the space of nearly ten years. These were stimulated, in various ways, by the work I did on a report for the Council for Science and Society, *The Acceptability of Risks*, between 1973 and 1976. I produced drafts for the chapters; these were then reviewed and modified by a working party; and the whole text was finally edited before approval and publication by the Council. The report is too long to reproduce here in its entirety; and I feel that none of its separate sections would read well if taken out of its context in the tightly structured argument of the report. Although I do regret not seeing it republished, it is better to settle for the work which is all of my own composition.

The first section is an introduction to the subject, adapted from an article originally written for the journal *Physics Education*. In it I discuss the uncertainties inherent in the scientific study of risks; and I draw out the policy consequences of this aspect of risks research. This work on risks has led to my most recent researches, conducted in collaboration with S.O. Funtowicz, on uncertainties in quantitive information. Our joint book, *Uncertainty and Quality in Science for Policy*, is due to be published by Kluwer Academic in 1989.

The second section is based on a lecture presented at a conference on 'Technological risk: its perception and handling in the European community', held in Berlin in April 1979. This was sponsored by DG XII of the European Community, and it was held in the reconstructed Reichstag building, next to the Berlin Wall. It was set up as an attempt at a dialogue between scholarly critics of civil nuclear power and some influential persons in the research section of that industry. An unforeseen event gave added point to the conference: the accident at Three Mile Island. Some of the nuclear power people showed obvious concern, and also a sense that their credibility would henceforth be seriously affected; but others carried on with superb contempt for the assorted critics and radicals, those present no less than those absent.

The third section is extremely brief, but even it has an interesting story. The essay on which it is based was sent to the editor of the journal *Minerva*, who was a good friend of mine, as a sketch for a fuller piece. It was a development of ideas on quality control, that I had worked out in connection with science in my book *Scientific Knowledge and Its Social Problems* (1971), and which were still not popular. The editor offered to print the sketch as it stood immediately, as a comment on a long article that was just then ready for publication. I accepted the offer, not knowing anything about the article. This turned out to be a programmatic manifesto by a very important person, Wolf Häfele, the leader of the energy study at the International Institute for Applied Systems Analysis and also a well-known proponent of nuclear power in general and the fast-breeder reactor in particular. His paper very boldly stated the difficulties affecting any analysis of the risks of nuclear reactors, and proclaimed that there *would* be an answer. My little piece, arguing qualitatively about regulation rather than quantitatively about risks, gave another impression.

Finally, the last section is based on an article, 'The political economy of risk', which was written so that I could publish some ideas on risks that could not be expressed so explicitly in the report for the Council for Science and Society. It appeared in *New Scientist*, and was later republished in a booklet, *The Risk Equation*. Were I to write it again, I would be more explicit about the great variety of risks, so that the 'risks triangle' is significant only in some cases. On the other hand, I would emphasize more strongly that the imposition of a risk is a form of oppression. Indeed, in the economies known as 'socialist' or 'centrally planned', one may say that the imposition of risks on workers, neighbours and the natural environment has partly replaced profit-taking as the leading form of oppression. The imposition of risks, and the weaknesses of their regulation, have certainly become very sensitive, politically and ideologically, in recent years. Also, the question of why there should be such wanton imposition of risks in the absence of a profit motive could become an important focus for deeper studies of political economy in general.

RISK ASSESSMENT—A SCIENCE OF UNCERTAINTIES

Risks are very much in the news now; and the study of risks has assumed great importance for policy purposes. It is also a very useful example for the philosophical understanding of science. Until very recently, it was assumed on all sides that when 'science' was brought to bear on a problem of public concern, it would provide assured, objective facts from which the correct policy conclusions could be derived. This faith was shared even by those who worked in the fields from which the facts came, in spite of their personal experience of the extreme difficulties of producing information of adequate quality. It was in this spirit that the first quantitative studies of risk acceptability were begun in the later 1960s in connection with civil nuclear power. After only a decade of research and argument, the proponents of risks research had become much wiser and perhaps also sadder. For in spite of the apparently 'natural' character of the phenomena, there remain irreducible and important uncertainties in any assessment of a risk of a technological or industrial system. Moreover, the social and personal elements of a risks situation cannot be separated off from the scientific and engineering elements. Risks are in their way a total phenomenon; and must be studied as such.

Here, I will use examples primarily from nuclear power; this is appropriate, since this was the issue around which the science of risk assessment was created. I will try to show that while there is an objective 'scientific' core to any decision on risks, this is conditioned strongly in its interpretation by inexactness, uncertainty and value commitments. Simply citing strings of numbers without qualification is, in this area, *not* the scientific approach but rather a variety of pseudoscience.

The study of risks is very much an 'applied' or 'mission-orientated' activity. There is no organized body of knowledge achieved for its own sake, nor an elaborated structure of theoretical concepts. The 'scientific' part of the study of a particular risk is therefore always related to a practical task of management; it necessarily aims at results that are immediately useful for policy, rather than being elegant or theoretically deep. The work is all very empirical, indeed exploratory. Ideas and methods are still subject to modification and debate. There is no exclusive expertise which requires years of specialist training for its possession.

For our present purposes we may consider the task of risk management as divided into four phases: assessment, evaluation, decision and execution. The first one looks most like 'science'. The 'intensity' of a risk is measured by its 'probability' and 'harm' jointly (most simply, but not necessarily, by their product). In the next phase 'values' enter; to determine its 'acceptability' the given risk is compared to analogous known or existing risks and also to possible risks of alternative decisions in the case of major policy choices. All this information is provided by experts and is then fed into a process of decision conducted by people in a political role. It is recognized that in many cases of risks (particularly those involving choices of new technologies), the 'scientific' input is insufficient to determine the correct answer to immediate policy questions and so 'politics' quite legitimately comes in. Finally there is the phase of 'execution' which will involve the establishment and operation of monitoring systems, both hardware and human. Since an unenforceable decision is the worst of all, the practicalities of monitoring are a valid consideration in all the previous phases of the process, even including the framing of the problems for 'assessment'.

I should say that this model is capable of refinement in many ways, depending on the purpose of the discussion. For example, even before assessment must come recognition of a risk. This is not a trivial affair; and first signs of a low-level risk are frequently based on uncontrolled, anecdotal information, which may well relate to other physical causes or even just generalized fears and suspicions. Public authorities must steer a course between chasing after every

33

complaint (incidentally producing public concern and disturbance in the process) and being too cautious and then being accused of complacency or collusion with those interests that create risks. Thus even before 'assessment' can begin, there may be a quite contentious policy decision on whether there is anything there to assess!

Risk Assessment—the Elements

The elements of a risk assessment are, in form, quite simple: measures of the probability of an occurrence, and of the harm in the case of its happening. One can even imagine O-level questions: given such components for several comparable risks, determine which is the most, or least, 'acceptable'. There are many cases, indeed the vast majority of those where risk assessments are made, in which the techniques can be applied in a straightforward way. These will be in the various fields of 'safety' — at work, on roads, with respect to fire, medicines or consumer products. So long as the following conditions are satisfied, a straightforward process of risk assessment can be entirely adequate, functioning as an analytical tool supplementary to 'common sense'.

1. The risk situation is simple with a few clearly separable causes.
2. It occurs so often that there is a strong base in 'historic data' for the various empirical probabilities.
3. The sorts of harm are limited in variety and are capable of meaningful measurement on a common standard (or a few such).
4. Calculated measures of 'intensity' are used for *comparison* between related similar risks as an aid to design or management.

When we consider the risks that come under public scrutiny, we encounter a dilemma that is quite common in 'science in society' problems. It seems often (though fortunately not always!) that the more important the risk for public policy as a question of human or environmental welfare, the more it diverges from the four conditions defining the possibility of its effective assessment in a scientific way. Indeed, one distinguished American nuclear scientist, impressed by the intractable problems thrown at him for decision, coined the term 'trans-science' (Weinberg 1972). This describes those urgent problems, typically occurring in risk assessments, whose *form* is quite scientific but whose *content* puts them outside the limits of technical feasibility. His example was low-level ionizing radiation from nuclear power stations, the statistical test of whose possible carcinogenic properties would (by techniques available ten years ago) require some eight billion mice!

For the moment, let us defer the difficult or insoluble problems and stay with the easier ones. How is an assessment carried out? It is not enough to see how often there are some bodies to pick up and cart away, after a particular type of accident. Each undesirable event must be analysed both for its *causes* and for its *consequences*. Accidents are relatively rare events that occur through 'commission' and 'omission'. First, there is a chain of situations, events or actions, themselves each harmless or of only mild harm, but which when combined produce the occurrence in question. But also, for the accident to occur, the normal routines and procedures whereby the above 'incidents' are monitored, corrected or otherwise prevented from concatenation must be absent or ineffective. One simple case of these could be a 'blind corner' on a road, which an occasional driver (most likely one unfamiliar with the road) takes too quickly, and where a warning sign is obscured for a period in early summer by an overhanging tree (before the tree-pruning team get around to it). All it needs is for an exceptionally careless driver or some distracting presence to send a car around dangerously *and* a stationary car or pedestrian to be in the way. Then that very rare event (relative to many thousands of safe passages through the year), an accident, occurs.

When experts analyse such accidents they fill in the places in a matrix, or 'tree', with all the various predisposing causes and incidents as inferred from this and related accidents. They can then see which are most significant, and thereby advise on the most economic and effective policies for improvements.

Similar to such a retrospective analysis for the management of existing risks is the prospective analysis of the risks of installations being designed. There the 'fault tree' is constructed by analogy with known similar units; the probabilities of failures or incidents, inserted at the 'nodes' of the structure, are derived from historic data. The overall probabilities of accidents of various sorts are calculated by the compounding of those of their antecedents. Those which are too high, by some standard of evaluation, are then redesigned.

The 'human' element, the causes by 'omission', does not enter explicitly in such models since it is known that the 'incidents' may themselves be the result of inattentions, malevolence or some other human cause. However, where the monitoring functions become very sophisticated or elaborate, this aspect of the risk becomes exceedingly difficult to model or quantify.

Risk Quantification in Real Problems

Up to now I have sketched the elements of simple assessment problems with an indication of where complexities occur in the causal analysis. Now we must consider the real and very challenging problems that arise from the significant degree of inexactness in all the quantitative measures and estimates.

First, and perhaps most obviously, there is the estimation of harm. Where this is mainly material damage, as in many fires, then some sort of cost of replacement may be a convenient and reasonable measure. But where people are at risk, calculations can easily go wild. How much is a life worth, in coin of the realm? There are a variety of measures, ranging from compensation awards through to average investment in safety per year of life saved. They have little in common in basis, calculation or result. Do we count lost earnings or suffering of self and family? Or do we also discount the costs to society of maintaining non-productive persons? There is no 'objective' cost of a life, nor any of non-lethal harm. Hence we may say as a principle *calculations of personal risk that invoke a monetary measure of harm are liable to be highly arbitrary or biased.*

Policy decisions are best based on an explicit measure of human injury. Traditionally this has been done, for the case of nuclear power, by numerical conversion of radiation dosage into cancer cases, but even this cannot encompass genetic damage to future generations. By some standards such harm is ethically impermissible even at very low incidence because of its irreversible effects on totally innocent persons.

Coming now to the measurement of probabilities, we are on ground that should be familiar to every scientist, for real quantitative science begins with a recognition that perfect precision is impossible; the real skill in using mathematics lies in the management of inexactness. Students know that every set of experimental readings has a 'spread', sometimes inappropriately called 'random error'. Indeed, one way that teachers can detect concocted data is when it fits *too* closely to the known theoretical curve! And the description of a quantitative result is at best faulty, and at worst meaningless, unless it is accompanied by an indication of its inexactness. This may be done by a very simple convention such as 'significant digits' or by some more elaborate notation. But in its absence we may find an implied precision which is totally false and misleading, especially in the case of estimate-statements like '2×10^{-6}'.

Such considerations apply even more strongly to statements of probability. I may say that the empirical probability of a particular coin coming up heads is 100%, but if that is the result of a single toss, my statement is really misleading. If I toss it, say, 10 times and come up with, say, 60% heads, what does *that* tell me about its possible bias? In fact, to have any rigorous meaning at all, probability statements should be the consequence of a *test*, organized around a particular *hypothesis*, to a *preassigned* confidence limit. Otherwise they cannot be distinguished from the results of a search for interesting strings of digits in a telephone directory.

The full theory of statistical testing and inference would take us too far afield from our present concerns. Let it suffice to establish two principles. The first is that every test, involving confidence limits, depends for its design on *values:* most simply the relative undesirability of the two sorts of error: 'pessimism' (the 'cry wolf' syndrome) and 'optimism' (or complacency). In a classic example, we apply different standards when sampling for rotten apples in barrels and for hypersensitive landmines in their cases. The second principle important for the assessment of statements about risk, is *every quantitative statement involving probabilities (or other estimates of uncertainty) must have some indication of its degree of inexactness.*

Finally, I must mention the more severe problems that inevitably arise in the assessment of the most important technological risks. The measurement and expression of *uncertainty* is a challenging but practicable task. But what to do about *ignorance*? Sometimes this relates to phenomena that are too subtle to be studied effectively, as in the case of low-level radiation. But ignorance may equally well apply to quite important contingencies that are not at all unlikely and where a formal risk assessment requires some sort of number in a box. One obvious case in point is terrorism, sabotage or other forms of 'malevolence'. There have already been a number of incidents of this character, directed at civil nuclear installations. How seriously should they be taken? Some policy decisions are easily settled by a purely qualitative analysis of the problem. Thus there are no known plans to site nuclear reactors in Northern Ireland, in spite of the absence of indigenous energy supplies and the consequent high price of energy there. Whatever quantities we might assign to the attentions of the Provisional IRA, they are too high under our circumstances. However, in the Third World, governments cannot be so fastidious, and with the approval of the International Atomic Energy Authority nuclear installations are set up in countries where there is no certainty of firm and stable civil rule throughout the planned lifetime of a reactor.

Less dramatic but equally important is the inevitable ignorance about the behaviour of technologies that are new or complex or both. For example, the 'fault trees' used in analysis of nuclear reactors have needed to be 'pruned' since the catalogue of *all* possible pathways and their interconnections would yield a completely intractable problem. Hence, in the US system, accidents resulting from several things going wrong at once have been excluded and situations of human error in response to crises cannot be modelled at all. Yet at Three Mile Island it was just such a combination that created a classic accident.

Even the probabilities that are inserted at the nodes of fault trees become highly inexact or even speculative under such circumstances. Without a long history of use, even the failure rates for pumps and valves are guesswork unless there is a special and expensive testing programme for each such component. It takes only a few such 'guesstimates' to yield a very different impression; four probabilities in a chain, each 'optimistic' by a factor of ten (well within a reasonable range of inexactness) will then produce a risk apparently ten thousand times less severe, which may well bring it up from 'unacceptable' to 'acceptable' on the scale. And in the absence of good historic data, such probabilities are derived either from theoretical models of a physical process or from experts' estimates—frequently reducing to guesses in both cases.

Judgements about Quantities in Risk Management

We can now see how the assessments of real risks for policy purposes may become a much less tidy affair than the simple calculation 'intensity = probability × harm' would indicate. This should be no great surprise to those who understand physical science. Indeed, the surprising thing is that some very abstract and simplified models of physical systems have, over the past few centuries, had such extraordinary and unprecedented power for human understanding and control of the physical world. But the particular interest of risks is that the complications to be coped with are not merely of the natural systems under study, but also of human beings, as we react to events and also as we try to describe paradoxical phenomena.

As a first example we may consider how qualitative judgements become very important, even crucial, in the expression of quantitative descriptions. Suppose we have an element of a fault tree, whose probability is known to within a factor of ten. If we write it by some suggestive convention, as (in computer notation) $p = E(-6 \pm 1)$, then we may convey a misleading impression of precision in the ± 1. But we cannot write 1.5 — that would be absurdly over-precise! How to indicate the inexactness of the inexactness? That problem must be left for another occasion.

Further, the choice of a 'representative' numerical value within the *band* of reasonable values of an estimate will itself have policy consequences. A string of most-pessimistic values would probably (!) involve overstating risks; and optimistic ones, understatement; yet what is sacred about those in the middle? Sometimes, if the calculations are not too complex, a statement of whether 'optimistic' or 'pessimistic' values are chosen (with a quantitative indication, necessarily inexact!) can be helpful for clarifying subsequent discussion. But a display of some values or other, without explanation or qualification, can convey information that is inadequate or positively misleading. Thus we have the paradox that, particularly in the case of risks, quantitative assertions require qualitative judgements of their inexactness if they are to have genuine, useful content.

Another case to consider is where the paucity of the data requires the use of quite complex judgements on probabilities, as inputs, to a decision. Here as an example we have the problem of cracks in the pressure vessels of the PWR reactor. There is a chance that such cracks, once established, will propagate rapidly and catastrophically when the steel of the vessel is subjected to great stresses, typically in the case of some incident involving rapid changes of temperature and pressure. This is more likely to happen with large cracks than with small ones. Also, remote methods for sensing cracks are relatively more successful for large cracks than for small ones. The risk calculation then involves the probability that some crack which escaped detection by being 'small' nonetheless would propagate rapidly by being 'large'. Numbers can be assigned to each contingency but they must have their inexactness, with respect to statistical confidence limits, and also be accompanied by technical discussion of both the testing and the consequence of failure. After all that, the question of the 'acceptability' of the risk of pressure vessel failure by crack propagation becomes hedged in a labyrinth of qualifications and explanations (Cottrell 1982). The final answer may then be 'obvious' to the experts concerned, particularly if all the indicators point in the direction of an 'optimistic' conclusion. But the inescapable presence of judgements about quantities describing uncertainties and ignorance cannot be denied.

The above example displays another characteristic feature of nuclear technology that distinguishes it sharply from other technologies and the run-of-the-mill risks that are managed with reasonable success. We can call this a 'zero−infinity' risk; or rather 'incalculable−immeasurable'. That is, the risks may well have been brought down below the point where numerical analysis is meaningful (say, one in a million). Yet the consequences of the most serious sort of accident, involving release of much radioactive material into the air and groundwater, are not to be contemplated as 'acceptable' in any way. This paradox cannot be resolved; in no way can nuclear materials be made benign.

In such cases, where the numbers, however forcefully stated, do not carry conclusive weight, other criteria are invoked. Rather as in a courtroom proceeding, the experts are assessed along with (or even instead of) their arguments. It may be very upsetting to scientists to be treated like the tame psychiatrists who are trotted out for and against 'diminished responsibility' pleas in murder cases; they deal in objective physical facts, not subjective opinions on mental states. But we have seen that while quantitative facts are still at the core of risk assessments, they are inevitably swathed in a variety of qualitative and value-laden judgements. For experts to pretend that this is not so, only decreases their credibility further. And this 'forensic' approach to the problem is not entirely inappropriate. For what is at stake is not the confirmation of purported knowledge, to be made at leisure by a community of scholars, but a decision on policy, to be made urgently by an agency representing society.

As the credibility of experts is eroded, it becomes ever more difficult to restore or even maintain it. The present severe plight of the American nuclear power industry is partly due to the ineffectiveness of the experts from the industry and from the Nuclear Regulatory Commission before, during and after the Three Mile Island accident.

More recently, observers of risks management have needed to reflect on the strange fact that it was university *students* in America who discovered a serious problem that had eluded all the experts for decades: the intense and long-lasting burden of radioactivity in the metals used as alloys in the PWR pressure vessel shell. These transform — for the worse — all the estimates of the costs and feasibility of decommissioning nuclear reactors (Norman 1982). Previous assurances by experts that 'there is no evidence of risk' then tell more about their methods than about the risk; and future assurances, however well founded, are inevitably discounted.

The science of risk assessment as we know it was created largely in response to the problems of the nuclear power industry. It was shaped partly for internal design methods and quality control and partly for public reassurance. Whatever else happens to civil nuclear power, this byproduct will survive as an indispensable intellectual tool for our coping with an increasingly complex and hazardous natural and man-made environment.

Those who promoted civil nuclear power had the sense of being revolution-aries—they had a vision of a boon for mankind of nearly magical proportions. They were doubtless men of intelligence, integrity and commitment. If there was a failing, it was of simplicity. Just as nuclear reactions are essentially straightforward as physical science, so (they thought) should the assessment of their risks be essentially straightforward as a review exercise. But as engineer-ing systems involving ageing, thermal stresses, corrosion and cracks, nuclear stations have proved increasingly troublesome. Similarly, the associated risks displayed novel and paradoxical properties: simple quantitative assertions would not suffice, and unpredictable human errors proved more important in practice than randomly occurring mechanical failures. The injection of politics, of the new 'environmental pressure group' sort, only further confused issues for the scientifically trained experts.

But all that is behind us now; the present question is whether the European nuclear power industry can escape the fate of its American parent. New industries, such as biotechnology, are providing challenges to risk assessment that are still more demanding, technically and practically as well. It is all a long way from the security of examination question exercises, but for any scientist who has wondered how to convert some messy experimental data by some reasonably honest process into an acceptable result, it should not be totally unfamiliar.

PUBLIC PERCEPTIONS OF ACCEPTABLE RISKS

When one considers the various public responses to the risks that it recognizes, and considers their great variety, confusion, and even inconsistency, one is struck by the magnitude of the problem of achieving public acceptance of the various risks that seem inherent in our modern technological order. I wish to stress right away the apparent inconsistency in the public's classification of risks as either acceptable or unacceptable; for even though I feel very strongly that the public has something important to say to the experts about the risks which are imposed on it, still it would be false (and also it would be incorrect and harmful to my argument) if I were to pretend that there is some instant wisdom available to the general public in its evaluation of risks.

There are several possible responses to this phenomenon of the public's fickleness, if I may put it so strongly. One is the simplest, technocratic interpretation, which is to use this as evidence of the incompetence and irratio-nality of the general public when faced with problems of a sophisticated, high-technology society. This type of public response to risk is then strong evidence against the extension of democracy in public affairs and for the restriction of genuine decision-making power to a technocratic élite. Given this response, there will doubtless be various techniques applied to lull the public into accepting what the experts know is best for it; but this should not be confused with a genuine attempt to meet the public's anxieties. A second approach is to take the public seriously, at least as a political force, and to try to see just what rational structure there might possibly be in its choices of risks to accept or reject. There might then be developed a taxonomy of risks, with some genera being found less acceptable to the public (regardless of their intrinsic degree of hazard). Then our policies which involve the creation of risks could be tailored to fit more comfortably with the public views or prejudices. This is still in the realm of a technical fix to the problem, in that it attempts to shift from a problem involving values to one where scientific methods, in this case at the administrative rather than the physical level, can suffice. Let me make it clear instantly that I do not oppose such taxonomies, but I have reservations about their effectiveness in solving a problem of this magnitude.

Finally, we may use this particular phenomenon, and the genuine crisis in government which it now threatens to create, to reconsider the whole field of risks, their production, their understanding, and their management. I am convinced that without such a deeper perspective, any attempts at management of the problem will be seen, and sometimes correctly so, as attempts at manipulation. And given the degree to which the problem of risks is political, then such attempts are liable to be rejected quite independently of their genuine motives and merits. My own thesis is that the peculiar structure of risks, both cognitive and technical, which is revealed by the variety of public perceptions of acceptance takes it out of the realm of scientific control on the technical side, and out of bureaucratic or manipulative control on the political side. For the management of risks in our present high-technology society, we must recognize that we can no longer apply the politics of 'economism', where quantitative differences can be negotiated between opposing sides; rather we must accept some features of the politics of 'ethnicity', where deep differences of values must be confronted and then used for the mutual education of both sides.

Cognitive Aspects

The first thing that we must appreciate about risks is their totality in human experience. Every human action (or even a decision for inaction) involves some risk, and the risk from any given action has ramifications for all other areas of human experience. Therefore, the hope that one can give a taxonomy, an evaluation, and finally a technical fix to the problems of risks is as ambitious as trying to put all of human experience and values on to a scale of measurement for mathematical or political manipulation. The variety in the public perceptions of acceptable risk partly reflects the variety of life itself. Our understanding of risks encounters certain quite severe difficulties which, I believe, are unique among problems of an ostensibly experimental or scientific character.

There are three basic contradictions in our cognition of risks. In many important senses risks are incalculable, unimaginable and uncontrollable.

For the first, we may observe that unless a hazard is so very common that the probability of occurrence is right up into the range of percentage points, then it lies below the limit of where anyone can normally make consistent calculations with quantitative estimates of probability. When we consider major hazards, of the sort where damage of an occurrence is very great, but the probability is very small, perhaps down to one in millions or even billions, then the phenomenon is like losing on a gigantic lottery. It is then in the realm of 'luck' rather than of a calculated gamble. The impossibility of calculating the risk in a gambler's way leads to a deeper sort of contradiction, namely that it is extremely difficult to imagine the hazard as affecting oneself. The attitude 'it can't happen to me' may indeed be the appropriate one for a sane and healthy person. Avoiding or preventing the occurrence of the hazard cannot then depend on a lively imagination of the outcome, but on some other considerations of costs and benefits, deriving perhaps from the system of control of the hazard. Finally, I would say that risks are conceptually uncontrollable, in the sense that one can never know, either in advance or even in retrospect, whether one did *enough* to prevent a hazard from being realized. Even in retrospect one is still left with two questions: how much more action would have been necessary to prevent it? and would such action have been within the bounds of reasonable behaviour? Thus all three contradictions are facets of the same phenomenon.

Now I am not advocating that all risks are totally incapable of being subjected to the processes of ordinary reasoning. Certainly, we do calculate probabilities, we do act with caution and prudence, and we do try to prevent the occurrence of accidents. However, my point is that the application of logical and mathematical reasoning, personal imagination and prudential measures does not have such a close relation to experience, either good or bad, that we can claim to be in control of the phenomena, either perceptually, personally, or technically. The reasoning involved in talking about risks is probabilistic rather than simply causal—i.e. we do not have simple chains of inference, inductive or deductive, and simple lines of confirmation or refutation, as we do in other areas. The inadequacy of causal reasoning, combined with these basic contradictions in thinking about risks, leaves us without adequate tools for their comprehension and management.

Probability Calculus

Some might argue that the application of a probability calculus to the analysis of risks solves these problems. I would strongly disagree. 'Probability' (in this sense of quantified likelihood) is an extremely new idea in our culture; only a few centuries have elapsed since its very first conception. The meaning of probability is multiple and, in each sense, obscure and confused. Also, the application of a probability calculus (even under such reasonable rules as we possess) to any real situation is (if properly done) as far more complex exercise than is realized by all except a very small minority among expert practitioners. Strictly speaking, any probability has meaning only when fiducial limits are attached to it; and furthermore, to be quite strict, and probability assertion has meaning only as a result of the testing of a hypothesis about an experimental situation. Certainly, we can quite effectively use probabilities as loosely and unrigorously as we use most other scientific concepts and tools; but we must face the fact that this is, as yet, a new and very rough tool, quite imperfectly understood. To blame the public for inconsistent reasoning with probabilities, when so much nonsense is purveyed by certified experts, is hardly fair or useful.

The burden of my argument is that reasoning in the scientific mode, either causal or probabilistic, does not suffice for getting us through the arguments involved in the management of risks. In other areas of experience where this is the case, we can replace or supplement scientific reasoning by a sort of 'personal' knowledge. In this, belief can be based partly on authority, and values and the decisions they constrain are based partly on personal affiliations. Indeed, that is the sort of reasoning which actually holds society together; the great insight of conservative political philosophy, as well as the force of conservative politics, is that explicit reason has only a minor and marginal role to play compared to unquestioned custom and tradition in society. In the areas of technological risks whose acceptability is now in question, this 'conservative' support is not available in full strength. First, the problems themselves have a technical component which calls for a large element of scientific discussion; this is in principle antithetical to the personal, 'conservative' approach. Moreover, the very novelty of the problems takes them out of the realm of the customary; here they lack that mellowness of age, which enables the conservative type of authority to be developed.

The political problem of risks is in these ways analogous to pre-revolutionary situations in societies under stress. In these the conservative style of resolution of tensions and conflicts becomes ineffective quite simply because it is no longer accepted. Societal cohesion must be maintained, if at all, by other means. Thus the problem of technological risks has structural features which put it in a distinct class, being capable of effective control neither by a purely scientific analysis (resting on an accepted expertise) nor on a 'personal', conservative, type of authority (on which our society normally depends for its smooth running). In consequence, when there is a polarized debate on risks, appeals from the authority of one side, whether based on scientific expertise or on political charisma, are very vulnerable to refutation or rejection. And because of the cognitive structure of the problems, there are in them no adequate internal barriers against a debate slipping totally out of control, with the two sides losing that element of dialogue which is necessary for a genuine resolution.

Technical Aspects

Any discussion of technological risks must begin with a reminder of the great reduction in the hazards to life which has taken place, at least in the rich countries of the world, over the last generations. Life is now safer than it used to be; not merely are we better protected against micro-organisms that use us as hosts, but also in all aspects of daily living and travelling, there is no doubt that we are safer as well as cleaner than ever before. In the poor countries the situation is far more mixed. There have been some very dramatic reductions in the hazards of life, particularly in the cases where Western medicine and sanitation are appropriate. But many traditional hazards survive, and now they are supplemented by high-technology hazards exported by ourselves in the form of many new practices and pollutants. Here I cannot go into the trade in 'bads' or 'dyscommodities' which now parallels the trade in 'goods'; at the present time it is partly an exchange of environmental toxicants (from the rich) for human ones (from the poor). Any serious discussion of risks in the global context would need to incorporate this aspect.

Concentrating my focus on the technological risks of the advanced societies, I will say that in general they defy an approach to their reduction that is based on scientific analysis and piecemeal hazards engineering. For examples I will consider two possible exceptions, the first real and the second apparent. With aircraft accidents we have a situation rather beautifully under technical control. The possibilities for mechanical failure and human error are scrutinized in the light of the rare accidents and incidents that occur; and, given the very large number of repeated hazardous situations, there are enough of these to support a probabilistic analysis. Hence they are controlled in order of severity, and the mode of transport becomes safer all the time. By contrast, the causes of road accidents are complex, and lie deep in political and personal attitudes and values; speed and drugs are still the main cause of death and injury on a scale which, if inflicted by a political enemy, would be totally unacceptable, and perhaps even destructive of the social order.

This contrast is most striking in connection with the risks to pedestrians, which are systematically underplayed in all official and industry pronounce-ments in spite of constituting an epidemic of violence; and particularly the risks to children, which are orders of magnitude more prevalent than the risks of the traditional diseases. Since strictly obeyed speed limits would signi-ficantly reduce the scale of these assaults, we have here a good example of a social 'acceptability' of a risk imposed on some for the sake of convenience and gratification for others.

The case of automobile accidents, then, is only partly a technical question; it is now even more a political, social and moral problem. But the same was true of the health hazards of the Victorian industrial cities; and by gradual, many-sided reforms (which, of course, required heroic campaigns for their accomplishment) they were eventually conquered.

However, the characteristic hazards of modern times, those which (to the chagrin of the associated experts) cause more agitation than the endemic disease-type hazards as from automobiles, are very different. These are of the 'major hazard' sort, where the maximum estimated probability of an occurrence is very low indeed, but the possible damage from an occurrence is exceedingly, or unacceptably, high. It should be fairly well accepted on all sides that such hazards, particularly in their more remote effects, are in the realm of what Weinberg (1972) has so aptly called 'trans-science': where scientific data, however necessary for a partial exploration of the problem, will be impossible to compile for its total resolution. Moreover, the structure of the hazard, as a concatenation of possible causes and effects, is always complex and depends strongly on human vigilance and commitment. Hence the probabilities which are assigned at the nodes of an analysis depend more upon moral factors and judgements than they do upon repetitious events like the throwing of dice or the random variations of mechanical equipment; and they should therefore have very wide fiducial limits indeed. When one carries such quantities with their 'error bars' or estimates of inexactness through a complex calculation, the result may quite likely have such a wide band of inexactness as to lose all effective meaning as an estimate of an absolute risk. To pretend otherwise, and to use hyper-precise numbers (just the digits with no indications of inexactness) in a calculation, is to compromise scientific integrity. To proceed further, and to compare the results of two such exercises applied to quite different sorts of risks, involves losing political credibility as well.

Looking at these 'major hazards' as a class, we can see that, up to the present at least, there has been a tendency for them to increase in severity through causes arising out of our prevalent styles of science, technology and administration. In the first place, the division of intellectual and managerial labour in a large bureaucracy with its attendant constriction of vision from any one vantage point makes it possible for hazards to grow unnoticed from within the bureaucracy. Indeed, there are significant cases on record where bureaucracies either denied the existence of obvious hazards, or tossed the problem around from office to office, since a recognition and action would have been too costly in personal terms for any one individual.

Also, in this period we have witnessed the dominance of a 'gargantuan' style in technological design. This affected first oil tanker ships, and then nuclear-powered electricity-generating plants (outside France). The technological or financial rationale for this growth was always thin, particularly when design was considered in the context of construction and operation. But in the culture of bureaucracies, bigger has always been beautiful in a variety of ways; and so our major hazards have inevitably become more concentrated. This trend may now be reversed through changes of style and aesthetic; some of our major hazards may thereby be alleviated, but the essential problem will remain as one characteristic of our high-technology society.

The final technical aspect of hazards needing discussion is rather delicate, and my viewpoint may be considered contentious. This is that the competence of those responsible for managing hazards is liable (more than in ordinary

45

science or industry) to be inadequate to the task. Hence in those areas of our technological society where quality control is most crucial, it can be at its most difficult to achieve. Evidence for this is supplied by the published enquiries into disasters in the USA, such as at Three Mile Island and Challenger. Indeed, the continued occurrence of 'incidents' of various sorts in American civil nuclear reactors has been important in depriving the industry there of what was left of its credibility after the near-catastrophe of 1979. Why Americans should have these problems more severely than other nations is a problem that could be answered by 'the anthropology of quality control', a topic beyond my concerns here.

For an analysis of 'major hazards' we note first that they are liable to occur in technologies that are complex or novel to some significant degree. There have been no opportunities for the development of the craft skills whereby small-scale mishaps are monitored and contained, and a craft wisdom developed of how systems can go wrong and be righted. Also, new installations, with their combination of inexperience of operatives and instability of operating conditions, are particularly at risk. Further, the problems of analysing and containing hazards are as yet not standard or salient in the training and outlook of scientists and engineers; courses in such topics are conspicuous by their absence in formal curricula. Further, the bias of the leading schools in risk analysis, towards formal probabilistic models and away from craft experience and intuition, predisposes all concerned to concentrate on the scientific aspects of the problem and to ignore the human and moral aspects. Thus the major nuclear power accidents have all resulted from 'errors' of sorts that were not included in the models. One might say that a theoretical scheme for hazards that omits the category 'a disaster waiting to happen' is likely to be an abstract exercise, providing comfort to some but otherwise not much use.

This analysis would be incomplete without a reminder of the strains and distortions on practice to which the large-scale innovative technologies are particularly prone. Three Mile Island was finished in a hurry so that the owners could obtain a tax rebate; and with the Space Shuttle NASA had to prove that it could accomplish an impossible mission. In this latter case, the burden of proof of hazards was explicitly imposed on those who warned; if a system had operated safely two dozen times already, this was effective evidence that there was nothing to worry about this time. Finally, we should also keep in mind the tendency of bureaucracies to stick to decisions once taken, however insecure their foundation, because of the political costs of change and of public admission of error.

The same considerations hold in the case of hazards which affect the natural environment through pollution, either chronic or potentially disastrous. There it is common to find a 'David and Goliath' situation, where an embattled community, commanding resources in background education and self-taught expertise, engages with a slow-moving bureaucracy whose relevant expertise is inexpert in the ways I have described. My own education in these matters began with a consideration of the story of the proposed nuclear reactor at

Bodega Head, California. In this pioneering case of environmental conflict, Pacific Gas and Electric, with the co-operation of the University of California, fought for years to defeat an opposition which maintained that the reactor was on a shelf of rock that sloped down towards the sea, less than half a mile from a branch of the San Andreas Fault. Asking myself how this could happen, I began to articulate the ideas that are developed above. In the case of major hazards, an analysis which treats them as a purely physical problem is bound to be misleading, ineffective and in the long run counter-productive.

Social Aspects

Having reviewed the difficulties in the way of a scientific approach to the analysis and control of major hazards, we can now see how these affect the social aspects of their management. In any problem of decision there will be one party (at least) which must go away dissatisfied; and for decisions to be accepted, those making them must be accorded legitimacy by all the parties to the debate. In the absence of such legitimacy, debates will tend to be resolved by simple coercion; or, alternatively, those who lose in a particular decision will feel entitled to carry on the struggle by whatever means. Thus the risks problem brings out in a particularly sharp form the phenomenon which Habermas (1976) has called the 'crisis of legitimacy' of modern society. For the authority of those who make decisions does not, as in former days, derive from a merit based on blood or wealth; it derives really from what the Americans have called 'the consent of the governed', based on the competence with which authorities exercise their functions. Now, we have just seen that in the case of risk problems, such a competence has a severe inherent limit. The trans-scientific character of the problems themselves, the immaturity of the sciences which occupy crucial positions in any argument, and the absence of a logic whereby inexact estimates can be translated into sharply defined conclusions and decisions, all seriously compromise any claims of a deciding authority to scientific competence of the traditional sort. Yet, in the absence of a scientific competence, what other basis is there for its necessary legitimacy?

The character of the outcome of realized hazards leads to difficulties in any negotiation on their accepted levels. After all, we are dealing here with the possibility of injury and death, perhaps on such as scale as to produce severe social dislocation and damage to the fabric of civilization. Few will now claim that harm of such a character can be reliably or usefully represented on a monetary scale to any degree of exactness.

This means that we cannot rely on what has been called the 'intersubjective comparability of utilities' on which our economic analysis has depended as a fundamental axiom.

Negotiations over hazards therefore cannot be easily reduced to the same sort as negotiations in economic affairs, even those which produce coercive outbreaks, as in strikes over pay. In that case, in the last resort, there will be a compromise somewhere between the two positions on a basically quantitative scale, perhaps as modified at the fringes for political or psychological effect. Here the only quantitative scale is one of inexact probabilities, and these are qualifying an event which at a high probability is absolutely impermissible. Moreover, the juggling with probabilities can easily take on the substance of a ritual; very roughly speaking, a risk of one in a million (on some appropriate scale) is considered 'acceptable', while one in ten thousand is definitely not (except in the work-place). Now, that is a factor of a hundred, which is really not much of a definite band in which to negotiate, when the risks themselves are so imperfectly known.

Yet we must not ignore the economic aspect of any existing hazards. When we are reminded that the amelioration of a hazard would be impossible or counter-productive because the remedy would cost too much, we are thereby shown that someone is, in effect, putting lives and limbs at risk because it is cheaper to do so. I must hasten to say that the action need not at all be undertaken in a cold-blooded spirit; the basic contradictions of hazard analysis affect the reasonings of those who impose hazards on others just as much as those who inflict them on themselves. It could be that a more skilled management of uncertain quantities could ameliorate some of these problems; if experts could avoid the traps of hyper-precision, and reason in orders of magnitude when appropriate, then it could at least be clear when there is a scientific foundation for distinction among risks, and when the problem is in the ethical or political/economic realms. Regardless of the self-conscious understanding of any of the agents, it is possible to see cases of the imposition of risks on others as a form of oppression. Indeed, this style of oppression might be characteristic of our affluent high-technology society, as distinct from those others where the strong have oppressed the weak by simple overwork and underpayment, along with lethally hazardous conditions.

One further feature of technological and environmental risks should be mentioned, as a corrective to some simplistic ideas that are held by many theorists. This is that only rarely is it possible to make a simple 'decision' by which the problem is resolved once and for all. Rather, the management of any large-scale hazard is a continuously evolving process that may extend over decades. In the case of industrial plant, it can start with the first intentions to design and build, continue through construction and start-up, be modified but still present as a monitoring task during normal operation, and finally produce new sorts of problems in decommissioning and disposal. Each of these phases has its characteristic scientific, engineering and political aspects. And while bureaucracies, unlike individual protestors, are eternal, citizens' movements can persist a long time, and it only takes one victory on their part to stop a project forever. Hence we would do well to stop thinking of simple 'decision-making' on risks, and concentrate instead on the complex ongoing process of managing risks.

Consequences of Failure

The problems of risks, from technology and the environment, are not central to our societies; we still worry more about employment and inflation. But they have been growing, in size and severity; and all the indications are that they will continue to do so for the foreseeable future. Looking at them as a task for management by the institutions of society, I have argued that they present new challenges. For by their nature they deprive those institutions of the traditional supports by which their legitimacy is maintained; and yet the work of these institutions is uniquely sensitive to the trust placed in them by those who are affected by their decisions. This combination of importance and fragility of the institutional management of risks derives from the cognitive, technical and social aspects of the task.

Although the multiplicity and variety of risks problems precludes any simple assessment of success or failure (unless there should be some overwhelming threat that is coped with with greater or less success), overall it will eventually be possible to have some assessment of the success of the management of risks in any given nation. That success will be related to the achievement of a consensus on risk management, so that those who lose on any particular issue will not feel obliged or entitled to carry their grievance outside the constitutional channels. It would be as well to consider the consequences of a failure of effective management, and the resulting breakdown of consensus.

The failure of a consensus in any area of public concern may take some time to show its effects. For in the absence of a crisis, the routine work of government and society can continue more or less undisturbed. It is only when a new, serious challenge is presented, and cannot be met because of a lack of intellectual or moral resources, that there is a discovery of a degeneration that may be irreparable. In the meantime, there are only trends, any of which may be contested.

The most notorious example of the effects of a failed consensus on risks management is the nuclear power industry in the USA. Although some plants are still going forward, new orders stopped a very long time ago, and there are famous cases where protestors either stopped a reactor or even drove a utility into bankruptcy. Those responsible for the development of genetic engineering are well aware of the importance of the 'dread' factor in the public perception of risk, however much they may consider such fears to be groundless.

These localized technological and environmental risks have brought into being a new sort of politics, where NIMBY groups (Not In My Back Yard) join with ideologically based pressure groups to fight off LULU plans (Locally Unwanted Land Use). This might be merely an enlargement of the politically active consituencies, to match the development of the problems of managing technology, except that such groups can become militant and coercive to a degree that is inconsistent with their general social location. One reason for this is the breakdown in trust in the institutions that are planning the LULU,

49

and also in those that are supposed to be regulating the problem on behalf of society and themselves. Further, they see themselves as victims of a policy which imposes severe costs on them on behalf of an impalpable generalized benefit for all of society. It would be hard to assuage this grievance except by instituting a new principle of compensation for local risks; and no government is eager to open up such a new source of claims on the public purse.

One result of this new source of confrontation is that a new militancy in political action has developed, and spread even to traditionally deferential and law-abiding societies like England. The earliest manifestations of this activity were in connection with protests against motorway plans, and even more, against the rules under which enquiries were held. This brought a partial victory; and since then the major investment decisions, as on civil nuclear power, have all been accompanied by lengthy enquiries which gave at least a show of concern for risk and environmental factors.

So long as such struggles are focused on proposed new developments, they may be seen as marginal to the ongoing political and economic life of a society. They do become a serious nuisance when the disposal of wastes is in question. The sheer bulk of ordinary wastes, the menace of toxic wastes and the special horror associated with nuclear wastes make all aspects of this problem particularly fraught. We are all learning the truth of Barry Commoner's axiom of ecology, 'Everything has to go somewhere' (Commoner 1966); and there is no 'somewhere' that is free of political or environmental worries. Of course, it is possible that the rejection of such wastes, for deposit or even for transport, will eventually force the waste-producing authorities to think again about what they are doing. It would be no bad thing for such political struggles to induce a transformation of consciousness (it has already happened in the case of nuclear weapons); and following on that a change in the style and values of the technology itself.

The issue might become more serious, should there be some major challenge, perhaps on the analogy of a Chernobyl accident where the radiation was approaching the acute danger level, or perhaps in the framing and implementation of plans to move populations away from land likely to be flooded and then submerged through the rise of sea-level in the anticipated greenhouse effect. There are many other possible threats to the stability of any of our societies; and those concerning risks and the environment are by no means guaranteed to become the most salient. However, they are there, and will certainly grow before they decrease. Hence as a problem in government, they deserve serious consideration.

Remedies and Recommendations

Since the political dangers I have just described are in many ways inherent in the character of the technological risks we now face, there is obviously no simple way out of them. All that one can do is to suggest measures which could lead to a better understanding of the problem, and eventually towards its amelioration in various ways.

Starting at an immediately practical level, I believe that we could do well to have a close scrutiny of technological design as it has developed in the post-war period, and an examination of the sorts of styles, values, and fashions which have operated, perhaps quite unconsciously, in major spheres. The influence of vested interests and institutional pressures of various sorts could well be brought into such a study, so that we would have a better appreciation of the shape of that thing which must be submitted to social control, if we are to have a consensus, or indeed survival.

I see the problem of risks not so much as one of decisions as one of regulation, and I have also become keenly aware of the difference between the national styles of regulation in America, Britain and continental Europe.

I believe that attempts to transfer ideas and techniques from one culture to another may be frustrated in the absence of an understanding of the influence of social and cultural context. Certainly, a study of contrasting styles in some sample field (as I have seen in the case of recombinant DNA research) could be quite illuminating.

Stepping back slightly from everyday practice, we might review our attitudes to the 'participatory' aspects of decision-making on major technological risks. How much do those in authority still view them as a nuisance, a diversion from the real tasks that must be endured for strictly political reasons? I would suggest that we would do better to welcome them as an essential part of technological development in the modern world. For the problems involving technological risks *cannot* be reduced to exercises, puzzles for solution in one or two established exact sciences. The various sorts of fragmented certified expertise are no longer competent to predict and control all the manifold unexpected and undesirable outcomes of new developments. The problems should be seen necessarily as a dialogue rather than as a linear demonstrative style. The greater the variety of viewpoints, the more effective imaginative insights will be achieved.

The time and resources spent on such methods at the outset of developments may seem large at the time. But they are always a very small fraction of the total cost. And their sheer savings, in avoiding redesigned or aborted projects later on, can be significant.

This change of approach to the management of risks would involve important changes of attitude. In the first place, it appears that a set of attitudes which may be called 'scientism' may well be too rigid or even brittle to be allowed to survive unchanged in this coming period. Certainly, we should be able to recognize that in many important fields the certified (academically trained) expertise does not have a monopoly of competence in all aspects of the problems. In the USA (a country more open and pluralistic than the UK in many ways) they already give standing to local amateur 'public interest groups', lending them financial support and even helping them organize training programmes for their own home-grown experts. A similar process is just now

51

starting in England, at least with respect to financial support. Of course, to relax the claims of certified expertise to a monopoly of competence in particular areas has its own dangers. However, when one is in a situation where all the problems are trans-scientific and where the relevant sciences are frequently immature, the pretence of a monopoly of expertise is one that can become counter-productive. Consequent on this, we might as well begin to revise our image of science itself, and reconsider which sort of natural science should be the paradigm example.

Relevant Science

For a very long time the 'real' science was considered to be physics, with its combination of precise experimentation with powerful mathematical theory. The triumphs of physics in these past three hundred years do not require any elaboration here. But it may be questioned whether this is the science whose characteristics are the most relevant to the problems we now face, and to the sorts of solutions we can achieve. If one were to consider toxicology, climatology or nutrition, or even energy forecasting, we would then encounter a very different picture indeed. Here we do not find scientific knowledge rolling back the frontiers with ignorance, and its applications steadily increasing human power, as on the old scheme. Rather, we find ourselves in situations where facts are uncertain, values in dispute, stakes high and decisions urgent. One traditional image of science was that of a map, where the representation was becoming more accurate without limit; now we have a reality that is changing more quickly, under human disturbance, than we can keep up with in our scientific mapping.

I would suggest that our conception of science should shift in the direction of these new problems and areas of expertise, in our work of popularization and teaching. This would of course be a vast undertaking, with many changes of attitude, style and power consequent upon it. But for an effective use of science in an era when risks are certain to increase before they abate, this would seem to be the only appropriate vision.

If I were to think of the most urgent well-defined educational task, I would suggest a reconsideration of mathematics as it is used for describing the world of experience. For a very long time we have been accustomed to thinking of mathematical statements as essentially precise, and admitting of no inexactness in content or formulation. Now, every competent scientist in a healthy experimental field knows that all of his quantitative assertions are inexact, and he or she will have conventions for expressing that quality. However, in most fields, particularly the mathematical social sciences, and in nearly all teaching in educational establishments, this feature of mathematics is barely recognized. An educational reform here would be as difficult and frustrating as in any other area, to be sure; but I feel that on this conceptual change, a great deal would depend.

Finally, we should recognize that science as a societal possession is ready for a change as deep as any in its history in modern Europe. Hitherto it has been the possession of a small, self-perpetuating élite, who have been wonderfully effective guardians of its quality and commitment. Now that science has become on the one hand an industrialized branch of the productive machine, and on the other a means to the containment of the risks inherent in production, it can no longer plead the innocence of its philosophical or academic periods. The experience of technological and environmental risks has shown that outsiders, even self-taught citizens, can make a real contribution to science, if not in research findings then in the highlighting of problems. Conversely, the impotence of experts, as shown in the Chernobyl fall-out fiasco, as well as in the Challenger disaster, was an important object lesson in the limits of science when applied to real technological or environmental problems. It has been said many times recently that the hubris of particular groups of scientists has led to their embarrassment; perhaps the triumphalist ideology of science, so strong and so plausible for so long, has led them astray. Now is the time for a reconsideration of how science can best serve humanity, and the area of techological and environmental risks would seem particularly well suited for being the focus of such a reflective effort.

THE SAFETY OF SAFEGUARDS

Safety has become one of the most salient issues in technology policy. After a record of centuries of progress, in which our world became more safe as well as more comfortable and pleasant, we now find ourselves with large-scale, basic technologies where safety is critical, and yet where it seems increasingly difficult to guarantee it. Civil nuclear energy is the most prominent case here; and by reflecting on the problems of that technology, which few can now claim to have been definitively solved, we might gain some insights into the general problem of safety as a task where technical factors are inextricably combined with those of the social and moral spheres.

It must be hard for someone trained in an older school of science or engineering to admit that some problems are insoluble. Particularly in America, it had seemed that given enough resources, anything could be accomplished once the national will was there. The atomic bomb project set a precedent; and the moon landings showed that even the most visionary plans could be realized. But both of these projects were simple in their goals and also endowed with a special enthusiasm and commitment. Other sorts of projects, not enjoying such fortunate circumstances, were not similarly successful. Even as the moon-shots were proceeding, it was remarked that it seemed to be easier to organize a safe journey to the moon than one across Central Park in New York City. Again, organizing an ongoing civil nuclear power industry that would provide electricity that was clean, safe and cheap called for skills and attitudes that were very different from those of the Manhattan Project.

Even within more traditional engineering fields, the present period has provided many examples of problems that cannot be solved, at least within any conceivable constraints on their social context and resources. Perhaps the first of these was traffic in towns. Nothing seemed simpler than to enable all automobile owners to exercise their democratic freedom to drive their cars wherever and whenever they liked; if too many were using a channel at its given capacity, then the planners and engineers could simply increase the capacity. This policy has seemed to work in Los Angeles, at least for traffic movement; but then that is a city without a centre, where commuter traffic is as diffused as all other. In the case of cities with centres, it was discovered after a couple of decades that providing storage and even access for all possible commuter cars would require a destruction of that centre to which they would be heading, on such a scale as to deprive it of anything worth going to. So the commuter-car problem was eventually recognized as 'effectively insoluble'.

The problem of safety is different from that of highway engineering; but if anything its management is even more dependent on the social and moral context of an ongoing operation. Whether it is soluble, to an adequate degree, in any given culture is a contingent question; there may well be some where it is, and there are doubtless some where it is not. My purpose here is to explore the elements of the safety task. For this I shall apply insights about the behaviour of people in an institutional environment and of technological systems in a natural environment. Since the problem of safety is largely one of control — including monitoring and, where necessary, applying corrections — my argument depends on an analysis of 'safety control' as an institutionally organized human activity. I identify three principles of rule-governed behaviour which are relevant to systems of control intended to ensure safety.

We may start with the old question: *Quis custodiet ipsos custodes?* — Who guards the guardians? No system of control involving human agents is self-controlling as a whole. The hierarchy of control is, in a sense, uncontrolled or open-ended at the top. No matter how many elaborate checks and sanctions are formally built into a system of control, they will operate only to the extent that there is an effective commitment for them to do so, in spite of their inherent personal costs of the controllers. We then have the principle of the 'open-endedness' of such a system, and the need for commitment at the top of any hierarchy of control.

We draw the practical conclusion that there is no guarantee that the socially 'best possible' system of control in a given environment will be adequate to its intended functions. In the case of the global safety of nuclear energy systems, the point might be translated into a maxim: 'Do not circulate weapons-grade plutonium in a country where the chief inspectors can be bribed'. Whether even this restriction would eliminate safety control systems inadequate to their function is something about which experts might argue.

It follows from the first principle that every human control system needs a meta-system for its own control. Since this relation iterates without end we immediately see that 'ultimate' control in any human system must be informal, personal, even partly tacit.

That feature of control systems interacts in practice with another property of all systems of rule-governed human behaviour, namely, that it is necessary for operatives to violate the rules sometimes in order to accomplish their assigned tasks. Instead of arguing this in detail, I will simply point to the phenomenon of disruption through 'working to rule'. Hence, it is strictly impossible for a control group to enforce perfect adherence by operatives to any set of formal rules. They must be allowed initiative to accomplish their tasks as they see fit.

This inherent informality and imprecision of human control systems has important consequences for all work governed by standards of adequacy of results. The degree of quality which can be effectively achieved, even within a purely technical possibility, will depend on the commitment of the operatives. A management, however committed itself, cannot arbitrarily define and enforce standards. If the work-force refuses to pay the personal costs of achieving them, the standards will eventually be jettisoned in the interest of the accomplishment of more obvious goals, as formal — or formalistic — 'completion' of tasks. Thus, we have the second principle: the 'incompleteness' of the controllability of tasks, and the need for commitment at the bottom of the hierarchy.

Thus, for there to be effective control, of quality or of safety, it is necessary for those both at the top and at the bottom to be committed. In regard to quality, the Japanese are fully aware of this; in their industries, all ranks share in the positive inducements and negative sanctions whereby group morale and commitment is fostered. In relation to safety, the combination of these two principles can explain the enormous variations between institutions, or even within one institution in its earlier and later phases; NASA is a good case in point here. This last example reminds us that no amount of external enthusiasm or pressure can ensure that control of quality, or even of safety, will be adequate for the performance of the required tasks. It is a matter of the organizational culture, one of those aspects that is impossible to quantify and yet which is crucial for the success of management.

The third principle relevant to systems of control is the 'degeneration' of routine tasks. There is not enough 'motivational capital' to go round to cover the multitude of boring, repetitive tasks on the diligent accomplishment of which all monitoring — and hence safety-engineering — depends. It is no answer to 'automate' them. This may reduce their quantity, but it cannot change their quality. Also, using iteration again, we see the need for the routine human task of monitoring the system of automatic control. Applying this principle, we can understand the otherwise astounding reports of lax security at American civil nuclear installations. It needs no arguing that here, as in the former two cases, the institutional, social and moral aspects of the human environment are crucial in the containment of the degenerative effects of this situation.

The importance of these three principles of human behaviour in systems of control becomes clearer in the light of a fourth principle, relating to technological systems in their natural environment. In recent decades it has become common sense to think in terms of cycles, so that for any process of manipulation of materials, energy or information, there are phases both 'upstream' and 'downstream'. There are no infinite sources, nor any infinite sinks, available as solutions of problems in the real world. In the nuclear field, as in many others, engineering is coming to encompass the tasks of managing flows through all the phases, each one requiring its own appropriate systems of control. With study, some of the 'downstream' phases are revealing themselves as more problematic than those of the central, profitable operation. Thus we now have the problem, which is currently the topic of strongly conflicted politics in the USA, of constructing a repository for the storage of long-lived nuclear wastes that will be 'safe' for at least ten thousand years.

Partly under the influence of external pressures like those of the above example, there is developing as new appreciation of technologies in their natural environment. We are no longer confined to consideration of the safety problems of 'nuclear power stations'; rather the safety of the whole, complex 'nuclear fuel cyclic system' is the issue. The processing, handling, storage and transport of ores, fresh fuels, spent fuels, reprocessed fuels, temporary hot wastes and permanent cooler wastes, as well as the decommissioning of plants and disposal of *their* products, are all equally important in principle. At each phase, the hazards are different, including varied attractions for diversion of materials and terrorism. Perhaps more than any other technology, civil nuclear power has (partly through the operations of the political process) forced an awareness of these aspects, because its materials, particularly in the 'downstream' phases, are so particularly problematic.

These latter phases may yet come to present more problems than the 'central' ones, as part of the general problem of waste management which steadily becomes more acute in our industrial culture. Even though the engineers no longer completely dismiss wastes as 'garbage', a problem lacking in interest or prestige, we are still a long way from a general recognition that 'waste' is a pathological symptom of a technology. And certainly, all the reward-structures of our society act against a proper appreciation of the problems of wastes. Hence we can anticipate a period, some decades hence, when after a quite lengthy interval of trouble-free operation of nuclear reactors, the problems of decommissioning and disposal will obtrude. They may well be costly in all sorts of ways; and yet they will provide none of the rewards for reinforcement of safety control at the top, or the bottom, of the relevant institutions. Of course such a prospect is speculative, but it is not on that account irrelevant. The 'downstream' problems of nuclear energy will have to be solved; and that task will be undertaken in determinate contexts of commitment and morale.

When we consider the operation of such a system, we can do more than observe this or that particular hazard. On the basis of these, we can raise the question of whether the institutional, social and moral environment can sustain adequate systems of safety control. Hoping not to be culturally chauvinistic, I must say that I would be distressed at the prospect of the installation of such a hazardous cyclic system in a Third World country lacking in appropriate technical skills and political stability. What of a relatively unskilled and unstable European country? What of ourselves?

Nuclear reactors are — so far — unique in civil life in the degree to which the physical engineering of their matter and energy systems requires extraordinarily high standards in the social engineering of their systems of safety control. If these fail, now or at some time in the indefinite future, life on this planet will be endangered. Yet these systems of control are vulnerable to the effect of 'open-endedness' of control at the top, 'incompleteness' of controllability of tasks at the bottom, and to the 'degeneration' of routine monitoring tasks. All these possibilities are more acute, and no less serious, in the 'downstream' phases of the nuclear materials cycle, when there are fewer external supports for the morale and commitment, at the top and at the bottom, necessary for the maintainance of effective control. In these respects the hazards of civil nuclear energy are particularly sensitive to the quality of the culture in which the technology is located.

Relative to the conditions of society as we now have it, even in the most advanced centres, there is no guarantee that the problems of safety through the full cycle of nuclear energy are effectively soluble. This is of course an important issue in technological policy. In addition, it opens perspectives of a philosophical sort: for here we have a case where the 'hardware' of a technological system is so critically dependent, for its proper functioning, on the 'soft', social and moral, aspects of society. In this way, nuclear power may have contributed not merely to our comprehension of risks, but also to our understanding of the nature of technology as a human creation.

THE POLITICAL ECONOMY OF RISK

The subject of risks is as varied as human experience itself; each variety of risk can illuminate another aspect of it. Here I will concentrate on those risks where it is possible to identify three parties: those who impose, those who endure, and those who regulate the risks. Clearly, these are 'roles' rather than individuals, since each of us takes chances, risks the consequences, and controls the hazardous actions. But there are some situations, notably industrial and occupational risks, where the three roles are relatively distinct. There, social and power relationships between workers, management and inspectorates are as important as science in any realistic analysis of industrial risk. A shift in this balance of power would be a prerequisite of any policy for the more effective control of industrial risks.

There is no doubt that quantitative studies of risks are essential for their scientific analysis and effective control. But their results cannot be treated like weights, that are simply balanced against estimates of 'values' in the determination of 'acceptability'. Science, power and ethics are intimately related in every assessment of risks. The more we know about risks, the more we understand how their management is conditioned by the goals and values that are dominant in society. Through a greater awareness of the problems of controlling risks, we can come to scrutinize and eventually to refine them. And a realistic analysis of the relations involved in the 'political economy of risk' is necessary for any real improvement in their control. Such a study requires a new sort of scientific work, in which the committed amateur can make a contribution along with the certified expert.

Some risks, particularly those occurring in ordinary experience like car accidents, can be described quite well by statistical methods. By relating statistical indicators of personal and political reactions to risks, we can obtain some idea of the practical limits of 'acceptability' of the various sorts. But the more we know about these limits, the more complex and even bizarre they seem. For example, pressure groups concerned with particular industrial or medical risks will argue endlessly about hypothetical scenarios, while the twin drugs of speed on the road and alcohol are allowed (and, by official inaction, encouraged) to regularly claim thousands of victims each year.

Any effective policy of risk control must come to terms with such paradoxical features of risks. I believe that they can be expressed in terms of three 'unthinkables'. First, as a matter of personal psychology, hazards with a low probability are unreal; we have no intuitions to help us balance costs and payoffs when the odds against losing are ten thousand or one million to one.

Secondly, and related to this, is the severe difficulty of studying hazards scientifically. Elaborate calculations of the probabilities of complex harmful events are all too likely to be mere pseudo-precision, for accidents and disasters do not follow the statistical model of successively picking balls out of separate urns.

Finally, there is the moral dilemma of anyone who imposes a risk on another, through their activity as designer, inspector, supervisor or worker. A zero probability of harm is just impossible; but if harm occurs, there will always be the question, 'though I did my best, was it as good as it *should* have been?'

These three 'unthinkable' dilemmas cannot be suppressed in the day-to-day management of risks; for that reason risk management cannot become a 'matured science' where standard exercises suffice for ordinary competent practice. Although there is a great need for more competence in risk management, any attempt to create a closed world of certified expertise would be deceitful, and (in the present climate of public involvement in science) ineffective. Some might even question whether there is any chance of a rational dialogue on strongly contested risks (as those of nuclear power and its 'downstream' phases of reprocessing and disposal). Certainly, the subject is difficult; but I would argue that to ignore the political economy of risks, pretending that it is all a question of statistics and perhaps psychology, makes any effective progress on risk management all the more difficult.

The Risk Triangle

We can make a start on managing risks as a social phenomenon by recognizing that there are three sides involved in every hazard: those who create it; those who experience it; and those who regulate it. Sometimes all the 'sides' come together in the same person (say, a mountain-climber). But for most techno-logical risks the sides are largely separate. Although all share in creating, experiencing and regulating risks, broadly speaking, in industry it is managers, workers, and health and safety inspectors whose basic responsibility and commitment lie on the three different sides of the triangle.

Since risks are so difficult to study objectively or even to imagine, it is only natural that the way each 'side' sees a hazard depends strongly on the values and expectations of its role, and that this perception will be very different from that of another side. Hence a manager need not be callous or inhumane to allow a hazard to persist even when warned about it; he just doesn't necessarily see it the same way as others. Nor need the worker take it too seriously, especially if he or she has real 'danger money' to compensate for an unreal slight chance of future harm, or, as is often the case, does not know the extent of the risk. This argument does not, however, excuse crimes: no doubt a murderer or rapist sees the crime in a different light to its victim or to a policeman!

Another consequence of the risk triangle is that the style of the control of risks will mimic, and be influenced by, wider social relations of power. A hazardous environment (at work or at home) is a part of social powerlessness. Hence all debates on risks have an inevitable and inescapable element of politics in them. Although bargaining on risks certainly involves the paradoxes of 'the three unthinkables', a risk policy that excludes such bargaining is all too likely to serve the interests of only one side of the risk triangle: that with the most power to shape perceptions and values.

Recognizing this basic structure makes it easier to isolate the influences that make the control of risks much more than a technical exercise. For example, the government agencies that regulate risks work in a bureaucratic context, where 'success' is assessed by many criteria besides the satisfaction of their publicly stated function—most notably the classic civil service aims of depart-mental well-being and a peaceful life. Such constraints, when added to the difficulties of imagination and analysis mentioned above, can lead to a total fragmentation of perception and responsibility among agencies charged with regulation. Further, mechanistic solutions, such as 'more flow of information' can be counter-productive. Faced with more memos, people throw away *all* the 'bumf'. The existence of such influences, analysed by Barry Turner (1978) in *Man Made Disasters*, indicates that the modelling of disasters as the outcomes of series of independent random events is so misleading as perhaps to contribute to the mentality in which disasters occur.

We can better appreciate the actual role of science in the management of risks by putting aside the traditional 'public knowledge' image of science, and thinking instead of 'corporate know-how'. Management, and also regulators, desire (or are even legally required) to keep to themselves much of the knowledge about risks that gives them power. And the data that are collected, indeed the very categories in which they are cast, reflect a conception of the problem that is influenced by the perceptions and values of the 'side' that has the power to collect and process the data.

All sides of the risk triangle are involved in its dilemmas of 'designing for death'; but the official regulators are particularly vulnerable to corruption of their work. In reality, they depend on the goodwill of managers to get improvements carried out, despite the great formal powers they may hold. This forces them to accept unsatisfactory conditions in the short, medium and even longer terms. Yet, through all this, they must present themselves to the public as effective and sole guardians of safety. When the workers actually running the risks react cynically to the inspectorate's claims, the regulatory agencies are driven still closer to management, in order to preserve their public image and self-esteem. The end result of this process is that factory inspectors have often appeared to workers as little more than adjuncts—even adjutants—of management, trapped by their dependence on the philosophy of persuasion.

This is a harsh judgement, and I know that many sincere and dedicated personnel in the inspectorates will think ill of me even for publicizing it. It may be that the many successes of the inspectorates are all small-scale and quiet, and their few failures large and notorious. Be that as it may, there have been enough exposures of highly unsatisfactory conditions by journalists, in the press and TV, to establish the point. Certainly, the failure of the old Factory Inspectorate to protect workers against known asbestos hazards at Hebden Bridge, Yorkshire, and in east London, is something that cannot be denied or explained away except in terms of the corruptions of impotence. Of course this impotence is decreed and enforced by the political masters, who keep the inspectorates starved of personnel, funds and powers; but the personal dilemma of inspectors is no less cruel because of that.

The corruptions of impotence may also help to explain a phenomenon that is familiar, and disheartening, in the field of industrial hazards. This is the 'careless worker', who seems indifferent to the well-posted hazards, or might even seem to take changes deliberately with the firm's property and his or her body. Certainly, there will always be some, of whatever social position, who welcome risks; the prevalence of dangerous sports is proof of this. But we can also imagine the reactions of someone who knows that they are required to 'accept' risks, perhaps even some which are officially guarded against, in the interests of getting through the job on time. They may feel that no one, neither regulators or even trade union officials, has any real concern for their safety. Hence the reaction to helplessness is apathy, demonstrated in apparently irresponsible, even irrational behaviour.

With this approach we can understand the workings of the Superstar Technology phenomenon. (This is the name of an early report of the Council for Science and Society, drafted by Professor John Ziman.) This refers to the problem of regulating an industry where all the recognized expertise is influenced by those being regulated. What happens then is not merely that the data become disputed, but the identification of the risk problem itself becomes a matter of institutional politics, with the powerful side eventually defining what seems to be a purely scientific problem. A clear example of this is the debate of the 1970s over the possible hazards of recombinant DNA research. There the problem was deliberately restricted to immediate laboratory hazards, rather than being extended to wider issues of environmentalism and ethics. Also, within the narrower problem, the burden of proof was imposed on objectors, so that unless they could demonstrate that a particular hazard was real, it was not taken seriously for policy, as distinct from regulatory ritual. This was confirmed by one of the more reflective of the 'insiders', Daniel Callaghan, at the forum of the National Academy of Sciences in March 1977.

Since risks are so deeply embedded in the human condition, no simple device will solve the problem of achieving effective or 'fair' control of risks. A change in the balance of power around the relevant risks triangle is a precondition of improvement for the regulation of any risk. Such a shift depends both on formal measures, and no changes of consciousness and of conscience; the two aspects interact. We should think not of a once-for-all solution, but in terms of cyclic processes, of advances on different fronts according to opportunity and effectiveness. And we should never forget that to every action that threatens existing relations of power and privilege, there will be a reaction. The Latin motto, *Quis custodiet ipsos custodes?* (Who guards the guardians?) should be displayed on the portals and letterheads of every inspectorate!

In this context we can see a function for strong and independent trade unions and community groups in the partial redressing of the imbalances of power in the risk triangle. The British Health and Safety at Work Act, providing for official safety representatives from among the union membership, was a major advance in this respect. Outside the work-place, risks are usually too diffuse for there to be any effective organization of those who endure them. Only on some special issues, notably traffic and pollution hazards, is there now a regular, recognized practice of communities organizing to protect themselves against those who impose the risks and the regulators also, if need be.

The study of risks is a clear example of the sort of science that is now emerging as salient in the management of our high-technology society. Here, as in the fields of resources and environmental problems, the established scientists have lost their professional monopoly of legitimate expertise. This does not affect the position of the traditional academic scientists, who have generally engaged in such problems only on an individual basis. What has become questioned is the scientific authenticity and authority of those who work for agencies as employees, or who sit on expert committees in the belief that the problems are not substantially different from those in the laboratory. Many of the important issues have been opened up, and indeed much of the relevant research done, by journalists, students, activists and pressure-groups. In this sort of science, the political commitments are open and self-conscious rather than being smuggled in through values concealed as 'common sense'. The maintenance of quality is achieved through public debates in a variety of forums, no less effectively than through private peer-review and journal refereeing. Thus the management of risks is, as well as being important in itself, an example of how there could emerge a 'critical science', combining objectivity with commitment in the study of nature, as already occurs in other fields of learning.

'Risk assessment — a science of uncertainties' was adapted from an article first publised as 'Risk assessment — a science in controversy', J.R. Ravetz (1982) *Physics Education* **17**, 203—8.

'Public perceptions of acceptable risks' was adapted from an article first published in *Science and Public Policy*, October 1979.

'The safety of safeguards' was adapted from an article first published in J.R. Ravetz (1974), *Minerva* **12** (3), 323—5.

'The political economy of risk' was adapted from an article first published in *New Scientist*, 8 September 1977.

References

Commoner, B. (1966) *Science and Survival*. London: Gollancz.
Cottrell, Sir A. (1982) 'The pressure on nuclear safety' *New Scientist* 25 March 773—6.
Habermas, J. (1976) *Legitimation Crisis*. London: Heinemann.
Norman, C. (1982) 'Isotopes the nuclear industry overlooked' *Science* 215, 377.
Turner, B.A. (1978) *Man Made Disasters*. London: Wykeham.
Weinberg, A. (1972) 'Science and trans-science' *Minerva* 10, 209—22.

Recombinant DNA Research:
Whose Risks?

The debates over the hazards of recombinant DNA research (or, under its British title, genetic manipulation) were among the most important in the field of the social relations of science in the 1970s. I was fortunate in being a participant observer, my knowledge of the political and social aspects compensating for my ignorance of the biological technicalities. My involvement began when I was invited to join the Genetic Manipulation Advisory Group (GMAG), probably because of the reputation I had gained from my work with the Council for Science and Society on risks. This was in late 1976; I attended one meeting of GMAG, and then went on a study visit to the Institute for Advanced Study, Princeton, which had been planned long previously. There I found the hazards debate in full swing; and using my American contacts, I soon found out who was who. I even attended the classic public meeting at the National Academy of Sciences in March 1977, where Jeremy Rifkin launched his campaign, in the style of the 1960s, against the research. Shortly thereafter I returned to England, and played my part as a member appointed to represent the public interest on GMAG, for the duration of my two-year term of appointment. My writings on my experiences were mainly transcripts of lectures; from these I have now produced this account.

The coming of age of physics was marked by the development of nuclear weapons, with the horrors of Hiroshima and Nagasaki, and later the tragedies of those scientists, like Oppenheimer, who could not keep on the right side of the power structures. With biology, it happened on a smaller scale, in the absence of any perceptible threat to humanity or indeed the environment; only a few distinguished careers were destroyed, and it was all over in five years. At the beginning, molecular biology was an exciting and well-known field of science, thanks partly to the great discovery of the DNA double helix and thanks also to the effective publicity about that discovery. There was the usual speculative talk about what these techniques could eventually do for humanity, but nothing was, or could be, promised. By the end, the community of scientists found themselves embattled and somehow tarnished, having been publicly accused (however falsely) of forming a self-serving élite; and the excitement of these techniques was then being expressed by venture capital coming in on a large scale, so that leading scientists were simultaneously performing the two roles of scholars and entrepreneurs. All this happened most openly and dramatically in the United States; the contrast with Britain, well-mannered and well-managed, is striking; and the contrast with Continental countries, where the scientists simply regulated themselves as they saw fit, is more striking still.

This brief episode forms a fascinating history in its own right, and has been studied by several competent scholars. My purpose here is to review it briefly in the light of some important lessons that it can provide in connection with debates on risks. In some ways it was like a revolution, not a neat replacement of old by new, but a sequence of events that, once triggered, followed out a logic of its own until the forces of innovation (or destruction) were exhausted and a new normality could be created. Perhaps because for a time no one was really in control, the debates were more open even if less conclusive; and from the succession of issues that formed the subjects of the debates among the various parties, we may appreciate an important property of such episodes. This is that when (as in this affair) the science is not conclusive, then what is actually debated will depend to a great extent on who sets the agenda of debate, and therefore who controls the forum. Furthermore, if the issue is contentious then this may be recognized at the time. The debate is then conducted at two levels: on the substantive issues as chosen; and on the question of the choice, its scientific appropriateness, political fairness, and procedural justice. This multilevel debate occurred openly at a crucial point in the history of the American effort to control recombinant DNA research. Since such clarity is relatively uncommon in risks debates, the DNA episode is particularly instructive.

This history also has implications for the philosophy of science. For in such debates it is impossible to make a neat separation of an objective, scientific core from its subjective, political meanings for interpretation and policy. All the actors in the affair had their own agendas, none of which was completely determined by such scientific facts as may have been available. Of course, this does not imply that the actors on either side were anything less than honourable and competent in their own sphere. Nor does it imply that there is never anything there in the science other than the products of a negotiation. What we have in these difficult risks debates is a mixture of the objective and subjective, the scientific and the political, which by its nature is inextricable. Perhaps a study of such debates will help us to get beyond the either/or thinking that so hampers our attempts to understand the social aspects of science, and to appreciate the need and the possibility of an enriched logic for studying such problems.

The other important feature of this episode is the neat contrast it offers between the American and British styles of administration. In this regard it might be something of a minor classic case, since the issue is quite self-contained, without any complications of party politics or diverging political philosophies. The styles of management of the problem in the two administrative cultures were so characteristic of each that the whole affair might have been written as a script.

The outcome of the affair is not particularly encouraging for those who consider greater public involvement in discussions on science policy as a good in its own right. The sporadic character of the American interventions, and the nearly total absence of public debate on the British scene, serve as a reminder that citizens' activity in relation to science can occur only when there is some issue so urgent that the wall of incomprehensible expertise must be breached. This may be happening at the present time in some places (such as West Germany) in connection with the large-scale genetic engineering industry. But that is another story, whose history is yet to be told.

The Beginnings: Classic Microbiological Hazards

We must remember that when the trouble first began, in the early 1970s, this was after nearly two decades of the most exciting period in living memory for biology. From the initial discovery of the genetic code (the term is not merely a metaphor, as we shall see) in 1953, there had been great progress in actual manipulations with the material of heredity, splitting and re-joining it at will. As yet, it was still only on the easiest of materials, mainly in well-known micro-organisms such as *Escherichia coli*, a common gut bacterium, and then mainly on some free-floating rings of DNA called plasmids. It was a slight worry that the easiest way to mark particular sites was with a gene conferring resistance to particular antibiotics; but it was not difficult to avoid the risk that these could somehow spread resistance to antibiotics in medical use. However, problems were being noticed, particularly when other micro-organisms, more obviously pathogenic or even possibly so, were used.

To explain this, I must introduce a few technicalities. The manipulation, or splicing, of genes is not done on individual copies, but by the mixing of many organisms in or on a nutrient medium. Furthermore, to effect this operation, it is necessary to have strings of DNA that are as small and simple as possible; even the main hereditary material of a bacterium, in a nucleus, is usually too large for the operation to succeed. Hence the use of the small extranuclear plasmids, with a few thousand or even a few hundred base pairs. Alternatively, there are viruses, also with a simpler genetic structure, and some of them are quite well studied because of their importance for medicine. These simpler structures, on which the actual manipulations are performed, are called the vectors. When after a mixing some of them are presumed to have the desired recombinations, they are then introduced to a host, most commonly *E. coli*, which can be easily and quickly multiplied, or cloned up. In that way, millions or billions of copies of the vector, with its recombined DNA, can be produced; they can then be extracted and analysed.

The only catch is that viruses are somewhat mysterious organisms in their behaviour, especially when compared with the classic bacteriological pathogens. Some are plainly pathogenic; with others, it is not so clear, and it is not at all easy to be sure that any virus that cohabits with humans is truly 'safe'. Hence the earliest concern about the hazards of this research was in connection with the viral vectors, not the bacterial hosts. This concern was developing in the echo of a near-catastrophe in which the National Institutes of Health had been involved. It had been discovered retrospectively that some twenty-five million Americans had been inoculated with an attenuated polio virus which had been contaminated with another virus, SV40, which causes tumours in simians (monkeys). If this had been pathogenic in even a small minority of cases among humans, the consequences would have been dire. Hence the officials were justifiably nervous about any manipulations that might lead to a spread of pathogenic viruses, or even a threat or hint of such an event.

Then as the pace quickened, and increasing numbers of researchers joined the work, these generalized worries began to take real and unpleasant form. Some researchers were worried that the micro-organisms in their cultures really required trained and careful researchers for their safe handling. In the classic fields involving dangerous pathogens, this was no problem; people would not presume to involve themselves with materials that were beyond their competence or their facilities. (In British there already existed a Dangerous Pathogens Advisory Group to monitor research done with the most lethal organisms.) There were well-known craft skills and safety routines whereby an experienced worker could quickly decide whether to allow someone in their lab; the classic example is going to a basin to wash one's hands after a preparation: does the candidate look for the elbow-taps? If not, they are out. In this way, a club of experienced and committed researchers had generally maintained quality and safety in the work. But in this new research these organisms were not being studied in their own right, but simply as convenient carriers of the genetic information that was of scientific interest to the researchers whose experience and commitment lay elsewhere.

Hence by 1973 there was an inceasing concern about the safe handling of the viral vectors, with the knowledge that the inevitable fringe of 'cowboys' could possibly do something really irresponsible and dangerous. Attempts by individuals to control who received samples had proved futile or even counter-productive. There was a growing sense of unease, not very sharply focused, about all the various problems of this new research. It is important that many of the researchers were young, with a political and social awareness that had been sharpened by living through the events of the 1960s. There was a sense of determination to avoid being drawn into a situation that would be analogous to that of the scientists who co-operated with the military in the Vietnam War. But just what to do, and how to assess the problems of such risks as there might be, was not at all easy to decide.

The Andromeda Strain Hosts Hazard

The affair went public in 1974 with a classic statement, in the form of a letter to *Science*, signed by Paul Berg and ten other leading researchers, which described several classes of potentially hazardous research, covering most of the interesting work in progress, and called for a moratorium on research in those areas until the hazards had been assessed and safety standards adopted. It was quite unprecedented in the whole history of science for a group of scientists to call a halt to their work, and trust to the force of consensus to ensure that colleagues in other countries did not cheat. If Leo Szilard had been successful in his efforts to get such a moratorium among the much smaller group of atomic scientists in 1938, the subsequent history of the world would have been much simpler and safer.

This was indeed the finest hour of these scientists; and it is understandable that they should have become bitter when, so soon afterwards, the public (or at least those parts made visible) turned their idealistic move against them. This happened for a variety of reasons. It seemed by the force of the announcement that there *was* some genuine hazard, even if it was not specified in detail. Then, when a scant two years later they announced that it was all under control, again with an absence of scientific detail, that public was puzzled and (given the inevitable changes in attitude) suspicious. There is a deeper background here; especially in America, generations had been raised in fear of 'germs', which were always lurking, ready to attack from such places as toilets, sink-drains, even one's mouth. To be told by the scientists that some germs were so dangerous they wouldn't handle them was reasonable; to be told soon afterwards that it was all right, they're safe now, was not.

Further, there is the question of what sorts of hazards were being advertised by the scientists. These had nothing to do with the issues of incompetent or careless handling of pathogenic organisms as such. Rather, the fear was focused on the possibility of pathogenic features being transferred across species, since DNA had been shown to survive and function in new host species. The areas of concern involved the enhancement of the pathogenicity of organisms, either by antibiotic resistance or by the insertion of genes capable of causing cancer. Although viruses were mentioned, it was only in connection with the cancer problem. Thus the focus of concern was now clearly concentrated on bacterial hosts, carrying the risks either of enhanced resistance to antibiotics or of some carcinogenic property.

The leaders of the research community were thus facing a cruelly paradoxical problem: how to reassure the public that they were going to restore safety to a set of totally hypothetical microbiological hazards? In the letter they were very honest about the weakness of theories and the paucity of data on hazards; and they stressed the need for research. But there were systematic difficulties as well. In order for these to constitute a genuine health hazard, there would need to be a most improbable sequence of events, involving the escape of the affected micro-organisms, followed by a transfer of

67

their undesirable properties to wild strains, and then for these to become vigorous and infectious to humans. It was all rather remote, and in its way unreal. From the outside, one could have compared such risks with those of viral infection in cowboy labs of researchers and technicians, who were largely women, and (in America) totally lacking in the protections at work that trade unions can provide.

Once the moratorium was announced, it was obviously urgent to organize research to assess those hazards; but before this, there had to be some means of creating a consensus on what those hazards were. Running recursively backwards, this would first require a conference, and (earlier still) some consensus about its organization and agenda. Quite soon some leading researchers went against the moratorium idea, and criticized and indeed ridiculed all hypothetical hazards when they were articulated in any detail. On the other side, the environmentalists and radicals were beginning to stir. The researchers' shift of problem, to Andromeda strain bacterial hosts from research cowboys' viral vectors, had probably occurred without any single conscious decision, and had the great merit of substituting a neat, scientific problem for an embarrassment on which one might well be reluctant to confide in the public. But it was now well on its way to imposing its own logic on any attempted solution, scientific or political. (The term Andromeda strain comes from a famous science fiction story about an infection from another galaxy, by its nature impossible to control or predict.)

Another feature of biological hazards made their self-imposed task yet more difficult. As the discoverers of the double helix had said, the essence of the genetic mechanism is not so much a substance as a code: information, rather than matter or energy, is the crucial agent in this system. In physical and chemical systems the dangerous things are material, and can be traced and, wherever found, reasonably assumed to stay put, or to move by recognizable channels, or to disintegrate harmlessly. In biological systems, the information constitutes the hazard, and it is carried on self-replicating units; the problems of assessment and control of the hazards are therefore enormously more difficult. Here the information can move in small numbers of invisible carriers; if even only a few copies survive passage through some barrier, they can multiply again, and moreover pass their messages on to hardier relatives. So dilution and attenuation are effective only in the most extreme degree. All this was common knowledge to those working with dangerous pathogens; experience of cases of smallpox and other infectious diseases spread by unlikely routes in labs and hospitals had driven home this lesson. To attempt to impose the rigours of a dangerous-pathogen lab on DNA research would be ridiculous; but there was no calculus of quantifiable risks available which could provide guidance for the defining of controls and barriers of graduated levels of severity.

The Berg letter opened the way for discussion of further hazards, which were to provide a bridge between the medical risks it discussed, and other, speculative risks whose discussion at that point might well have sent the whole affair out of control. The basis of the scientists' alarm was the discovery that genetic material from one species could be inserted into another, and not merely be reproduced but also function there. This meant that the barrier between species, which had been thought to be nearly absolute in nature, could now be bridged at will, by mankind. The adverse consequences of this are difficult to specify in detail, and no one claimed that monsters and chimaeras were going to be produced overnight. But there was among some a sense of awe that something like a central taboo of the natural world was being breached; and we should at least stop to think about it before rushing in to exploit it. This wider problem was mentioned by others, and when it was introduced, the researchers' response was simple: first, that such things have occurred in nature; and secondly, that it is hard to imagine such a man-made creation being sufficiently hardy to become a hazard.

In the discussions of such issues we have the beginnings of a struggle over the choice of the salient problem, rather than in the unnoticed, probably unselfconscious shift from viral vectors to possibly pathogenic bacterial hosts. The scientists could label the broader concerns as speculative and unrealistic, but this was in respect of a programme for biology that was artificially narrow. Some biologists, including the most distinguished among them, had been publicly speculating for decades in a Faustian mode about the modification of life, for the improvement of humanity under scientific guidance. When the rhetoric of promise of recombinant DNA approached the earlier visions, it is not surprising that critics took the more extreme versions seriously as the *eventual* outcome of the research.

Hence by the time that the conference on risks was organized, the issues were already complex, and the lines of future conflict taking shape. It was held in February 1975 at the beautiful conference centre at Asilomar, on Monterey Bay in California, and is remembered by that place-name. It was remarkable for happening at all; but the things that did not occur there were of comparable significance for the unfolding of the story. First, there was a paucity of experts in the fields relevant to assessment and control of the hazards; even a most enthusiastic bacteriologist who supported the research and ridiculed the Andromeda strain hazards, Dr B. Davis of Harvard, later complained that his talents had not been utilized. A leading public health official in California told the press that he learned about the conference from the newspapers. The one distinguished public health official who was there, an Englishman, had always said publicly that this hazard is minuscule compared with the breeding of resistant strains of pathogens through the widespread inappropriate use of antibiotics. Hence it is fair to say that at Asilomar the hazards problem was kept under the control of the DNA scientists, who in this area were amateurs.

Furthermore, the problem was kept within the confines of the Berg letter's statement. One participant from Europe who had hoped that this conference would act in the spirit of Leo Szilard, and at least open up discussion on the questions of the future of this nascent technology, went away embittered. Since every researcher who wanted to stay in the game, or race, knew that he or she had to be there, the pressure on the organizers for places was severe; at first they tried to economize on space by excluding the press, but the attempt failed, leaving a certain amount of ill-will. In the space of a few days the organizers had to create the theory and framework of a programme of risk assessment and regulation, and secure the consensus of a research community of highly ambitious, individualistic scientists. A measure of acquiescence was achieved after a sobering lecture by a lawyer on the sorts of legal liabilities that might fall on institutions or scientists, should some of the hazards be realized. And the elements of a solution were provided by another British member, Sydney Brenner, with a proposal for 'crippled bugs' that would grow in the artificial conditions of lab cultures, but die off with convenient promptness as soon as released.

All that accomplished, the researchers went home, and the most concerned scientists, mainly those at the National Institutes of Health, embarked on the Herculean task of contructing guidelines. These were to define standards of safe practice in terms of the two sorts of containment, physical (equipment and standard procedures) and biological (degree of crippling) appropriate for each possible class of experiment; and to produce a comprehensive catalogue of classes and their containments. Since practically nothing was known about the infectious behaviour (in this context) of most of the organisms being used, all the categories had to be based on conjecture about the hazards and about the degree of conservatism necessary to cover uncertainties. Naturally, any such category could be criticized as too severe to allow research to proceed, or too lax in protection. By this time the American style of regulation was in operation, with ample facilities for observation and comment by all interested parties, including those critical or hostile in any way. The environmentalists were becoming steadily more alarmed at the way the affair was being managed; and their criticisms were being relayed to community activists wherever they might be preparing for struggle.

At this point, in 1975, reassurance might have been achieved if there had been a 'crash programme' of large-scale research in risk assessment, as recommended in the Berg letter. But this did not happen, in spite of money being made available by the NIH. After Asilomar, several labs started work on the engineering of Brenner's crippled bugs; and as the difficulties in this became apparent, it was abandoned nearly everywhere. The paucity of serious risks research, in spite of the advertised official good intentions, is a constant theme throughout this whole history; a study of the reasons for this could be illuminating.

The Political Struggle for the Agenda

By this time, the environmentalists and radicals were becoming alarmed. It seemed that problem and solution were firmly in the hands of the professionals. Americans are quite sophisticated about 'the regulation game', and know well that self-regulation can be primarily devoted to self-protection by a professional group. Moreover, at those universities which decided to look into the risks problem on their own, it was soon clear that for the administration and leading scientists the question was not whether, but how soon, DNA research would be promoted. In a pattern which has become characteristic of American environmental politics, there was developing a coalition of citizens concerned for their localities (the NIMBY—Not In My Back Yard groups) with ideologically orientated national pressure groups, against a threatened LULU (Locally Unwanted Land Use). This could feed on traditional towns-people's resentment of universities, as being arrogant and overbearing as well as exempt from local property taxes.

It did not help the researchers' public image when in 1975 a book was published that was a sort of sequel to the famous *The Double Helix* by James Watson (1968). Watson was well known as an aggressive type, given to vociferous and rude comments about any and all who opposed him, as well as occasional remarks that gave offence to women. He was also one of the earliest defectors from the Berg letter, and an abrasive critic of all attempts at regula-tion. In this new book, the great discovery, and Watson's relations with Rosalind Franklin and her project manager Maurice Wilkins, were viewed from a rather different perspective in the book *Rosalind Franklin and DNA* by Ann Sayre (Norton, New York, 1975). Briefly, Sayre's argument was that Watson had used the gullible Wilkins to obtain, secretly, X-ray photographs that were the confidential property of Dr Franklin. This is uncomfortably close to academic theft; and the author argued further that this information was crucial in Watson and Crick's making the discovery before Franklin herself. Watson's book had already caused a great stir by its frank display of his all-too-human emotions and motives; now the demystification, indeed degradation, of the scientific calling was carried a step further.

The crisis came to maturity in 1976, itself the centennial year for the United States. And it was natural for the great confrontation to occur in Cambridge, Massachusetts, the home of Harvard and MIT but otherwise a working-class suburb of Boston with a strongly ethnic population. There the coalition comprised local politicians with many grievances against the great universities, together with university-based radicals whose campaigns dated back to the 1960s or even further. There had to be an incident that triggered the confrontation: this was a plan to construct DNA research facilities in an old building suffering from an ineradicable infestation of ants; a plan which, moreover, had not been notified to the civic authorities.

In some memorable public hearings and offstage debates, the issues were both of the safety of the DNA techniques as to be practised, and the attitudes and behaviour of the scientists and institutions (or of the interfering, demagogic politicians, depending on your point of view). A leading scientist at the NIH, Dr Maxine Frank Singer, came to the hearings with a set of the official guidelines hot off the press, assuming that these would demonstrate the sense of responsibility of the research community; instead she was asked at the outset, 'Whose side are you on?' As it eventually turned out in practice, the Boston area was the one place where citizens' involvement in regulation was attempted seriously and where it was successful. A committee of laypersons was appointed to review the regulations, within the confines of the narrow hazards problem, and eventually came up with a broad approval of the official scheme.

By this time, later 1976, the original concern with scientists who were 'cowboys' or simply incompetent in handling potentially dangerous pathogens, had been nearly forgotten. As the debate polarized, the issues went correspondingly to the extremes. There was a conference on hazards at Falmouth, Massachusetts, at which a consensus was obtained informally on all sides that the chances of an accidental disease epidemic were extremely low; this was then advertised as universal scientific agreement that the techniques are 'safe'. On the side of the critics, public leadership was being assumed by Jeremy Rifkin, of the People's Bicentennial Commission, now retitled People's Business Commission. His battle-cry was that the scientists were not merely playing God, creating new life-forms, but worse yet, doing so for private profit and concealing their conflicts-of-interest when they made public pronouncements on safety.

The achievement of a crippled bug, a version of the common *E. coli* that needed a variety of artificial nutrients for survival, did not soothe the critics' feelings. It was significant that this creation, named chi-1776 in honour of the bicentennial, was the only such successfully engineered organism, and that its creator was not a mainstream DNA researcher, but a bacteriologist at the University of Alabama Dental School, Roy Curtiss III. True genetic engineering, as opposed to changing genes where it happened to be convenient, was still in its infancy.

The climax came in March 1977 with an all-American event, an open forum at the National Academy of Sciences in Washington, at which proponents and opponents were paired off in public debate. By this time tensions were running very high, and the leading scientists were feeling quite embattled. Newspapers and television were replete with jokes and cartoons depicting the scientists as manufacturing new monsters daily; and a liberal senator from Arkansas introduced a bill that by implication treated all this research like germ warfare. Worse, Rifkin's rhetoric had been shifting from radicalism to populism with a religious tinge. Even his Cambridge radical colleagues became a bit nervous at his repeated references to church-goers. The separation of church and state, or rather the exclusion of organized religion from matters of intellectual policy, was an issue that polarized America between liberals of all religious views, and the religiously conservative who were later to be named 'the moral majority'. Biologists in particular had the threat of creationism hanging over them; and after that, who knows what could come. Rifkin was playing a very dangerous game, perhaps much more so than he realized or cared; but for the biologists, liberal, intellectual, and many of them Jewish, his brand of populism aroused very primal fears. Hence the issue of debate was threatening to move right away from biology in whatever form, and into some deep and unresolved tensions in American public life. (As an historian's footnote, I must say that at the time I lacked sensitivity to this dimension of the affair, perhaps because of my long absence from America.)

At the NAS symposium itself, Rifkin attempted a replay of the 1960s. In press statements the weekend before the meeting began, he denounced the agenda, the organizers, and their public and covert sponsors. Thus his leaflet with an alternative agenda started with: 'What are the moral, ethical and theological implications involved in the artificial creation of new forms of life?' He also made vague threats about disruption if his demands for a changed agenda were not met. There was a compromise on these, so that a representative of his group could make a statement at the very beginning of the conference. Undeterred, he had his young activists planted in the hall so that at the official opening, they unfurled banners at various strategic locations. (One of them, quoting Adolf Hitler, 'We will create the perfect race', was held in front of the speakers' table; a mischievous press photographer caught it at such an angle that it could seem to be the drop-cloth, and more mischievous editors printed it.) The speech by his colleague Ted Howard was more measured; he simply pointed out that this issue would be with us for a long time, and the ethical and humanistic dimensions could not be willed out of existence by the research scientists.

The debates themselves had a rather tired air, since the paired participants had been boxing in similar rings too many times already. The scientists were very strong on their assurances of present microbiological safety; the critics were equally strong on their concerns for future dangers of all sorts. The scientists also did not resist the temptation to wrap themselves in the mantle of freedom of enquiry and the quest for truth; although as good citizens they agreed that technological development should have no immunity from regulation of its hazards. In all the debating, there was no real dialogue, only a public display of both sides being outwardly polite to each other.

At the conference was one genuinely tragic figure, a sort of Brutus character. This was Robert Sinsheimer of CalTech, who had been a leader as researcher, administrator and statesman in the community. But a few years previously, at the peak of his career, he had begun to ponder on the question of whether scientists could guarantee that these discoveries, which would eventually yield great power, could be controlled for human benefit. After exploring this theme in a number of lectures, he found that he could not solve the problem, and became progressively more disillusioned with his colleagues although not with the ideals of science. His research output dwindled, and a visitor from Cambridge solved the big problem that had guided Sinsheimer's researches and earned a Nobel prize thereby. By the time of the NAS symposium, he found himself in an unlikely alliance with the radical, anti-science critics. His former colleagues and students felt betrayed, for his presence among the ill-assorted opposition figures transformed their public standing. There was much bitterness about his defection; and unpleasant

73

rumours about his motives circulated. Soon afterwards he resigned his Chair, and became an administrator in the University of California system.

Re-Entry, and Transformation

After 1977, the debate dwindled. The critics had had their chance, and in the absence of a demonstrable present hazard, their vague and generalized warnings and complaints were ineffective. Intensive lobbying on Capitol Hill ensured that no unwelcome legislation would get through the Congress. Successive conferences were devoted to displaying the consensus among the scientists that the Andromeda strain risks were indeed minimal, and that the original guidelines could safely be relaxed. The earlier fears about the cowboy scientists were effectively allayed by the guidelines, which prescribed equipment and lab discipline for the more hazardous operations which, even if not always obeyed to the letter, did at least serve to curb any really outrageous excesses. In 1979, the operation went international, and a conference at Wye College, England, worked on the relaxation of the standards for viruses. At that event there were detailed reports of experiments on hazards; and by their paucity, simplicity and crudity they conveyed an impression almost of contempt for the whole exercise.

One result of all the public agitation, certainly unintended by the critics, was that this field became more notorious than it would have done on the basis of its current scientific achievements (or indeed its palpable hazards) alone. The claims of its practitioners, that it would soon be producing substances yielding great benefits to humanity and commensurate profits to investors, eventually became plausible. At first there were only the glowing statements by the early entrepreneurs, who had been among the pioneering researchers in gene-splicing. But by the later 1970s, industrial investment in respectable amounts was coming in, and an increasing proportion of the leading researchers were doubling as businessmen.

For a time this seemed to be causing considerable concern among those raised up in traditions of 'little science'. To be sure, it is always possible for an individual scientist to wear several hats, and to speak freely about his academic research while being discrete about the other. But when a community becomes involved with two radically different systems of intellectual property, value and etiquette, it is hard for it to retain its integrity. Whereas high-energy physics became bureaucratized through the sheer scale of the necessary equipment, DNA research tended to become commercialized through these entirely natural and unavoidable developments. Seen in historical perspective, it is part of the transformation of the social activity of science, from its 'academic' phase to 'industrialization', where the size of the enterprise, the scale of individual projects, and the proximity to profitable technological development all combine to produce corresponding changes in the social relations and then inevitably in the ideology of the work itself.

The British Model—Consensual and Closed

I personally experienced the culture-shock of rapid transition from the American system to the British; only a few weeks separated the NAS forum from my next meeting of the Genetic Manipulation Advisory Group. Going on an early morning train to London rather than to Washington, I found my way to the Ciba Foundation, just up the street from the hallowed BBC, was allowed in by the concierge, sipped coffee with my new colleagues, and then went into the closed, windowless meeting room. One or two meetings afterwards, we found on entry that our table spaces had been provided with texts of a declaration about the Official Secrets Act, awaiting our signatures. (This statement itself may make me liable to prosecution under the Act.) I decided not to sign, leaving my conscience free to blow the whistle if my duties as representing the public interest required it, and also knowing that I would be liable under the Act regardless of my signature.

The Genetic Manipulation Advisory Group was the outcome of the British approach to regulation in this field. Soon after the 1974 letter, a committee of enquiry was formed, consisting of eminent and independent scientists under the chairmanship of Sir Eric Ashby; it recommended that there be a supervisory body so that the research could proceed safely. This was planned by a second committee, chaired by Sir Robert Williams; and GMAG came to be in late 1976. As an example of design of regulatory agencies, it had several interesting features. In the British mode of minimal regulation, it functioned by the voluntary co-operation of researchers; it had no enforcement powers of its own. However, all its work was done in the closest collaboration with the Health & Safety Executive; so anyone who ignored the Group's 'advice' or otherwise contravened its recommendations would immediately have the HSE down on them. Thus, the Group could have the reality of power without its outward trappings or formal responsibilities; a device truly worthy of a mandarin.

Doubtless because of its creation under a Labour administration, with Mrs Shirley Williams as the Minister responsible, GMAG had some uniquely progressive features. First, the Group itself had the researchers as a minority presence: eight places, with two for employers, four for employees and four for those nominated to represent the public interest. Thus the workers and public between them had a representation that balanced the researchers and comprised nearly half the Group. In practice, the categories overlapped considerably, since two of the 'employees' were active researchers, one of the researchers was an industrial manager, and one of the 'public' representatives was the polymath editor John Maddox. Hence there was never a polarization on an issue based on conflicting perceptions of what a problem was about.

It is worthy of reflection that three of the members were American in their origins, and another was frequently in America and had an American wife. It goes without saying that considerations of the sort raised by the Cambridge (Massachusetts) radicals, to say nothing of Jeremy Rifkin, were totally absent from the agenda at GMAG. But since there were also absent from public discussion in the country at large, one could hardly expect GMAG to go looking for trouble by taking them up. As a public interest member, I was representing a constituency that was totally unorganized, and perhaps even non-existent! I saw my job as monitoring the regulatory machinery as it was being constructed and put into operation, including such things as checking that people in positions of responsibility (such as Biological Safety Officers) were already trained or committed to getting training. I learned that one of the most important techniques of my task was checking the 'matters arising' against the minutes of previous meetings. It was all too easy for small items to be forgotten from one meeting to the next!

It could be that it was easier to promote this innovative model for GMAG against the inevitable resistance just at that time, because in 1973 there had been a scandal over a smallpox outbreak in a hospital near one of the few laboratories licensed to work on that virus. The whole affair was extremely confused for a long time; but it was clear that the self-regulatory Dangerous Pathogens Advisory Group had not succeeded in preventing this accident. Hence, the radical idea of giving the workers and public interest some say in connection with this hypothetical hazard, even as a reassurance exercise, was less vulnerable than it might ordinarily have been.

A second progressive feature of GMAG's constitution was that the Genetic Manipulation Safety Committees which each centre was required to institute were to have less than half their members from 'management'. This term was offensive to many academics who, in spite of having responsibilities, power and pay on a managerial scale, still wanted to think of themselves as just first among equals in a community of scholars. This hint of a trade unionists' conception of a laboratory was strengthened by another provision, that the committees were to consider the scientific merit of proposals as part of their assessment in passing them to GMAG for advice. The origin of this seems to have been the point that if you are asking people to do something dangerous, it is only proper to show them why it is worthwhile. But since the hazards covered by GMAG were agreed to be only 'hypothetical' at worst, it seemed to some that this provision was an invitation to mischief. However, the Group was not inclined to stir things by changing the regulations with which it was constituted.

As the meetings ground through their lengthy agendas of assignment of categories to proposed experiments, it gradually became clear to me that the scientifically competent members of GMAG considered the hazards to be not very real at all. Early on I took it on myself, as public interest representative, to suggest that GMAG sponsor research into the risks that it was regulating; this was actually the second point of its remit. This proposal received no support, and raised some influential opposition. This was based on the very sensible point that if you tell the public you are researching into the risks, then they will believe that there are some, and become alarmed, all unnecessarily. I then wondered what people were doing on GMAG, especially the scientists who would meet for a long day's work once a month to engage on long, earnest discussions about the category in which to place some particular ambiguous experiment. Eventually I decided that it was largely a cosmetic exercise, designed to reassure the public and also ensure that researchers kept a generally clean shop. In that way scandals would be avoided, which is the great desideratum of any Civil Service, and of the British in particular. (Much later, GMAG learned that the HSE had commissioned a research project on the supposed fragility of the American crippled bug chi-1776. Also, a sub-committee of GMAG commissioned research on the transfer of some plasmid vectors in common use, with results that I discuss below.)

It should be said that GMAG did its bit to keep the labs up to scratch. Even if the categorizations of proposed experiments were to some extent arbitrary, the site visits were most definitely not. There we could see how at even the most prestigious lab, with the most safety-conscious staff, little (and sometimes big) things could go wrong unnoticed. To some extent (though in my view insufficiently) we functioned like a good safety inspectorate, being a conduit for complaints that could be made to us without fear of victimization; we could then make enquiries without disclosing the source of our particular interest.

Scientific questions did become very significant at a crucial juncture for GMAG. One of the subcommittees was charged with assessing and then validating the safety of hosts and vectors. They were able to commission experiments which demonstrated the decay rate of particular populations under particular circumstances. But whether any such number could stand for safety was a question that they (perhaps imprudently) faced squarely, and then promptly admitted defeat. This put GMAG into a crisis; the basis of our categorizations hitherto had been a table which, according to Sydney Brenner, had been drafted by him and inserted into the Williams report over his protests that it would be accepted as definitive in spite of being nothing of the sort. The table was being questioned as more information came in; and now it seemed impossible to create any sort of scientific basis for categorizations. Just at this point (late 1977) it seemed as if the Americans were set to dilute their standards to the vanishing point; and only GMAG would be there to hold the line for safe and proper operation. (No other country then had both the resources and the inclination for such an exercise.) So Sydney Brenner was prevailed upon to overload himself to the danger point yet again and produce a scheme for categorization. This he did within a few weeks; and with interpretations and modification by various GMAG members, it became the standard biohazards analysis scheme for the UK and remains so to this day.

It may be significant that the only really serious disagreements on GMAG were concerned with institutional politics rather than science. The first concerned the status of the trade union members. At one point they said that they wanted to consult with the Trades Union Congress before agreeing to some policy; this was challenged on the grounds that they were at GMAG as independent members representing an interest, not as mandated delegates of the organization that had been asked to nominate them. The issue was taken up to the Minister, and the 'gentlemen's' status confirmed. The most serious struggle concerned confidentiality. Given the traditional, semi-paranoid concern of British industry with secrecy, it was not surprising that firms were reluctant to have their proposals viewed by the whole membership of GMAG. They did have a point, in that if one of us merely mentioned something about a proposal to a rival, that could count as 'prior disclosure' and nullify their patent rights. And the sanctions over us, consisting only of the Official Secrets Act, were not really effective. There was a proposal to have a small chairman's committee review such proposals; and the employees' representatives were adamant in their opposition to this, on the grounds of the remit of GMAG and also of their responsibility to their members. This issue, with its ramifications, came close to splitting GMAG, until an acceptable British compromise was found.

The political temperature was finally raised in late 1978, near to the end of my two-year term. First, the most prominent trade union in the industry, the Association of Scientific, Technical and Managerial Staffs, organized an open meeting on genetic manipulation. This was well attended, but the only critics were a very small group from the British Society for Social Responsibility in Science; and they were not on the platform but on the floor with a single strident leaflet. Shortly afterwards there was a television programme, the second on the subject. For the first, in early 1977, the producers had needed to come to America to interview me, as the only mildly critical person with a British accent that they could find. In this second, the critical voices came from America; the programme could be considered as sensationalist, and was ill-received on GMAG. And then in December 1978 I was rotated off GMAG, for reasons that may be discovered in 2008 when the thirty-year rule permits.

I was later told that after that first two-year session, GMAG settled down to a routine, to the point that the public interest representatives eventually found themselves with not much to do. This clarified my own ideas on what that initial period of GMAG was all about. Its function was only partly in the performing of ritual categorizations; more important was the work done on the margins of the meetings' agendas, in the piecewise construction of a framework for regulation. This was done formally through the drafting and approval of guidance notes on a variety of topics for safe and proper procedures, and informally through the establishment of precedents and understandings on a great many detailed issues. Since, as it turned out, there were no realized hazards which would test, or strain, the machinery of GMAG, there is no proof that the machinery was effective or even necessary. But as an exercise in the enlargement of the idea of regulation in the British context, it had a significance beyond its size or original remit. Not long after GMAG was established, the regulatory climate in the UK changed drastically, so that the example of GMAG was not likely to be followed up. But providing that memories are kept, the example of GMAG will be there, when the tide turns again.

Conclusion

Early in 1979 I was invited to do a brief front-page article for the journal *Trends in Biochemical Sciences*. The editor, although a strong proponent of the research, clearly thought it good journalism to have a piece from me. He could even have intended a minor scandal, since the issue would appear just when everyone was awaiting news of the Wye conference on relaxation of safeguards for research with viruses. For that, I coined the term 'high-intensity science'; and although my definition got lost when the text was cut by the editors, I recall that it involved manipulations of information rather than of matter or energy. Because of this, relatively modest inputs of capital and labour would be sufficient to produce results of great power, in all the aspects of knowledge, applications and hazards.

Equivalent to my thousand words was a cartoon, showing a scientist and a layperson both looking at a packing case labelled 'Environmental Risks — High-Intensity Science'. The one is holding his telescope backwards, and proclaims, 'Ah, yes! Precisely as my scientific colleagues anticipated! The risk is vanishingly small.' The other, viewing frontwards, shows great alarm, and shouts, 'Good grief! It's even worse than I feared! The risk is COLOSSAL.' Nearby is a journalist with a press-card from the '*Daily Trash*', whose tabloid front page consists of the headline 'NEW CANCER SHOCK HORROR REPORTS are totally untrue'.

The world of academic science was doubtless turbulent and stressful for its practitioners in all sorts of ways. But in relation to its environment it was insulated and peaceful to a remarkable degree. That is all gone now; in retrospect the insulation of academic science may be seen as a transitional phase, between its predecessor in natural philosophy, never far from ideology and hence politics, and its successor in industrialized science, so very close to industry and (through its hazards) to another sort of politics.

The cartoon in *TIBS* symbolizes the new sorts of debates that take place around science. They may well determine the course of research that is done (unless the research communities can always maintain total control of the regulation of their hazards); and yet they cannot be conclusive scientifically. Is it all a matter of prejudice, through which end of the telescope one chooses to view? Is there so little possibility of consensus that the gutter press has a free run? In terms of the system of ideas that grew up for explaining and promoting academic science, these questions cannot be answered. If we need some absolute criterion of truth or objectivity in science, then we will surely be disillusioned and fall prey to subjectivity and prejudice. But if we can develop a new understanding of science, that sees it as part of life and society, then debates like those on the safety of recombinant DNA, which are bound to recur so long as we have a science worth pursuing, can be better comprehended and hopefully better managed as well. That is the purpose of historical sketches like this one, indicating by example the sort of philosophy of science that we will need to have.

For the past century, progress in technology has increasingly depended on the applications of scientific research. Starting with synthetic chemicals and electricity, and proceeding through nuclear power and now micro-electronics and biotechnology, industry depends increasingly on substances and processes which have no precedent in traditional, craft-based manufacture. As this development continues, each innovation both promises more good and threatens more evil. Also, commensurate with the greater scientific and social sophistication of the whole context of innovation, the problems of possible risks are recognized at the outset. In its way this is great progress, since it becomes less likely that a new technology will become firmly entrenched in the productive system before anyone realizes its problems.

The path to regulation of such nascent technologies has some characteristic problems of its own, which might be taken as one of the main lessons of the recombinant DNA debates. One of the main difficulties at the early stages is in the identification of what risks might eventually prove salient. Since these will depend on how rapidly the different sectors of the technology develop in the future, and how they will interact with each other and their total context, locating the crucial point is necessarily very speculative. It is no wonder that there must be a lengthy learning period, during which there may be considerable confusion and error (as seen retrospectively). Even that shift from 'research cowboys' viral vectors' to 'Andromeda strain bacterial hosts', so fateful for the course of the debates of the 1970s and beyond, can be seen as nearly unavoidable, given the circumstances in which the leaders of the responsible scientists were grappling with these unprecedented tasks.

If there is one systematic point to be made, it would be on the problem of criticism. If the burden of proof is put upon critics, they will always be at a disadvantage, since the only thing that they can rigorously prove is our ignorance of the future. To have some effect they will then tend to concentrate on the two extreme ends of the spectrum, either publicizing particular cases in which they can interest the media and the public, or raising long-term fundamental (and necessarily inconclusive) issues of ecology, ethics and perhaps theology as well. Neither is conducive to a reasoned scientific debate; but if that has already been impaired by the implicit assignment of burden of proof by those who control the agenda, those whose function is to call for reflection must then seek other forums.

Acknowledgements

I owe thanks to many individuals, here and in the USA, with whom I had illuminating discussions about the problems of regulating recombinant DNA. I would like to make a special mention of Max Weintraub, then a student at the University of California, Santa Cruz, who researched the evolution of Robert Sinsheimer's ideas. My analysis of the 'cowboys' problem is based on Michael Rogers' article 'The Pandora's box congress', *Rolling Stone*, 19 June 1975, reprinted in J. Watson and J. Tooze, *The DNA Story*, San Francisco: Freeman, 1981.

Hardware and Fantasy in Military Technology

Those of us who have studied the philosophy of science are familiar with the way in which, earlier in this century, the practice of science revolutionized its philosophical analysis. After many decades in which science seemed to be accumulating permanent truths, by some infallible method, usually inductive, it all changed suddenly thanks to the revolutions in physics at the largest and smallest scales. Einstein's relativity theory showed that our deepest intuitions about space and time, and with them the axiomatic foundations of the science of mechanics, can be wrong. Shortly afterwards, the theories of quantum mechanics put causality, the continuity of natural events, and the presumably limitless extent of our knowledge of nature, into question. Rather later, the ethical questions of science, which for a very long time had seemed totally unproblematic, came to the fore, first with nuclear weapons and then with the deleterious side-effects of our sophisticated science-based technology.

In that latter case, there can be many difficulties in assessing actual and potential harm from particular industrial processes; and so ethics and epistemology can interact in (for example) environmental risk analysis. But hitherto there has been no occasion to question whether the material things that might be causing the harm do actually *exist*. Indeed, such a question, about a chemical or a factory, might seem quite nonsensical. That may well be; but we know that some (though not all) of the apparently nonsensical questions can lead us to new insights about the reality which we inhabit and construct. I shall argue here that the question of existence becomes salient, and indeed quite crucial for policies of all sorts, in connection with the weapons systems of the nuclear age. As my title indicates, the dividing line between hardware and fantasy in nuclear weaponry may turn out to be as culturally conditioned as that between matter and energy in pre-Einsteinian physics. Should my argument be correct, there can be important implications for all future debates on defence policies.

Up to now, however, there has been no occasion to question technology from the perspective of our knowledge, or of the reality of the things claimed to exist. Indeed, our whole conception of reality is a 'materialist' one, in which things that used to be called 'spiritual' are of dubious status at best. In so many ways, the example of science, in particular the mechanics of small particles and all those sciences cast in that mould, has been taken as the paradigm of all knowledge. Correspondingly, there have been numerous attempts to establish the foundations of our values in our knowledge concerning the real, material things. The symbols of our civilization are the great technological achievements; and however problematic some of these may have become recently, there are certainly no effective challenges to them in the minds of the great mass of people both rich and poor.

Of course there are always those who denounce this or that area of technology, or perhaps even our technological reality as a whole, as misguided or evil. But even they are constrained to use it, and to live within it as a fish within water, flying to conferences at which they read word-processed papers on the beauties of the simple or spiritual life. So there can be no question of the reality and power of our system of technology as a whole. Some might argue that it is now on a self-destruct course, that with the uncontrollable pollution and degradation of the environment. Should there be some vast ecological catastrophe, leading to social upheavals and the disruption of our finely tuned systems, *then* eventually the survivors could look around and remark that those things once called (for example) sixteen-track stereos and compact disks are no longer 'real'. For even if some objects are still lying around, they can (in this post-apocalyptic scenario) no longer be used as intended. Some stray shaped bits of metal and plastic, which (with their strange iridescence) might find a use as magic pendant charms, are no longer the 'thing' (e.g. a record with superior qualities of sound reproduction) as described in its pristine state. The 'compact disk', as such, exists no longer.

This hypothetical example is far from sufficient for the establishment of my case; but we can use it for the insight about what is 'real' in the case of a sophisticated technological device. Let us try another example, rather more familiar. It is said that in certain cities of the USA it is unsafe to leave a car parked by the kerb. It may be 'vandalized' (actually, recycled), so that tyres go first, then perhaps wheels and brakes; the windows are smashed and any saleable parts removed; if it is the right sort of model, the engine itself might be lifted out. At the end of all this reprocessing, it is no longer a 'car', it is scrap, which once had been a car. Now, to determine the precise point at which it ceases to be a car and becomes scrap may well be impossible. But that is not a case for worry, for one of the oldest philosophical puzzles in the world is devoted to just this phenomenon of a continuous change between discrete categories, such as diluting wine with water until it stops being wine. If someone argues that the thing at the kerbside is still a car, then we can let it be towed away, further dismembered and finally the shell crushed into a block and the loose parts shredded. Somewhere along the line there is a phase at whose end there is no car, and common sense dictates that this occurs before the total physical disintegration of the object.

The point of this somewhat lugubrious example is that a thing, even something inanimate like a car, can in its way 'die' and cease to be. When there is no practical prospect of its performing its function, or being restored to a state where it can do so, we begin to recognize that it is passing out of existence into non-existence. Another way of putting it is that the quality of the device is being degraded by stages (where quality relates to its performance and costs of maintenance and restoration); beyond a certain phase, the quality is so low that the thing no longer can be said to have any, and therefore cannot be said to exist. In the first example, we had individual copies of material things perhaps surviving intact, but in the absence of the total support system (such as high-quality electricity supply) they were useless and hence, as the named device unreal. In that case we could speak of a class of devices (compact disks) that becomes unreal, while the individual copies are unchanged, the reverse of our example of the single copy of an automobile being recycled at the kerbside while the class of automobiles still lives and flourishes.

My examples for all this discussion are necessarily somewhat out of the ordinary, since our total technological system has means for ensuring that quality, both of large subsystems and even of individual copies, is kept up, very far from those low, abysmal or abyssal limits where the degradation of quality threatens the very existence of the thing. Certainly complaints of low quality, both of copies and of systems, are legion; but the presence of a market, supplemented by regulation, ensures that people hardly ever find themselves having purchased a non-thing rather than an inferior thing. However, there is no automatic guarantee that all systems and copies will be 'good' in all relevant respects; certainly, there is no discernible lower limit on what is sold or foisted on to the poor and ignorant, locally and globally, in the way of shoddy, inappropriate or deleterious things.

To find an example where things are produced which have some of the properties of the post-apocalypse compact disk or the kerbside recycled automobile, we must therefore look in some special sector of the economy, where usefulness, consumer choice and regulation are so weak that there is no 'floor' at all under the quality scale, a sector where things can be so low-quality that they are not really the named 'things' at all. If this were in some odd, eccentric corner of the economy, then this would be just another essay in consumer advocacy, finding yet another evil, or aberration in the market economy, to be sorted out. But, as my title indicates, I am here talking about a large and significant sector of the economy, and one which has dominated much of our political life for a very long time. For a variety of special reasons, the sector of military procurement is lacking in the various protections of quality, to the point where it is realistic and relevant to say that we have been and are spending money on things that do not and cannot exist. Most notably, the Strategic Defense Initiative (SDI) is an example of this; and it is very useful for my philosophical analysis since it is so bizarre that there will be less resistance to my paradoxical thesis in this case. What other important examples come under this category of zero-quality non-existent systems, will be for others, more familiar with the details, to decide.

The SDI as a Non-Thing

This is not the place to recapitulate a lengthy debate; one simple anecdote will have to suffice. This was a public debate on Star Wars, conducted between two American gentlemen, both of impeccably Establishment, military-orientated careers and views. The defender had conspicuously little to say; he showed that the problem has a history, that we now have no shield against enemy rockets, that he is concerned for peace, and that he too appreciates the inherent impossibility of some of the design features (as a ten-million-line computer program that must have no bugs on its first real run). The critic enjoyed himself hugely, and based his argument on considerations of quality: by examples, he showed how any possible design is in many respects hypersensitive to defects. For example, the mirrors that are to reflect the death-rays to the incoming rockets must be polished to a near-perfect smoothness lest they absorb some of that highly concentrated radiant energy and disintegrate instantaneously. Any sort of flaw could be fatal to their performance — a tiny crack, a piece of chewing-gum, etc. Of course that brought the house down; what is more likely, in America, than that some careless assembly-worker or bored soldier would place his chewing-gum on the mirror and forget to collect it?

All this was before the Challenger disaster, and the shooting down of the Iranair plane in the Gulf, so that the problems of quality are even more plausible now than then. But what might still cause difficulty is that a system can be deliberately *designed* to be so hypersensitive to quality, that under any remotely realistic circumstances it could not be said to exist, or to have a chance of existing, at all. Even if that could be imagined as an abstract possibility in some philosophical game, it is difficult indeed to imagine its happening, and on such a vast scale as the SDI. So my argument must not only show that these non-things are conceivable; I must also show that they really do happen. The non-things are there, and have an importance of their own as believed-in-things. Fantasy and hardware are not, then, in totally separate categories; in the nuclear age they can become indistinguishable. Out of such a paradox we might arrive at a deeper understanding of our technological reality as a whole.

As I say, the SDI is an excellent case in point as a non-thing. What is indubitably real about it is the extra money appropriated annually by Congress for the work. (To the extent that existing programmes are deprived of funds on behalf of this new one, and then existing work carries on with new titles so as to attract continued support, even that financial reality is relative.)

Beyond that we have an 'initiative' which could never (once the opposition had presented its case) be seriously defended in public, nor indeed even *defined* with any precision. It became a shifting assemblage of speculations and computer-art videos. Some of its imagined hardware had been considered and rejected; the rest was unfounded fantasy. There was a single experiment at its base, a highly improbable result concerning X-irradiation emitted from a small hydrogen bomb explosion; by some undreamed-of technology, *this* was to be aimed and focused in the instant of disintegration, thereby producing the death-ray against enemy missiles. There might, of course, be some potentially real things lurking behind it (which may be why the Russians have been taking it seriously); among these are communications satellite systems which might transform our present *ballistic* missiles to ones with on-course *guidance*, thereby greatly enhancing their accuracy.

But the SDI survived in good strength through the Reagan administrations because it was one of the President's fancies, along with Nicaragua. It not merely threatens the quality of civilian research into computers (the country's main line of defence against the Japanese), but also has all sorts of distorting and corrupting effects on technological R&D and scientific research. Those with extensive experience of federal programmes designed to eradicate this or that social evil within five years will find none of this surprising. But what is different in this case is that real hardware is being designed and built, at enormous expense in money and resources of talent, which is so palpably a non-thing. Fortunately, the self-correcting mechanisms of a (relatively) open society have come into play; and following on a growth of healthy scepticism among people and politicians about 'conventional' nuclear weapons systems as proposed, there is now little enchantment, outside Reagan and the looney right, over Star Wars. I am writing this before the election of 1988, so it is pointless for me to predict how the SDI will fare in the immediate future; but it is hard to imagine its carrying on unscathed into the 1990s (though this may be one of those predictions I shall come to regret!).

Quality Decontrol in Military Procurement

Nothing in politics happens in a vacuum; and so even in the Reagan administration there had to be some precedents and practices that gave the SDI some semblance of plausibility. This pre-existing context can be analysed into three phases: capture of quality control; the 'baroque' design effects; and what I might irreverently call 'Zen and the Art of Nuclear Deterrence'. To the first, the classic source is the book *National Defense* by James Fallows (New York: Random House, 1981). There he quotes case after case where even the most humble tools of the soldier, including his rifle, were the victims of distortion and degradation of quality through bureaucratic and commercial pressures. For those interested in the philosophy of quality control, there are fine examples of imposition of inappropriate criteria, such as testing a rifle by its performance when used by marksmen under competition conditions, rather than in some simulation of battle. All this was in the cause of keeping the M15 (later M16) rifle, a foreign import, from being seen to be clearly superior to the traditional American product. Such practices go a long way back; in his *In the Name of Science* of 1966 (Quadrangle Books, Chicago), H.L. Nieburg described how defence contractors accomplished the 'throwing away of the yardstick' whereby their projects and products could be independently assessed.

It can be profoundly shocking to discover how the distortion and degradation of quality of performance can be imposed, in spite of what would seem to be its obvious consequences on the ability of one's own troops to fight and even to survive. The reasons for this can be as various as those of any corrupted state. We need not always invoke the 'Milo Minderbinder effect', from the *Catch-22* character who brought the principles of free enterprise, for which he was fighting, into the battlefield itself. The eminent physicist Freeman Dyson tells how he struggled vainly for many months to secure a slight modification of the standard Second World War British bomber, so that it would not be a death-trap for the fliers once hit by enemy fire. Those who opposed this were doubtless the well-educated, charming, highly principled mandarins who would be scandalized at the thought of the unsophisticated corruption by which the American system is bent from its stated objectives.

In all such cases, we can say with certainty that mechanisms of quality control are defective. The users of military equipment are remote in all ways from the purchasers, and hence the market is far different from that envisaged by Adam Smith. Also, the purchasers and regulators are subject to many pressures and inducements; since they must have some expertise in the materials on offer, they must therefore be familiar with, and in many ways useful to, the suppliers. However, quality control is not absent altogether, because in the end there is some hard reality testing in field conditions. Even if sample copies of a system perform miraculously well in 'controlled' trials, there can be notorious mishaps in practice, too significant to escape notice in any society where state control of communications is incomplete. The Aegis system for identification of aircraft is a recent case in point.

All these degenerative tendencies become more severe when the weapons system become 'baroque' in the sense discussed by Mary Kaldor in her book *The Baroque Arsenal*. Another way of describing the phenomenon would be hyper-sophistication, together with design by committee. Partly because of the enormous expense of new weapons systems and even of individual copies, there is always great pressure on their designers to make them perform optimally over several different sorts of functions. That this exercise is to a great extent a matter of bureaucratic power politics needs no saying. Then there are inevitable tendencies to changes of design in midstream, and to overly complicated designs in general. The result can be systems which were conceived and designed with the best and most honourable, uncorrupted intentions, and yet which have to be (or, better, should be) abandoned halfway through the process because they become quite impossible to manufacture according to the specifications as demanded and promised.

Those systems which do survive to the stages of manufacture and use will always be sickly, in a sense. Design changes and retro-fits produce dishar-monies and incompatibilities within the completed system. It is difficult to see a way to reverse this process, except by an international agreement to ban the gun. For, when they do work at all, each latest model is (in some contexts at least) vastly superior to its older rivals, so that victory can depend on its posses-sion. So the world's military forces are in a sense 'hooked' on increasingly baroque weapons systems, in spite of their accelerating costs and increasing susceptibility. We may say that in this case, the mechanisms of quality control are further constrained and distorted by the sheer difficulty of specifying what is the design and what are the desired performance criteria.

Quality in Nuclear Weapons: Can the Unthinkable be Thought?

All these tendencies to the degradation of quality control operate even more strongly in the case of nuclear weapons. The dividing line between some of the 'classic' nuclear weapons systems and the SDI is, in retrospect, not so completely sharp; this is because of some logical properties of the theories under which nuclear weapons are justified, deployed and designed. First, we can say that there has been enormous progress for humanity over the last quarter century. The message first proclaimed by nuclear disarmament campaigners, and then derided by all the establishment intellectuals, is now a common-sense proposition that guides the policies of the two greatest powers. This is that there can be no such thing as major nuclear war. Here is another example of a non-thing, analogous to those I have discussed already. In our part of the world, we all accept the definition of von Clausewitz that 'war is the continuation of diplomacy by other means'. Now, a real exchange of nuclear weapons would most probably kill all the diplomats along with the rest of us; hence diplomacy would be discontinued, and the event would have been something other than a war. One could call it genocide, or a holocaust, or perhaps ecocide; but not war. Of course there is no *certainty* about this, but, especially since the 'nuclear winter' debates, the probability is so high that it is decisive for policy purposes.

This means that there is something unique about the various explosives and their systems for delivery: they cannot be used in a war. I should mention a possible exceptional case: sometimes there is reason to believe that their real use *is* contemplated, as in a 'counter-force first strike', which would be intended to disarm the enemy and keep us safe from retaliation. In that case a 'war' is contemplated, however one-sided it might be; and there are occasionally great debates on whether some development could make that option more attractive to one side, and therefore destabilize the arms race

87

further. But, given what is now publicly known about the deficiencies of existing weapons systems, that option, which would require extremely accurate weapons lest it rebound catastrophically, is always more of a theoretical, long-term concern rather than an immediate policy.

In the above example I have provided a hint of how convoluted the debates on nuclear weaponry can and do become. Because they threaten total annihilation, the logic of their possible uses is just very different from anything we have seen hitherto. In the normal scenarios, the weapons are designed, or perhaps better, intended *not* to be used. They are there as a 'deterrent' against some matching system on the other side. Essentially, their use is that of a bluff: one hopes it will succeed without being 'called', but one must be prepared for that most unwelcome eventuality. Now, how is there to be any quality control in that function? It would require some grave crisis, or a realistic simulation of one. The last real one was over Cuba; and the more we know about that, the less it seems possible to simulate such a thing realistically. Hence any quality control on particular designs of nuclear weapons systems, rests distinctly in the realm of uncontrollable speculation. Worse, we might consider the problem, how can there by any serious design at all? It is totally impossible to fine-tune the performance characteristics of a device of mass annihilation around some nightmare scenario of misunderstandings and panic among the world's leaders.

Fortunately for the nuclear weapons business, this difficulty has been circumvented; the procedures have been well described by Sir Solly Zuckerman in *Science Advisers, Scientific Advisers and Nuclear Weapons* (Menard Press, London, 1980). What starts the process is not a strategists' scenario involving mad Russians, but a weapons lab with a device they hope to market. Around its properties they imagine possible physical uses, and then the sorts of crises that could precipitate the threats to such uses. These would best relate to weapons already in existence on the other side or thought (or conveniently imagined) to be under development there. With such a sales pitch, all it needs is glossy brochures, realistic computer-art videos, and some sympathetic congressmen. Then the public learns of a new threat in the form of a 'gap' or 'window', to which our brave lads in the labs have fortunately in the nick of time dreamed up the answer, for only so many gigabucks. Thus the fantasy spawns hardware, whose only real function is to generate cost-plus contracts for itself and its offspring.

Of course there is a sense in which this is corrupt; for the public is being sold a succession of systems whose real function is not the sort of public benefit as stated, but rather a covert, private enrichment. But it is hard to see how it could operate otherwise, at least in a country that is leading rather than following in technological development in the field. When Herman Kahn wrote his famous book *On Thermonuclear War*, he referred to the calculating with megadeaths, in tens and hundreds, as being 'unthinkable' in its moral horror. He was not then aware that this property made any attempted rationality (such as his own) purely theoretical and speculative; once the test of reality is brought in to the planning of nuclear warfare, its logical impossibility obtrudes on and then dominates the process. So, half-cynically one might say that the system of design as described by Sir Solly Zuckerman is as good or as bad as any, given that a society somehow believes in such a thing as rational policy for nuclear defence. From that fantasy of illogic, all others flow.

When such corruptions of reason and of process are so necessarily involved in the design and production of nuclear weapons, it is only natural, indeed inevitable, that their quality as physical systems, should totally lack controls. By analogy with the previous case, we may speak of them as hyper-baroque, lacking any chance of reality testing to contain or dilute the effects of unstable specifications and over-design. Indeed, before the SDI ever emerged from its murky origins, there were cases of weapons systems whose quality was publicly seen to be right down there near to the point of nullification. The most famous case in point was the MX system, which was to be carried around on trains in a gigantic network of underground tunnels, all to cope with a technicality of a treaty as yet unsigned. Faced with NIMBY (Not In My Book Yard) protests on a correspondingly large scale, the promoters shifted designs repeatedly, until it was quite clear that the function of MX was simply to keep the Air Force in the missiles business. The notorious Cruise missiles certainly played a part in the growth of a world-wide radical feminist movement; but their computer map-reading program never worked, the copies of the missiles performed but indifferently on tests, and the whole thing was abandoned halfway through its production run. Examples of 'nuclear junk' that never did work and never could work are there in abundance; the question is whether there ever was a nuclear strike force that could have inflicted serious damage on Soviet targets, rather than random genocide all around.

Thus, in the technical sphere just as in ordinary civil life, corruption is indivisible. If one part of an enterprise is rotten to the core, then the others will surely be infected. What makes nuclear weapons unique is that the corruption does not even depend on the (inevitable) moral frailties of the responsible agents; it is built into the very conception of the things, as devices whose use must be a non-use, and that non-use to occur under conditions that are strictly unimaginable. In another civilization, 'nuclear deterrence' might even become a Zen riddle, like making the sound of one hand clapping. But outside the monastery, in that big business of war, it had to become corrupt. Logical self-contradiction in these conditions leads not to instant enlightenment, but to intellectual fantasy and technical and social corruption. The SDI was only a natural extension of nuclear weaponry by other means, its fantasized hardware only a more pure version of what had gone before.

The Emperor's Bombs

Like anyone who is making a point they consider original and important, I must explain to myself and to my readers why it has not been taken up before.

There has been no lack of debate on nuclear weapons at all levels, and it is surprising that this point should have waited so long, perhaps until the problem is well on the way to resolution, before being made. One thing I can say about it is that I have indeed been making this point, in occasional lectures and articles, over the years; but I never found the slightest interest expressed in it. From this I concluded that either I am very eccentric indeed, or that the reluctance of my various audiences, even those in the anti-nuclear movement, to engage with this problem, is itself a topic for reflection.

First, I should say that my detailed observations have no novelty at all; everything I say about the deficiencies of nuclear weapons systems is and has been freely available in the public prints. Furthermore, my theories of the attitudes of those in charge of the weapons systems are supported by statements of knowledgeable people, reported in the press. Some years ago there was a minor scandal in America, about the 'electro-magnetic pulse' (EMP). This had been known since the mid-1960s at least, as a product of H-bomb explosions, that could derange even heavy-duty electrical switchgear, to say nothing of electronic systems. It was clear, to all who cared to know, that after a nuclear exchange of any significance, all the world's communication systems would be disrupted or destroyed. Moreover, there were techniques for 'hardening' such systems, making them less vulnerable to the pulse. But to institute these would have been very expensive indeed, and research on them would deflect funds from more glamorous projects. So the EMP was ignored, until there was evidence that the Russians were taking it seriously. Then there was a rather belated recognition; and at the time (1981) *Science* magazine quoted one defence official as saying: 'The philosophy that says a nuclear war is never going to happen has pervaded the military and its contractors to the point where they do not mind building self-defeating systems' (W.J. Broad (1981) 'Nuclear Pulse', *Science* **29**, 1009 ff, 1116 ff, 1248 ff).

Although this is an isolated statement, and as such not the strongest of evidence on its own, it fits so perfectly with the objective phenomena of the multitude (perhaps majority) of unworkable nuclear and hi-tech weapons systems that it is the obvious solution to the problem. And yet, what could be done, philosophically or politically, with such evidence, unless by someone who had already got to the same point as myself? Unless one has already gone beyond respecting nuclear strategy and nuclear weapons as the products of serious intentions, such a statement could only provide an invitation to further conundrums of the sort (usually involving comparisons of the dangers of various weapons systems and strategies) in which many anti-nuclear intellectuals have entrapped themselves. For we might ask, is the world safer with people like that running the show? Is this a case of 'laudable corruption'? Should we encourage them to keep on building self-defeating systems, as a contribution to peace? I do hope that such questions have an initial plausibility, for in my view they reflect a conception of the phenomenon that lacks roots in the analysis, logical and material, that I have been making, of hardware and fantasy. The reasons that there has never been a systematic appreciation of the problem of 'nuclear junk' lie in the ways that nuclear weapons, in spite of all their moral horrors, are 'natural' to the ways of thinking of nearly all of us.

I believe that the nuclear weapons industry, culminating in Star Wars, could survive for so long in spite of being so fantasized, because it has an inherent plausibility in several basic aspects of our world-picture, and then also because its exposure would threaten some fundamental beliefs of ours. Those who admired the emperor's new clothes were not simply frightened and venal; social stability and social solidarity were at stake. Only a child could have been innocent of the subversive consequences of that excessively penetrating vision of hers.

First let me discuss the negative side of the protection of the plausibility of nuclear weaponry, extending for a while even to Star Wars itself. Here we may have a case of a taboo, an unwillingness to imagine incompetence, corruption and mendacity on a scale that staggers the imagination. For me there are two analogous cases. One is in committed scholarship of various sorts, where there are heated debates, persisting for decades or generations, over the true solution of some problem. In Protestant religion there was 'the historical Jesus' whose career *must* be capable of reconstruction from the scriptures that authentically described it. In the philosophy of science there was 'the scientific method', which *must* be capable of articulation so as to explain the unique truth and rationality of science. When both of these quests eventually lost their plausibility, the world as a whole did not suddenly turn upside down; but many individuals went through deep crises, and the next generation in those areas of experience inhabited a reality that was subtly but definitely different.

The other taboo may be more acceptable outside America; I call it the 'Kennedy in Dallas' problem. Can there be places in the United States of America where it is simply unsafe for the President to go? The widespread need to find a lone, crazed assassin, rather than a web of persons involved actively or passively, reminds us how in America the Presidency, as distinct from any particular incumbent, *is* hedged about with a sort of divinity. Should the Presidency be exposed as just another part of the game (as was indeed the threat during the Watergate scandal), then something nearly sacred, that for many Americans has made their country something different and better, would be tarnished and corrupted. For this present case, I recall the title of that early book on the problem, *In the Name of Science*. That name, science, has a charisma in our culture analogous to that of the flag for Americans. Even though defence contracting is not traditional academic science, still there are enough connections, both in symbol and in practice, that the exposure of the universal degradation and corruption of quality in the one would necessarily rub off on to the other. The activities of the State in policy for defence science necessarily use some of the most eminent of the research community; if these should turn out to have been so gullible, or so complicit, then their standing, and then that of their community, would be compromised.

Perhaps in the management of the many individual scandals in the 'nuclear junk' field, we even see an analogy to the management of incompetence and corruption in American politics at the highest level. So long as each crisis can be contained, treated on its own, and treated implicitly (though unrealistically) as an exception to a general rule, then the symbols are safe. In politics, it was that assassination in Dallas, and later that squalid little crime organized in the White House, that threatened the symbols themselves. In defence procurement, we have not yet had such a shattering experience. Perhaps the very illogic of nuclear defence protects itself: since there cannot be an occasion for reflection on the quality of the equipment when used, there is no way in which the awful truth can be forced upon the public. The closest approach was the Challenger disaster, but that was very specialized, and in the civilian sector as well. All this discussion has been in terms of the American situation; for there, government in general is more vulnerable to public disillusion than almost anywhere else, and also the scandals are more open. If fantasy and junk in nuclear weaponry can survive there, then elsewhere they are quite safe indeed.

At the present time we may be witnessing the containment and resolution of the greatest fantasy of them all, the SDI. In the closing months of the Reagan administration, there is very little said about it; and it is now some time since there were accusations that the basic experiments by which the whole scheme was justified were themselves highly dubious. There were leaks, protests, splits and finally resignations in the key weapons labs responsible for the core of the programme. It may be that reality testing was accomplished in this case, by an effective combination of the integrity of particular persons with the rivalry between particular organizations. What will happen after Star Wars, particularly if the decline in antagonism between the superpowers continues, is hard to say. Being optimistic, one could imagine a situation where people begin to ask what was it all about, and go on to look critically at the whole enterprise. At that stage, perhaps the cultural need for defences of the nuclear syndrome will be decreased; and so it will be possible to engage with the grounds for its positive support within our general view of the world.

Here we are dealing with what might be called inherent plausibility, which strongly constrains a culture's reception of an idea. Before Galileo and Descartes, the idea of the earth at the centre of the cosmos had all the inherent plausibility; after them, the balance shifted. Before the work of Martin Luther King Jr the idea of political action through Gandhian non-violence had no inherent plausibility in the West. Until recently, the idea that national security is *decreased* by an increase of armaments was implausible, even though this paradoxical property of weaponry was established in various ways of individuals. Thus although many Americans keep guns at home, not so many carry them around for instant use on the streets; even the guns lobby does not press for a *continuously* armed citizenry. The British have long been known to keep their police forces unarmed in ordinary conditions; and there is no pressure to change this apparent invitation to violence. Hence there have been a variety of precedents available, and some of them used in argument, to show that security can be improved through controlled disarmament. After only some three decades, the balance of plausibility has been changing rapidly, and both the American and the Soviet leaders now know that (controlled) weakness brings strength.

This change in inherent plausibility might be quite an important one for our civilization, for it stands as an exception to the implicit logic whereby we relate ideas. For here we have a grasping of paradox, an appreciation that two apparently contradictory ideas have a deep inner relation. This is quite foreign to our mainstream literate culture, where logical entailment is the only accepted connection of ideas. Indeed, that thought-style, combined with the triumphant materialism of modern European civilization, is what made the development of nuclear weapons so seductively, nearly fatally plausible. Defence is secured by the ability to deter, repel and counter-attack; the greater these abilities, the better the defence, and hence the greater the national security. This is so logical, it could almost be a theorem in mathematics.

In spite of the abstracted megadeath calculations of the theory of games as applied to nuclear strategy, there was no real imagining of the thought-processes of the other side. The lesson in logic of the First World War, when both sides had the machine-guns that each had previously used so successfully against spear-throwing natives, was forgotten. This time around it was not merely the butchery of the best men of all the nations for a few yards of mud. Now we had the realization of the mad inventor's dream, 'a weapon so terrible that it would make war impossible forever'. But on all sides we still heard, 'If "they" have them, then we must have them too, and bigger'. It was beyond the wit of almost any expert, including the most erudite and authoritative, to imagine the properties and outcome of a duet in which each side was singing this same refrain. Of course, the reasons for this low-level awareness could be seen as largely political: if one has made the antagonist into a demon, then he is presumed to have no rights to self-defence, and by extension no thought processes either. But it is also possible to see a deeper cause, in an inability to confront a deeply paradoxical, self-contradictory situation that has arisen in the most natural way from ordinary circumstances and common-sense reactions.

We all know that the Bomb started as a deterrent against a possible Nazi bomb, and that once completed it was used both to finish the war with Japan and to make a show of strength to the Soviet Union. But once the Russians had followed suit, and especially once there were intercontinental ballistic missiles against which there is no defence, the logic of warfare, which had taken so many generations and centuries to elaborate, was rendered demented at a stroke. In the perspective of history, thirty years is not such a long time for leaders and theorists to turn their thinking around. While that was waiting to happen, all the corrupting tendencies of ordinary military procurement, aggravated by the baroque weaponry phenomenon, were heightened in the case of the nuclear weapons that had so suddenly become Zen riddles. Now at last we have learned that in the face of the technological ability to destroy civilization and much more, our inherited logic in political−military cause and effect must be discarded, and a logic of paradox and reflexivity must be employed.

As that lesson sinks in, we may be ready for the next lesson, that not merely logic but also reality can be paradoxical and dialectical. The idea that a piece of equipment may be a non-thing, and may attain that status by a continuous conceptual extension from being a shoddy thing, is contrary to the ingrained materialism of our world-view as much as to our linear logic. Having been taught that the only reality is in the atoms (or their successors), and that things like 'values' are secondary, how difficult it is to imagine that what makes a device what it is, is the *function* around which it is designed. From that principle follows the appreciation that if a supposed device can perform no function at all, then it is not an object, no more than a pile of scrap is an automobile. In the persisting belief that such non-thing is a thing, we have the primary fantasy, from which all the others, and their associated corruptions, follow. Thus we learn that hardware and fantasy interpenetrate as much as do strength and weakness, and indeed good and evil.

In the case of nuclear weaponry, and particularly in the most instructive example of the SDI, we may have an important example of the way in which the development of ideas as realized in practice eventually modifies the reality around them, and so fosters the creation of a new, appropriate framework of ideas for effective practice and indeed survival in that new reality. There are analogous developments in other contemporary problem areas, most notably environmental pollution and degradation; we see it clearly in the concepts 'waste' and 'disposal', both of which are paradoxical and lead to illogicalities though of not such an immediately apocalyptic sort. If our civilization is to survive through the environmental, social and cultural consequences of the material powers it has spawned, then philosophical lessons such as these will be as important as any of our scientific or technological responses.

Adapted from a lecture first given at Crown College, University of California, Santa Cruz, in November 1985.

2
HOW WE GOT HERE

It is not easy to draw a boundary around the problem of the roots of our present predicament. Some see it only as a temporary imbalance in the technologies of production and of conservation; others lay it to the post-war affluent society, or to the industrialization of the Victorian age. At the other extreme, it is possible to argue that with the displacement of hunter–gatherers by agriculturalists the ecological imbalance was set in train; and one can even speculate that for hundreds of millennia *Homo sapiens* has been disturbing the ecosystem. My competence lies within the last few centuries, and so I can most usefully concentrate on an epochal event in our intellectual history, the 'scientific revolution' of the seventeenth century. This was a revolution within science, but even more a revolution *about* science, a relatively sudden revaluation of its objects, methods and functions. Taking the traditional term 'revolution' for this historical event, I use it to illuminate some of its essential features, including the simple, prophetic message which defined it, and then the complexities inevitably introduced by success. The dream of power for all mankind over a natural world conceived as disenchanted and dehumanized is unique to our civilization among all others; and so this revolution in ideas may help us to understand our predicaments in the material sphere.

The term 'scientist' is a recent invention, scarcely a hundred and fifty years old; and so we can say that there was science before scientists. Then they mostly called themselves natural philosophers; and this term conveys a difference in how the role was imagined. We understand the scientific revolution better if we see its founders as self-appointed prophets of a new path to the True and the Good. Admittedly, this is easiest in the case of Francis Bacon, for he devoted himself more to rhetoric than to research. But the volume of his writings on non-scientific subjects provides us with many clues to his essential vision. The title of the second essay in this section includes the term 'reform';

and this is ambiguous, since Bacon's own religion was the product of a Reform. I show how Bacon's religious commitment shaped, even determined, his conception of the path for science. There are some surprises there, such as in his relating of his endeavours to the millennium; and Bacon's perception of charity as the essence of religion has made a deep impression on me.

Such an exalted view of science has been for a minority, even among its practitioners. Linking the past with the present, I show how the tradition of criticisms of science is co-extensive with the history of scientific research and speculation. The Socrates idealized by Plato appears otherwise in a famous comedy by Aristophanes; there he runs a school that unites godless philosophizing with crooked logic. This conservative criticism is echoed down through the ages, to the Creationists of today; but there have been radical critics as well, condemning science as élitist and inhuman. It is possible to see all those past critics as futile or irrelevant, as science accomplished its triumphant advance. But in recent times the criticisms have increased in volume, diversity and standing of their proponents. The ambiguities in the ideas of 'science' and 'scientist' have now become a source of weakness, as the community of science is now in a position of creating great powers while being deprived of responsibility for their use; a paradoxical state, which leaves it confused and vulnerable.

Such a state of affairs would have been particularly dismaying to one of the last great prophets of science, who reinterpreted the rationalist tradition in Marxist terms; this was J.D. Bernal. His vision was formed in the 1930s, when capitalism produced unemployment, scientific and technical stagnation, and Fascism; while Soviet Socialism seemed to contain the promise of a science that was planned, for the benefit of science and society alike. Although he had great influence on a generation of scientists and politicians in England, his vision was clouded, by the Bomb and by the subsequently admitted errors and distortions of Stalinism, just as the planning of science was becoming a reality. He turned to history for guidance; and wrote a magnificent survey that enjoyed enduring popularity in capitalist as well as socialist countries. But his Marxism could not really explain the shape of events in the past, any more than in the future; and his life's work remains as a monument whose relevance will have to await some eventual rejuvenation of Marxist thought.

The following essays provide a perspective, however fragmentary and incomplete, on the background to our present problems. If there is any single simple lesson to be drawn from them, it is that science in history is very far from being the collection and application of facts, directed by some inner logic of discovery and need. Ideas, ideals and illusions, as tempered by criticism and fierce debate, are an important driving force in the shaping of the science that is done and the technology that is effected. The lesson for the present and future is that science and technology can be similarly influenced, perhaps even more deliberately now than ever before, by public scrutiny and debate. This has already happened on a variety of salient issues, such as cruelty to animals and environmental protection; the task for the future is to ensure that accountability to the public is achieved by appropriate means, and does not degenerate into crude control by politicians.

What Was the Scientific Revolution?

From one perspective, the civilization we call Western, or better, modern European, is but one of a long sequence of civilizations, extending back for thousands of years towards prehistory. Indeed, it is prudent, particularly now, to consider it in that light, and to be aware of the possibility that it may now be turning towards decline and replacement. Although every civilization is unique in its own way, ours has special features that make it important not merely because it is our own and carries our fates with it. It has achieved a totally unprecedented degree of material power, enabling the earth to support previously unimaginable numbers of people in previously unimaginable conditions of material comfort and security. With this material progress has come an amelioration of social and cultural conditions for the great mass of people, so that even with all the continuing poverty in the world, there is at least a vision and a hope of a good and decent life for all. With this progress have come hazards; these affect not merely ourselves and our present civilization, but also the survival of any civilized life and indeed the whole living system of the planet. Hence our concern with understanding ourselves as a civilization now has a significance of genuinely cosmic proportions.

Such as understanding of ourselves will require all the perspectives we can achieve, from those of the poet and novelist to those of the scientist or philosopher. Somewhere in the middle, perhaps the broadest in scope but not in itself a complete synthesis, lies history: the study of the past, motivated though not dominated by the concerns of the present. In the case of modern European civilization, history is particularly appropriate as a path to understanding. The features that have made modern Europe unique, though discernible in retrospect in its various cultural roots, became decisive in the seventeenth century. Up to that point, one could (in retrospect) imagine Europe as just another empire, on the rise just when its rivals were decaying. But during that turbulent time, something happened to the educated common sense of the world in Europe, which interacted with the rapidly developing sciences of nature. Out of that union came the uniquely powerful body of theories and methods that is epitomized in Newton's *Principia* of 1687.

Those achievements in the study of nature had consequences in all spheres of educated culture. The radical thinkers of the Enlightenment adapted them as symbols for their own programmes of reform of philosophy and society. The innovators of the Industrial Revolution used the example and the results in their rapid, though piecemeal transformation of the basic forces of production. Out of these two currents came contemporary Europe and its cultural colonies, an empire on which until recently the sun never set.

Revolutions

We get a special appreciation of how the Scientific Revolution has shaped our consciousness when we study the works of its masters, and feel how 'modern' they are. Galileo's *Starry Messenger* (1610) reads like first-class popularized science, and Descartes' *Discourse on Method* (1638) unfolds its story through the familiar device of an autobiography of an intensely self-aware intellectual. The writings of the third great prophet, Bacon, support this point, for they now have a somewhat antique flavour; Bacon wanted to reconcile the accepted learning with the new, rather than replace it. We can concentrate on these three authors as our examples, because of the commitment and clarity of their vision, making them prophets rather than just innovators; this was well-recognized in their own century. Such apparent modernity is, of course, somewhat deceptive; each of these authors was expressing personal concerns that are forgotten to use now, and in any event they were exceptional in their own time. However, the direct intellectual ancestry is unmistakable; and so when we look for the events that have made the world-view of modern Europe what it is, we can start there. All earlier events can legitimately be taken as roots, or anticipations, rather than the crucial thing itself.

For the purposes of this essay, I accept as an historical event something called the Scientific Revolution. It is concentrated inside the seventeenth century. Its earlier benchmarks are the classic writings, such as Galileo's *Starry Messenger* of 1610, Bacon's *New Organon* of 1621, and then Galileo's *Two World Systems* and Descartes' *Discourse on Method and Essays* of 1632 and 1638 respectively. Its culmination is recorded in Newton's *Principia Mathematica Philosophiae Naturalis* of 1687. Other contemporary great works of science, such as Gilbert's *De Magnete* of 1600, Kepler's *Astronomia Nova* of 1609 and Harvey's *De Motu Cordis* of 1628, do not count, because they only recorded the doing of science and did not call for its transformation. The 'revolution' was localized in place as well, starting in northern Italy, but soon moving to north-west Europe, including France, the Netherlands and England. Within those constraints, somewhat conventional as are all in history, we can try to see what happened and what it means to us.

The Copernican Revolution is the dramatic centre-piece of at least the earlier part of the scientific revolution; in it the earth was displaced from the centre of things and set to spinning on its axis and orbiting about the sun. In cosmology it replaced the hierarchically nested universe of the Christianized Aristotelian scheme with infinite uniform space; and it also emptied it of the various intelligent agencies responsible for various theological and astrological functions, leaving it silent of meaning of its own. All this was accomplished partly by technical astronomy (Copernicus and Kepler) and partly by popularization (Kepler, Gassendi, Descartes and, most famous, Galileo). But a *proof* of the earth's motions was slow in coming; even Newton presupposed them rather than demonstrating them. Hence rather like the larger scientific revolution itself, the success of the Copernican revolution must be seen as much in terms of philosophy, common sense or ideology, as of scientific research.

The term 'revolution' now means the overthrow of something old and its replacement by something new; and this is how we understand the scientific revolution. The term was brought explicitly into the analysis of science by Thomas S. Kuhn in his seminal book *The Structure of Scientific Revolutions* (Chicago, 1962). For him, the scientific revolution in general, and the Copernican revolution in particular, functioned as crucial examples for his analysis. He also had an explicit picture of a reactionary or rigid old guard, unable to move quickly enough to resolve the contradictions (in his terms, anomalies) in its scientific practice. The analogy with political and social revolutions seems to be commonly accepted by scholars, and so we can call on it whenever it is fruitful for our analysis.

In general, we can imagine a revolution resulting from the maturing of various tendencies in an older order, which had previously seemed marginal or unimportant difficulties; but which rather suddenly come together and make it impossible for the existing structures to perform their necessary functions. In a genuine revolution, there is also an explicit ideology, a simple vision of a better world, that provided coherence and drive to the effort, inspiring the activists to their sacrifices. As the revolution consolidates, that ideology is rendered false or irrelevant, the new order becomes stable and conservative, and a new cycle begins. This is a rough model of revolution in the sphere of power; let us see how well it works for ideas and techniques.

The Ideology

In this case we can start with the ideology, for out of it came not merely the achievements then, but also the shape of everything since. This is a composite of the pronouncements of the three great prophets of the scientific revolution, Bacon, Galileo and Descartes. Very different in circumstances, style, doctrine and career, they offered complementary visions of what the revolution was about. In the words of Auguste Comte, the founder of the philosophy of 'positivism', the revolution was based on the precepts of Bacon, the concepts of Descartes, and the *expériences* of Galileo. They are a diverse set: the English humanist and jurist, the French metaphysician and mathematician, and the Italian 'physicist' and cosmologist; with only indirect acquaintance or none at all; and all ending their careers in bitterness and failure; but between them creating the synthesis of ideas and commitments that revolutized our knowledge and power over the natural world.

In this case it might be more accurate to speak of an ideological commitment common to all three prophets, rather than of an ideology as such. For while there was very little in detail on which their programmes all agreed, there was a common core to their commitment that can be defined. This can be expressed as follows: *The most valuable and powerful new truths are to be achieved by following a certain new method of studying the natural world considered as dehumanized and disenchanted.* This formula is tightly packed, and so I should discuss its elements in some detail.

The *value* of the work is best expressed by Bacon's aphorism, 'for the glory of God and the relief of man's estate'; for him (and also Descartes) their work was a calling, the redemption of mankind in his material existence, a task with strong millenarian overtones. Such a commitment was not new among philosophical visionaries in Europe; the novelty here was the invocation of material *power* as the means to the divinely sanctioned end. Previously, the highest good had generally been portrayed (for the élite) as something inward or contemplative, the cultivation of wisdom or even of religious experience. Now the path is seen as something external and activist, even when (as with Bacon and possibly Descartes) the spiritual component is essential. This theme of power was also no novelty for Europe, for magic had co-existed, in a frequently hostile interaction, with learning and religion from the beginning. For magic as such, our revolutionaries had nothing but contempt and scorn; in modern terms, they created the list of pseudo-sciences that has stood unchanged to this day. (We may say that this *negative* definition of science exhibits the essential connection between their revolutionary vision and our orthodox scientific common sense.) But they took over its aspirations, in a certain refined form; and this paradoxical act (one of the two key moves in the ideology) was crucial for the revolution.

One way that the ideology could sanitize magic was to make the craftsmen the surrogates for the magicians. On this theme there is more unity among the revolutionaries than on any other; each in his own way lauded craft practice as a better approach to knowledge than the book-learning of the time. Some historians have seen this theme as a confirmation of a Marxist interpretation; here was the unity of theory and practice which the representatives of rising, progressive class (then, the bourgeoisie) would naturally promote; and also here was a harbinger of the sort of science that would flourish under socialism. The first point is quite plausible, although it is not easy to identify any section of a bourgeoisie particularly on the rise just at this point in the early seventeenth century. The theme of power can also be seen as a reflection of the changing nature and status of certain practical arts in the preceding century, mainly those depending on mathematics and showing their usefulness for navigation, warfare and civic pride. Training in these mathematical arts was standard for young gentlemen of the time.

The theme of *method* was not particularly new; it had already been advanced in the previous century. Also, it is hard to find a common positive theme among the versions of the method that were advanced by the three prophets. Of course, they all proposed experience and reason, in some mixture, in opposition to the book-learning of the professors and the enthusiasm of the magicians. Perhaps the important unity here is the stress on method for *discovery* of truths, accepting that in their time mankind was largely ignorant; this was in opposition to those philosophers and theologians who believed in the existence of a satisfactory body of known truths, available to persons with the right training and attitudes.

The theme of *novelty* was somewhat daring in its own time; institutions of learning were explicitly charged with protecting tradition rather than challenging it; and in religion novelties had a very bad reputation, as they had led to the excesses of populist, radical religion during the Reformation. By contrast, Truth was a traditional goal in European thought; and this we understand as genuine, indubitable truth, known to be such with certainty. Previously there had been great debates between the adherents of theological truth against those supporting philosophy; but there was agreement that truth is there to be found. One element in the background to this new ideology was the rise of 'scepticism', in some important cases (notably Montaigne) a reaction against the idiocies and horrors of religious intolerance; and it is possible to see Descartes, and perhaps Bacon too, forming their philosophies in reaction to the challenge of sceptical denials of the possibility of achieving truth of any sort.

Perhaps the strongest novelty in this ideology was its commitment to the discovery of truth through the study of the *natural* world. For us it might seem strange that people should believe that they could solve problems of ethics and even of theology by this route; but for Bacon and Descartes it was quite explicit and programmatic (and at the core of their endeavours), and even Galileo gave hints in that direction. But after all, this is the dominant belief of our time: that the natural sciences, both by their accomplishments and by their methods, provide the example for all the others. Such a radical shift in priorities needs explanation. If we exclude the folk-history tale that the obvious successes of science and of the scientific method were the source for the new methodology, then we are left to find some motivation outside science itself. This could lie in a general disillusion with all traditional forms of knowing, achieved either through literature, philosophy or theology. These had failed to prevent the splitting of Christianity into perpetually warring factions; and the meaningful world that their symbols invoked was fading fast. Descartes' criticism of the pretentions of humanistic education in the *Discourse* is a masterpiece of destruction of a culture; Bacon, while more sympathetic and also more discursive, shows the same commitment.

Finally, we come to the principle that the natural world is to be considered as 'dehumanized and disenchanted'. This is the core of the metaphysical reconstruction wrought by the scientific revolution. In the first rejection is the well-known reaction against the philosophical system of Aristotle as interpreted by the modernized scholasticism of the sixteenth century. Its 'final causes' were the prime target of ridicule by the innovators, along with its 'substantial forms' and 'occult qualities'. It has taken a full three centuries for the natural philosophy of Aristotle himself to be rescued from the dustbin of history, to which it was consigned in those early modern polemics.

The *disenchantment* was not so clearly proclaimed by the revolutionaries, and its significance has become appreciated by historians only recently. The term refers to the denial of the existence of any conscious agencies or meaningful events, anywhere in the world other than in humanity and in our unique God. With this goes the denial of the prodigious effects that such agencies can produce with small or negligible physical causes. In the enchanted cosmos, there were highly developed rational sciences, such as astrology; there were practices in which the purification of external matter and of the soul were indistinguishable, such as alchemy; and there were many forms of divination, ranging from the most refined down to the most gross and superstitious.

It was the historians and critics of literature who first observed the rapid change in style and in figures of speech that occurred around the end of the Elizabethan period. They saw that this signalled a revolutionary change in the educated common-sense view of the cosmos. There is even a great poem to mark the change, that by John Donne where he laments,

> The new philosophy puts all in doubt
> The element of fire is quite put out
> All the world is reduced to atomies

although the poem is so early (1610) that it is more likely to be referring to the Renaissance visionary heretic Giordano Bruno than to the corpuscular philosophy which had not yet been announced. In the later seventeenth century there was an explicit awareness of the affinity between the new disenchanted natural philosophy and the new literary style ('plain' for the English, 'classical' for the French); and this was exploited for propaganda purposes by the apologists for the fledgling Royal Society of London.

In this disenchantment we find a powerful contradiction in the ideology, for the scientific revolution shared the theme of power over nature with the ancient magical arts. Yet it did not even debate with their devotees, but simply dismissed them with contempt. Thus Galileo, in a crucial passage in his great work on cosmology, pitied the late Kepler for having believed the astrological nonsense that the oceanic tides are influenced by the moon! Many sorts of knowledge about the natural world that had been highly regarded (though also strongly contested) including astrology and alchemy as well as many varieties of divination, quite suddenly, in less than a century, became objects of ridicule among all the educated classes. In this respect the modern

European educated common sense is unique among all the world's literate cultures.

This dismissal was not so simple as it might appear in retrospect; for the prestige of the ancient enchanted arts was just beginning its rapid decline at the time of the inception of the scientific revolution. For Descartes and Galileo, the crucial move was not so much the discovery of mathematics as a way to knowledge, as the disenchantment of the Pythagorean mathematics that was already extant as a traditional path to wisdom and enlightenment. For a contrast, we have Kepler's lifelong search for the harmonies of the Creation, and even more strongly the Englishman Robert Fludd with his cabbalistical proportionalities. As usual, Bacon was the least rigorous in his rejection of the old enchanted learning; he did not ridicule it, but rather condemned it, on two sorts of grounds. First, it made men slothful and careless in their study of nature, since it promised easy results, unlike the Puritanical message of a just reward for honest toil that his way offered. And second, it was simply implausible that gross effects should be the result of the small or insubstantial causes that are invoked in magic; and this commensurability of effects with causes was a strong support for the essential beneficence of science, until the advent of nuclear weapons in our lifetime.

There was a significant overlap between the activities of the pioneers of the scientific revolution, and those of the proponents of 'natural magic'. This was claimed to be the production of strange and wonderful effects by purely natural means; and indeed much of the popularity of science then and now is on just such a basis. One of the most successful of the natural magic school had a career that touched that of Galileo in several ways; he even had a claim to have invented the telescope. Outside the part of Europe where the scientific revolution was victorious, natural magic remained the vehicle for new discoveries; thus was von Guericke's great experiment on the power of air pressure announced to the world. There were even transitional cases, such as when the young John Wilkins wrote on 'Mathematical Magic', full of innocent wonders; and later he became one of the founders of the Royal Society. The total silence of the adherents of the new philosophy concerning natural magic is as strong an indication as any of the deep difference between them. For the prodigious as such was of no interest to these philosophers, as indeed not to science; and this is another indication of the deep change in world-view that underlies that revolution.

The most natural substratum for the disenchanted world of nature was that of dead, particulate matter. But this had the problem that it was perilously close to a well-known heretical position, that of the ancient atomists, notably Lucretius. Then and in more recent times this philosophy had served as a vehicle for anti-religious ideas; if we are only atoms, then we have no immortal souls, to be judged and punished after our deaths. Hence the Christian philosophers who espoused this atomism needed to ensure that their theology was such as to neutralize its subversive implications. Why they should have adopted such a position, known to be dangerous, is one of the more intriguing questions about the scientific revolution. One answer, provided by the French historian R. Lenoble, is that the whole movement was theologically inspired; and that in response to the threat to belief from the Renaissance natural philosophers (who could deny miracles on the grounds that *anything* is possible in Nature), there was a need for a world-view that was even 'harder' than that of Aristotle; hence the move to atomism, in spite of its recognized perils.

It should be noticed that Aristotelian ways of thinking did not die off so quickly; it turned out to be difficult, scientifically as well as theologically, to deny 'final causes' and design in the organic world. The ideological significance of Darwin's theory of evolution by 'natural selection' was that it was taken to complete the revolution in natural philosophy that had been started some two and a half centuries earlier; those who debated for and against 'Darwinism' in the later nineteenth century were under no illusions that this was merely a theory within science.

Reviewing this revolutionary ideology, or commitment, we see that the term scientific revolution needs to be interpreted properly if it is not to be misleading. What happened *in* science was an accelerated progress on several fronts, with foundations being laid for later achievements within the rising paradigm. But the deeper change in thinking was *about* natural science: its objects, methods and functions, in relation to its character as a means to knowledge and power. In this way we can understand how the Copernican theory became so popular among the learned, in spite of its scientific weaknesses and counter-intuitive perspective. Also, we can appreciate how this tendency in science, at first marginal to the enterprise of learning and even more so to that of industrial production, eventually came to dominate and indeed define them both.

Ideology and Practice

We are interested in the scientific revolution not so much as an expression of philosophies of the world, but for its significance in the creation of the science which now so dominates our culture and our life. Was this revolutionary ideology a consequence of the success of the experimental–mathematical sciences, a drawing of the lessons of what had made it possible? Or perhaps was it the rallying cry, after which the sciences were transformed into their present shape? Both these questions are deliberately simplistic in their phrasing, and so we should expect complex answers. For the first, a negative answer is a good first approximation. Bacon never did any science worth the name in our sense; Descartes formulated his grand designs on the basis of a period of work at the beginning of his career that was incredibly successful but also quite brief; while Galileo had rather more successful science and less programmatic talk, at least until he attempted the biggest job of all (proving the Copernican system) and failed.

As befits prophetic utterances, or revolutionary ideologies, they come before the really hard work, with a simple vision that makes the commitment possible. In historical retrospect, it is easy to query the extent to which they made much real difference. The new approach to science worked best with the sciences dealing with matter in its most abstract and general form, amenable to mathematical descriptions, and simple observations and experiments. These were mainly mathematics itself, astronomy, mechanics (extending from statics to dynamics and hydraulics) and optics; but these had already been well developed in classical antiquity, further refined in the Islamic period and brought to a new excellence during the sixteenth century. The revolutionary transformations of *doctrine*, as of the Copernican system and of Descartes' co-ordinate geometry, have tended to obscure the continuity of subject matter and method into and through the seventeenth century.

Outside these 'mixed mathematical' sciences, as they had been called for centuries, the record of success is mixed. Chemistry was transformed conceptually, as the 'corpuscular' philosophy replaced alchemistic or vitalist conceptions, but practice developed steadily without any sudden break-throughs. The story with biology is similar, and the line of progress even less clear. Harvey's discovery of the circulation of the blood was invoked as a great propaganda point for a 'mechanical' or 'corpuscular' philosophy, on the basis of the analogy of the heart with a simple pump. But historians have recently made it clear that Harvey himself was firmly in the Aristotelian tradition; and in any event his theory of circulation rendered the old Galenic unified physio-logical system implausible while not suggesting anything to replace it.

As to power over nature, we can recall that in the early eighteenth century, after the revolution was all over, Jonathan Swift could make a savage satire of the descendants of the scientific prophets in 'Laputa', as either addled philosophers or cynical 'projectors' who left things far worse than they found them on the estates of gullible country gentlemen.

Even accepting all these reservations about the accomplishments of the pioneers of the scientific revolution, it would be misleading and indeed unjust to dismiss their efforts as being more philosophy than science. Something immortal *was* achieved by the pioneers, each in his own way; and as the revolution consolidated in the middle of the seventeenth century, there was a 'generation of genius', including (among the English) Hooke and Boyle, and culminating in Newton. Afterwards the impetus flagged, so that by the end of the century English natural philosophy was largely a subject for theologians, eccentric gentlemen and satirists. Newton, semi-deified, was above and beyond it all as far as the public was concerned.

Thus it would be fair to say that outside a few favoured areas, what the scientific revolution accomplished for scientific research was a change in methods and explanations that *eventually* produced the edifice of established knowledge that we now take for granted. The fruits were delayed in their coming by anything up to two centuries or perhaps more. Hence we can say that the revolutionary ideology was not sufficient to bring about the instant transformation that it promised. Also we can query whether in the context of those times it was strictly a necessary change, in order that scientific progress could occur.

The assumption (common from then to now) that the great scientific achievements of the scientific revolution required *our* sort of metaphysics of nature and conception of method is falsified by a close scrutiny of the works of some of the greatest innovators. At the turn of the century, from the sixteenth to the seventeenth, there worked three very great scientists: Gilbert had just completed his researches on the magnet; Kepler was engaged on his earlier work in astronomy; and William Harvey was completing his studies in anatomy and physiology. Each of them made a great scientific discovery: Gilbert of the earth as a great magnet, Kepler of the laws of planetary motion, and Harvey of the circulation of the blood. Yet each of them lived in a world that was in some degree enchanted, endowed with world-souls or life forces, that were soon to be declared anti-scientific by such as Descartes and Galileo, and that would remain in that category until our time.

Thus the ideology of the scientific revolution was framed in contradiction to what was scientifically successful in its own time, and then failed to produce immediate successes on a broad front outside the traditional matured mixed-mathematical disciplines. We might even question whether in those fields outside what we now call physics, the adoption of the new paradigm was on balance a 'correct' strategy for scientific advance in its time. But such a question, like all the big ones in history, rests on counter-factuals, and so cannot be effectively pursued.

Historical Interpretations

Now, some three and a half centuries on, we are left with the consequences of that creative period, in a science that has unprecedented power in its own terms, but which has created the possibility of evil on a scale commensurate with that of its good. We have mentioned how the heritage of the scientific revolution includes not only our common sense of the world of nature, but also the secularizing, critical enquiry of the Enlightenment, and finally the industrial innovation and eventually the science-based technology that brought Europe to world domination. With this perspective of hindsight, we can return to the question of the relation of the scientific revolution to Europe, and for the sake of our understanding of ourselves, try to understand the scientific revolution.

For this, the work of historians promises much but in the event offers tantalizingly little. We still have to contend with a sort of folk-history that played its part in the ideology of science from that time until ours, which is the story of heroes. These were such as Galileo and Descartes, who made those essentially simple discoveries which form a part of the core of elementary science. How did they do it? Their secret was simple common sense and sound scientific method, which in their day was a great achievement since most men's minds were still captive to various distorting influences, either Aristotle or magic or metaphysics. There is a more sophisticated version of this tale, created by the first generation of critical historians of science. In this the great event is a change in Ideas, from the Aristotelian world-picture to a mathematical one, inherited mainly from Archimedes; and the transformation is exemplified in the mechanics of Galileo.

These folk-histories (with their variants) are now not so commonly told as they were just a generation ago; the recent transformations of science and of its consciousness make them appear naive in the extreme to those of us who know about the Bomb, ecology and acupuncture. In its place there have appeared some attempted alternatives, serving to demystify science and to exhibit it as part of the apparatus of social and political oppression. The most strident of these attempts is that of a feminist perspective. There, the scientific revolution has been interpreted through the theme of 'the death of Nature', where the disenchantment is seen as the destruction of feminine earth-consciousness by that of the alienated, phallic, patrial male. This works quite well at the level of consciousness, and even has its social correlate in the witchcraft craze (which lasted well into the seventeenth century) and the associated takeover of female medicine from the *sage-femmes* by men with university degrees. But it is difficult indeed to locate a strong feminine consciousness in previous ages in Europe, to say nothing of a feminist society existing within some millennia of the scientific revolution.

Rather more plausible at the moment are the sophisticated versions of Marxism. It is always useful to be reminded that literate culture has always been dominated by the classes possessing political and economic power; and that this culture will be deployed by them, on occasion quite self-consciously, for their material and ideological needs. The leading scholar in this new tendency has been M.C. Jacob; in her book *The Cultural Meaning of the Scientific Revolution* (New York, Knopf, 1987) she has shown how the 'new philosophy' of the seventeenth century was quite explicitly and unashamedly seen by its proponents as a means of protecting social stability during a period when it was quite precarious. In England it is most clear how the movement was of the centre, opposed both to the 'right', in the totalitarian Roman Catholic Church, and to the 'left', in the politically and religiously radical sectarians. Hobbes in particular is quite explicit on this, closing his *Leviathan* with a proof of the identify of the Kingdom of Darkness and the Kingdom of Fairies. For me the most telling incident of the whole episode, in this respect, is the Webster—Ward debate of 1654, just as the Puritan Revolution was winding down. In this, the radical John Webster called for an experimental science that was also Christian and Paracelsian; while his Oxford opponents had to admit that, in the last resort, universities were not primarily about advancing learning but about socializing the young élite.

This Marxist interpretation is given added strength by the political and cultural geography of Europe. The new approach to studying nature flourished first in Northern Italy, just before economic decline and the counter-Reformation sent the area into stagnation. The centres of excellence then moved to the expanding economies of north-west Europe, including France, the Protestant Netherlands and England. The Habsburg Catholic countries of southern and central Europe, and the war-torn fragmented German states, were left behind for a century or even two. Thus a rising capitalism (including for these purposes its statist version in France) was the background for the development and consolidation of the scientific revolution. Certainly, no one in the seventeenth century had any conception of 'pure science', an activity irrelevant to commerce, statecraft or philosophy; that was an invention of German professors much later on.

But it must be admitted that the correlation of the rise of capitalist modern science works best on a broad scale in space and time. Attempts to show that a particular class interest or stated need led to a particular great discovery have so far proved fruitless. Also, the Marxist approach seriously undervalues the significance of the 'absolute state' in early modern Europe. The rulers of those, big and small, were the effective patrons of most of the mathematical practitioners of the time, rather than some section of the 'bourgeoisie'. Galileo himself said (although admittedly in a letter applying for a job back in Florence) that he preferred the patronage of a Prince to employment by a Republic. What may be called a simplistic Marxism applies best to the rhetoric of that time, though of course it fits well with much of scientific practice now.

This account would not be complete without a mention of religion and theology. For many years the Galileo affair was taken as a type-case, of how religious institutions (and hence, by implication, religious belief) are antithetical to the progress of science. The fact that Galileo and all the other great scientists were believers, and many of them Catholics, was just an anomaly to be adjusted. Then the story became complicated, as some scholars discovered affinities between certain Protestant principles and the scientific endeavour, following on Max Weber's identification of the 'spirit of Capitalism' as related to the 'Protestant ethic'. There even developed a revisionist thesis, to the effect that the uniqueness of Europe, enabling the scientific revolution to occur at all, was located in its Christian tradition. Certainly there is much to be said on this score; the tendencies to a voluntarist theology (emphasizing God's unrestricted will) seem to have been associated with other currents in the new philosophy. But my inclination tends away from looking at such specialized intellectual currents as independent agencies in history. For me the most appealing theological argument is the one I mentioned above, where the issue of miracles (which was a political question as much as theological) was instrumental in turning men towards a corpuscular philosophy.

Roots of the Scientific Revolution

For myself, the guiding principle is that the workings-out of history are complicated, and therefore single-cause explanations are sure to be oversimple. My preference is to identify several roots of such a development, to see which were more general and which more specific to the time and cultural milieu; and from that to derive an assessment of the particularity of the event. The practical consequence of such an approach is that it can enable us to see more clearly both the variations within the process as it occurred in Europe, and also the possibilities and problems of reproducing it in other times and cultures. Such extensions are, unfortunately, far beyond the scope of this present essay.

We can identify four roots of the scientific revolution, all capable of being traced back for some centuries previously in European history. Proceeding from the material aspects, we first have what can loosely be called 'capitalism': a productive economy dominated by a market of relatively unfettered operators devoted to self-enrichment, rather than by organizations created for the service of the power and glory of an absolute ruler through military might and religious culture. (Notwithstanding everything I said above about the absolute state, in the matter of organizing *charisma* for state purposes, these rulers were incompetent amateurs compared with those of the East.) The second root can be seen as a cultural reflection of this economic style: a new conception of the good life for the élite, away from the contemplative virtues of learning, wisdom and religious enlightenment, towards an activist, manipulative approach to nature and society not merely for practice but also for the highest good. Then there is (thirdly) the technical background, in the recovery and development of the sciences and arts of classical civilization, first through their adaptations in the Islamic civilization, and then directly through 'humanism'. Finally, there is the most subtle and pervasive change of all, which fortunately can be documented by crucial shifts in evaluation of forms of knowledge; this is the dehumanization and disenchantment of the external world, to a degree that makes Europe quite unique among all the major world civilizations.

To deal with these briefly, the period of early capitalism produced a rapid development of techniques in all fields, but also crucial changes in the social relations of intellectual property and hence also in its evaluation. For in this period there developed a market, of a somewhat special form, for useful knowledge. There was a new class of freelance (*sic*) experts, of which both Leonardo da Vinci and Galileo were members. They relied mainly on patronage of the great and wealthy, but given the insecurity of such support, they had to advertise their skills publicly. This was done partly by books that they published, which necessarily gave away some of their knowledge to any reader, but which also demonstrated their prowess and their promise for their next employer. Such knowledge extended over many fields; but most significant were the techniques associated with conquest and war. Sciences such as navigation, surveying and fortification were crucial. They involved advanced mathematics, and so their practitioners could not belong to lower social strata; and they were also fields which gentlemen were expected to understand. Hence during this period there was a temporarily lowering of the barriers of snobbery between the 'liberal' and 'mechanical' arts. Descartes learned all the applied mathematical subjects at his Jesuit school; and Galileo taught them to his boarding pupils whom he took at Padua for extra income and future patronage. From this root could be seen to derive the respect for craftsmen among philosophers, and also their belief that through utilizing them, natural philosophy could accomplish what the magicians had always promised and never delivered.

An associated development in this same violent period was a change in the value system inculcated into the youth of the élite for the purpose of reproducing the social system. It had already been initiated in the Renaissance period with the famous 'discovery of man and nature' in the context of a professedly Christian culture. A symptom of this change is the work of Machiavelli, whose books replaced a centuries-old tradition of handbooks of advice to princes, which contained all the high-flown morality. Machiavelli was in his own way an idealist as well as a patriot; but he perceived that the realities of the baser human drives must be systematically mastered through fully explicit teaching, if there is to be any effective government at all. Francis Bacon summed it up when he announced the three grades of ambition for (élite) mankind, replacing the traditional set which were progressively less materialistic. For him it was a question of domination: at worst for oneself, better for one's nation, but best of all for the whole human race over nature.

All these attitudes would have been to no avail, in the absence of a technical basis for scientific advance. And this was there in good measure. Thanks to printing and to the market for expertise, published books in all subjects grew rapidly in number and in sophistication. At the beginning of the sixteenth century Europe was still translating and assimilating the scientific heritage of the Classical and Islamic civilizations; by the end of the century the work is fully matured technically, of a quality and style that can be read now without embarrassment or apology, in a variety of fields ranging from astronomy to anatomy. Hence when the new philosophical commitment was injected, there was some quite solid technical material for it to work on, at least in the more mathematical fields. With the steady development through the century in astronomy and mathematics, and the consequent transformations in cosmology and mechanics, the materials were available for Newton and his successors to create the vast edifice of science as we know it now.

The story as told along the lines of these three roots is self-consistent; and yet that driving commitment to a *particular* sort of experimental-with-mathematical explanation of nature, combined with that *particular* sort of belief in human power over a dead nature, is still to be explained. In other words, we can explain the rejection of the Christianized Aristotle in terms of a changing social and ideological function of knowledge; but the retention of magic's aims, combined with the rejection of its means and world-view, still calls out for explanation.

We can put the issue in terms of the question, why the three prophets of the scientific revolution, with all the differences between them, were completely consistent in rejecting those ancient sciences which most of their contemporaries were still willing to entertain. It is one of the few themes which they all stated strongly; and more than any other it gives their work a common modern feel. The background in cultural context seems to have been a quite sudden acceleration of a shift of sensibility, which had been proceeding for some centuries previously. In their own time there are many cases of world-views of great scientists which to us seem bizarre mixtures; thus the astronomer Tycho Brahe disproved the reality of the 'crystalline spheres' which on the Aristotelian theory carried the planets around in the heavens; yet he was an enthusiastic practitioner of astrology and alchemy. One can find roots or anticipations of the scientific revolution in Luther's insistence that the Bible is a plain historical document rather than a mystical allegory; or even in Aquinas' definition of miracle in terms of interference with natural laws. If there is anything uniquely European about this transformation of consciousness, it is in this hardening of common sense, to the exclusion of both non-tangible causes and prodigious effects, first from philosophical or religious significance and then even from existence.

The Heritage of the Scientific Revolution

In this essay I have been able only to sketch some ideas about the background and initiation of the scientific revolution. As we might expect, its career was very different in the different parts of Europe; from a start in Italy, it moved to France and then England, following the shift in favourable environment, both in economy and in politics. In the German culture area it came late and partially; the struggle for the elimination of enchanted philosophies of nature was won there only in the mid-nineteenth century. Elsewhere the old symbols were picked up and adapted to new ideological struggles, as with the *philosophes* in eighteenth-century France. In the Catholic lands of the Counter-Reformation, Galileo has remained a living symbol (for both sides) until our own time.

Inevitably, as the revolution consolidated, it lost its ideological aggressiveness. At the outset the battle was over the message to reach the literate (hence élite) public, and the first tactic was to bypass the established educational institutions and challenge their monopoly. Since it was always an affair within the élite sectors of society, once that institutional battle was won, the doctrines of the new philosophy could be devoted explicitly to the service of the stability of the ruling social and cultural institutions. In eighteenth-century France, Descartes became the symbol for a new conservatism, and in England, Newtonianism was invoked in proofs of the wisdom of the creator in

His fashioning of the perfection of the natural, and by extension, of the social world.

In the perspective of centuries later, we can ask whether there was something uniquely European about the scientific revolution, with both historical and policy questions in mind. For history, if we were satisfied with its uniqueness in time and context, then we could readjust our approach to the science of other great civilizations, such as the Indian, the Chinese and the Islamic. We could drop the perennial question of why they failed to make it, and concentrate on evaluating them in their own terms. For policies for the future, we can enquire about the chances for the spread of science *as we have understood it* outside Europe. The relevance of this is the challenge of the new East-Asian nations, from the small to the large to the gigantic. Although the social and institutional conditions for the flourishing of the best creative science have changed through the centuries, and there is now no need for anyone to re-invent the scientific revolution, still we may say that if the initiation of this very special cultural product was somehow unique to Europe, then its transfer to other cultures is still problematic. This is not to deny the scientific and technological excellence which can be and is achieved abroad. Rather, we have to consider the possibility of the appearance of a generation of genius, which provides inspiration and examples for many generations that follow. So far, nowhere outside Europe has this occurred on a large scale, even within any field of the differentiated science of our time. But of course it is still early days in the maturing of modern non-European civilizations, and so there may yet be surprises to come.

Finally, there is the biggest question of all, raised by the ecological threats that, in their urgency at least, seem to be a product of the technology that has emerged from the scientific revolution. These give new life to the questions of excessive powers of knowledge over nature, of which the magical tradition was explicitly (if mistakenly in its own case) aware. We do now create prodigious effects with very small causes; and the new problem of control has now emerged as basic to our exercise of power. In these respects at least the assumptions underlying the world-view of the scientific revolution need correction. Whether the new consciousness produced to meet these new challenges will require a modification of both the activist ethic and the dehumanized and disenchanted cosmology of the scientific revolution, is something that only the future will tell.

Based on an essay published in J.R. Ravetz (1966), *Indian Journal of History of Science* 1 (1).

Francis Bacon and the Reform of Philosophy

Of all the great figures in the history of science, Francis Bacon is the most enigmatic and controversial. Some even deny him any place at all in the history, for he did no worthwhile science of his own, and on what we now see as the major issues of his day (the Copernican revolution, and the introduction of the mathematical approach) he guessed wrong. Yet for several centuries his memory was venerated as one of the founders of modern science, as important in his way as Galileo and Descartes in theirs. This mixed and contradictory reputation extends over his whole career, and indeed began in his own lifetime. For someone whose towering genius was recognized from his childhood, and who devoted his life to service of his country and mankind with hardly an evil thought, he had a strange power of attracting condemnation and even emnity.

In his lifetime he enjoyed the patronage of the greatest of English monarchs, Elizabeth I; and under her successor rose to the highest judicial position in the land, Lord Chancellor. His published essays were influential in his lifetime and for generations afterwards; and so universal was his learning that for a time a strong school of literary scholars argued that he was the only possible author of the plays attributed to Shakespeare. Yet when he was just at the pinnacle of success, he was disgraced on a charge of corruption, and spent the last five years of his life a broken man.

His ideas for science were adopted by the founders of the Royal Society of London; from him they learned the virtues of patient empirical research, done in a socially organized framework. Later, his 'inductive method' was taken as the model for disciplined scientific enquiry. But in recent generations historians found his organizational schemes irrelevant to the real work of science, and his methods applicable only to a small and not very important part of science. The rescuing of Bacon's reputation was started by Benjamin Farrington, who saw in him a 'philosopher of industrial science', and who later (as he himself matured) perceived the significance of Bacon's spiritual endeavour. My own study of Bacon was stimulated by both these works of

Farrington; and historians are now more willing to admit arguments such as ours than they were at the time of the first publication of this essay.

In recent years, historians of science have come to see that the establishment of the new style of investigating Nature in the seventeenth century was different in many important respects from the tasks of consolidating and extending this work in later centuries. The greatest men were concerned with philosophical problems as much as with 'scientific' ones, and indeed did not generally make any sharp separation between the two classes. The debates that took place were similarly a mixture of technical and metaphysical considerations. And engagement on the work was in many cases at least as much participation in a movement, as the following of a profession. With the new appreciation of this complexity of the work of the scientific revolution, the old opposition between internalist and externalist approaches to the history of science can be correctly seen as the reflection of general philosophies of history imported into this special study. Each historian will naturally investigate those problems to which his interests and skills direct him; but no one would now deny that the adoption of a new philosophy of Nature produced a qualitative difference between Galileo and earlier practitioners of the mathematical arts, nor that Boyle's and Newton's interests included the experimental philosophy of nature only as a special part.

This ecumenical approach brings many advantages, not least the freedom from choosing sides in a sterile debate. On the other hand, it has its characteristic dangers, in blurring the lines of definition of the subject matter of the history of science. This is not so serious when it comes to distinguishing (for purposes of historical analysis) between particular studies in a natural science, from those in general philosophy, and from craftsmen's empirical investigations. It does raise the deepest problems for historical enquiry, at those points where the fields of enquiry involved have been subsequently excluded from the domain of genuine science. To argue, for instance, that magic and alchemy, or generally the Hermetic tradition, played an essential and positive role in the establishment of modern science is to contradict a tradition of the conception of science which goes back continuously to the earlier seventeenth century. To admit mystics and Rosicrucians into the respectable ancestry of our modern science may seem to involve a betrayal of the long struggle for the establishment of reason as the foundation of judgements in affairs concerning both Nature and man.[1] But we now know that we cannot simply exclude from the earlier history of science any man whose philosophy of nature would have been unacceptable to late nineteenth century German analytical chemists. Long ago Dr Walter Pagel exhibited the rich mixture of motifs involved in the work of van Helmont and his school; and more recently he has restored William Harvey as a philosopher rather than an hydraulic engineer.

Reason itself requires that we should not run away from established facts merely because they are uncomfortable to our inherited prejudices. Also, in this later twentieth century, the focus and emphasis of the ideological struggles involving science have changed suddenly from the versions that were current from the Enlightenment onwards. The completely natural powers provided to man by science are so great that sorcery has re-entered the vocabulary of discussions of science as a moral attribute.[2] And the Galilean style of applying 'disciplined experience and necessary demonstrations' to simplified and abstracted aspects of the natural world has in technical applications led to the micro-rationality of devices which each perform their assigned functions superbly but which in aggregate threaten the survival of our species. In reaction to these new problems, the long-submerged current of mystical thinking has surfaced again, not merely in the counter-culture of rebellious students, but even in influential currents in the new ecological thought and propaganda.

With these new experiences of the present, historians can and should have a new appreciative perception of the styles of thought that were suppressed in the seventeenth century. And as historians rather than propagandists, we can and should avoid a facile oversimplification of the complex and sometimes tragic interaction between styles of investigating nature which derived from opposed conceptions of that world and its relation to man and to God. In particular, the concept of influence (which more than any other carries the load of valuations) is a simple one only if we conceive intellectual history as a genealogy of ideas, hopping from book to book down through time. Rather, we should see the great philosophers as men grappling with the deepest and sometimes insoluble problems throughout their lives, adopting different provisional solutions, and thereby being open to different influences at different times; and also struggling with the relics of their own earlier thoughts as they change and develop.

In this historical framework, the real influence of those currents of thought soon to be damned as irrational can be established, without necessarily pitching the historian into the very deepest questions of judgement on the whole process of the establishment of the new philosophy of Nature. We need only imagine that some at least of the great natural philosophers achieved commitment to their life's work in a period of youthful enthusiasm and dedication; and spent their subsequent years in a struggle to retain what could be retained, and to achieve what could be achieved, in the face of the contradictions thrown up by harsh experience. Although such a pattern is commonplace in politics, it may seem entirely inappropriate to import it into the history of science. But the history with which we are concerned just now is of science in the largest sense; it concerns a movement for a Reformation in the philosophy of nature, in which the achievement of a particular sort of results by a particular style of research was only a part.

The career of each of the founders of the new philosophy of the seventeenth century can be studied in this way, and the differences in their achievements can be related to differences in their style and commitment. Thus, Galileo's Truth lay in a particular sort of realized mathematics, and his characteristic style can be seen in his very earliest production, the *Bilancetta*. On the deeper problems of metaphysics and ethics, he left very little evidence of concern; and even his theological excursions were in the nature of defensive polemics. For Descartes, the evidence of enthusiasm is there, but it is suggestive rather than conclusive for a direct personal involvement with Rosicrucianism.[3] However, the autobiographical accounts of meditations and insights, and the 'three visions', leave little doubt that Descartes was started on the road to his extension-and-motion ontology by problems of philosophy, and by experiences, which touched the roots of the problems of human existence. For Bacon, the case is easier to argue, and correspondingly less disturbing in its conclusions. Bacon was neither a successful scientist, nor a consistent adherent of the new ontology of dead matter. A demonstration that his philosophy of science was influenced, and even shaped, by non-scientific considerations may even offer ammunition to those historians of science who have all along wanted to throw him out of the list. But since the list of thoroughgoing professional scientists in the seventeenth century becomes shorter with each advance of historical scholarship, such prejudices may be allowed to wither away of their own accord.

Strategies for Reform

There is no need to argue the case that Bacon saw himself not so much as a scientist, but as an agent of Reform, where the term is understood in its sixteenth century rather than twentieth century sense. By contrast, Descartes can be considered as trying to accomplish the sorts of task appropriate to both roles; and Galileo might be said to have become a reformer only when the unreformed state of his audience's minds became a nuisance and hindrance to him. We can therefore expect that Bacon's involvement in systematic philosophy, and in experimental science, would be casual and incidental; his achievements correspondingly less important; and the significance of his essays in these directions for an understanding of his basic philosophy, minimal. We have also got beyond the earlier tradition in British philosophy which constructed a Bacon who proclaimed the 'inductive' philosophy of the later eighteenth and nineteenth centuries. Hence we are entitled to approach an understanding of Francis Bacon by an analysis of his strategy for reform in philosophy, and to use this as an interpretative framework for his many and varied pronouncements on the state of the world about him.

Any strategy for reform must include several distinct components if it is to serve as a coherent guide to action. Without arguing on the absolute correctness of any particular taxonomy, we may conveniently distinguish the following aspects. First, there must be a description of the present lamentable state, and an explanation for its occurrence. Second, there must be some characterization of the desired state, and also a guarantee for its possible existence. Third, there must be a plan for changing the bad present into the good future. And finally, there should also be some indication that the time is now ripe, so that recruits will come forward, and survive the inevitable temporary disappointments. To run this scheme on a familiar example, we may say that classical Marxism described the miseries of the proletariat and explained them in terms of the particular form of expropriation which defines capitalism; it was rather vague on socialism and on its variety of communism, but prided itself on its 'scientific' as opposed to Utopian analysis of their inevitability; its plan rested on the conclusions of the earlier phases of analysis, and involved the activation of the industrial proletariat rather than of other classes who might be oppressed or rebellious (peasants and young intellectuals, for example); and the ripeness of time was established both by the intensified struggle of the proletariat and by Marx's optimistic aphorism, 'Mankind sets only those problems which it can solve'.

For Bacon, a plausible analysis of the strategy for reform can be achieved without difficulty. The present ills are described in many places, in a variety of ways. Starting with the dichotomy between 'the Grecians and the alchemists',[4] we have the simile of the spider and the ant,[5] and the fine passage on the varieties of misguided endeavour in *Novum Organum* I, Aphorism 95.[6] For an explanation of present ills Bacon offers his Four Idols, perhaps the most original part of his entire philosophy. The guarantee of the possibility of improvement in philosophy comes from the example of the mechanical arts, both in their progressive character[7] and in their previous achievements in the absence of any contact with philosophy.[8] For the advancement of learning itself, the institutional form is sketched as Salomon's House in the *New Atlantis*; there we see a fine division of labour,[9] and a fully autonomous community of research workers, gathering and processing facts in a disciplined style. The plan for the improvement of philosophy is based on achieving 'colleges' where this sort of work can be done, and its correctness proved by its successes; and Bacon's own contribution is to provide the propaganda leading to the establishment of such an institution, on a Royal foundation. Finally, the ripeness of time is established by the numerous radical changes in the arts and in society over the few generations preceding Bacon's time; the frontispiece of the *Novum Organum*, with the Columbus of learning setting forth, symbolizes the argument.

Such a strategy for reform fits in well with what a twentieth century audience would expect, and as it is displayed in his writings it uses themes which must have been quite familiar to his own contemporaries. As evidence for Bacon's own views, it is not to be neglected; but it is evidence and not fact. All Bacon's published writings were propaganda; their function was to convert his audience, and their relation to his own private views was purely incidental. Indeed, the essays which he suppressed as unsuitable for publication have a style and content which is strikingly different from those of his published writings; and it was these essays that provided Farrington with the clue to the deeper interpretation of Bacon that he achieved in his second study.

There is strong evidence, from the history of Bacon's life and work, to indicate that the publicly announced strategy of reform was only a part, and not the deeper part, of his personal vision of the task. In the first place, on the matter of the mechanical arts, he knew not whereof he spoke. The three great inventions of printing, gunpowder and the magnetic compass were not first identified as such by him.[10] They were discussed by Cardano, and perhaps more significant, were dealt with in a popular French book, which was translated into English in 1594. The moral that Bacon drew from these inventions, that they were lighted upon by chance and owed nothing to 'philosophy', is not merely incorrect but would have been recognized as such by anyone then familiar with their recent history.[11]

Again, it is well known that Bacon's knowledge of the state of the sciences derived from his reading of books, and mostly general books at that. In retrospect, historians of science can discern fields in which great advances were being made in the period up to Bacon's life; in particular, anatomy, astronomy and mathematics. Bacon showed no recognition of these points of progress, but laid all of the sciences under his general condemnation. His conception of the ideal organization of scientific research could not have come from any examples within philosophy or the mechanical arts; but it is a natural extrapolation from the type of research appropriate to a programme for the rationalization of English law, one which was very dear to his heart. Indeed, his writings show an intellect trained in legal and literary skills, applied to this very different sort of work. His similes and rhetorical figures are nearly always taken from these fields and applied to natural philosophy and the arts; the cases where 'nature' provides the insights for 'man' are very few.

The conclusion of this line of argument could well be that Bacon was merely a literary showman, offering advice and instructions to people in a field of enquiry which he was too proud or too busy to learn properly. And, judging his published writings as propaganda exercises, such a conclusion would be hard to refute. But if we accept that with all the complexities and contradictions in his character, he was moved by a very deep commitment, this negative conclusion serves to throw up a new problem: what was he trying to do? If his programme for the sciences was not based on induction from personal experience of philosophy and the arts, wherein lay its driving force for him? Benjamin Farrington has provided the elements of an answer: that Bacon's deepest commitment was ethical and religious; and that the reform of natural philosophy was his choice of the strategic point for the achievement of the reform and redemption of mankind. To confirm and amplify this insight, I will show how a coherent and meaningful strategy for reform can be extracted from Bacon's affirmations in religion and ethics; and that this element is in fact essential for solving the historical problems raised by the technical and secular version of his strategy.

Bacon's Strategy for Reform

We need not dwell on Bacon's numerous criticisms of the state of natural knowledge in his time. The causes of this evil condition are in three classes: ignorance of means, corruption of ends, and inherent infirmities in human reason. In the first class we have the analysis of the sterility of school logic, and of the one-sided scientific efforts, either purely empirical or purely theoretical; and then the positive suggestions towards a method of true induction that comprise the second book of the *Novum Organum*. On the ends of the endeavour, Bacon describes the narrow and distorted ends then governing the various sorts of work,[12] and offers several formulations of the true ends of natural philosophy, as 'to establish and extend the power and dominion of the human race itself over the universe'.[13] As an explanation of the corrupted state of philosophy, he provides the Four Idols, which seem to be a deeper sceptical critique of human knowledge than the classical tradition provided, and indeed in some respects deeper than that with which Descartes grappled. Bacon starts with the defects of the mind itself, neither a *tabula rasa* of the empiricist tradition nor the true 'mirror' of the rationalists.[14] These imperfections are magnified in each individual, according to the peculiarities of his constitution and temperament. He is then subjected to the brainwashing of school, where he reasons with words that do not correspond to real things. Finally he comes to the theatre of higher education, where actors spout their lines devoid of all content.

At the naturalistic level, this explanation is self-sufficient, and indeed relevant to all times and places. But at the moral level, it has no meaning, except that of cynicism or despair. In itself, it certainly offers no clue to the possibility of reform; for any ordinary institutions would inevitably be corrupted by the prevailing tendencies to intellectual and moral decay. Bacon gave explicit recognition to the insolubility of the problem at this level, at the conclusion of his discussion of the Four Idols. There we read:

> So much concerning the special classes of Idols, and their equipage: all of which must be renounced and put away with a fixed and solid determination, and the understanding thoroughly freed and cleansed; the entrance into the kingdom of man, founded the sciences, being not much other than the entrance into the kingdom of heaven, where into none may enter except as a little child.[15]

Is this comparison a mere figure of rhetoric? It seems unlikely to be so, for two reasons. First, this call for a moral reform (the cleansing as well as the freeing of the intellect), the requirement of the innocence of the child, is Bacon's only answer to the sceptical challenge of the Four Idols. Second, and more important, the conception of human history which was a commonplace for Bacon and for his successors through Newton was that of a cosmic drama in which the successive acts were revealed in Scripture, and in which the

Almighty is ever-present. The analogy between the two kingdoms was not to be uttered lightly.

A stronger connection to the religious foundations of Bacon's vision is provided by a theme which is expressed in passages scattered through his published writings, and which dominates his unpublished essay, *On the Masculine Birth of Time*.[16] The absence of the true ends of philosophy is not merely an intellectual deficiency; it is a moral defect as well. In that essay Bacon runs through the list of philosophers, ancient and modern, calling them to the bar of judgement. He speaks of the 'sham philosophers' who 'debauch our minds', and of those who are worse still, 'the satellites and parasites of the great ones, the whole mob of professorial teachers'. Lest there be any doubt on this point, he concludes:

> But now I must recollect myself and do penance, for though my
> purpose was only to discredit it yet I have been handling what is unholy
> and unclean. What I have said against them is less than their
> monstrous guilt deserved.[17]

What is this 'monstrous guilt'? It is composed of spiritual pride, showmanship, dishonesty, and lack of true humility before Nature or pity for mankind. To put it in a single word, we may say, 'vanity'. Bacon mentions vanity in an important place in his published work, in the prayer which concludes the Plan of the Work of the *Instauratio Magna*:

> But man, when he turned to look upon the work which his hands had
> made, saw that all was vanity and vexation of spirit, and could find no
> rest therein.[18]

The same text is found in the *Meditationes Sacrae*,[19] and in the companion piece, *A Confession of Faith*, vanity comes into the cosmic drama:

> That upon the fall of Man, death and vanity entered by the justice of
> God, and the image of God in man was defaced, and heaven and earth
> which were made for man's use were subdued to corruption by his
> fall.[20]

A similar set of themes appears in a passage in the introduction to the *Historia Naturalis et Experimentalis*:

> For we copy the sin of our parents while we suffer for it. They wished
> to be like God, but their posterity wish to be even greater. For we
> create worlds, we direct and domineer over nature, we will have it that
> all things *are* as in our folly we think they should be, not as seems
> fittest to Divine wisdom, or as they are to be found in fact.[21]

The need for curing this vanity, as a prerequisite to any progress in philosophy, is expressed in the Preface to the *Instauratio Magna*:

> Wherein if I have made any progress, the way has been opened to me

by no other means than the true and legitimate humiliation of the human spirit.[22]

Later in the same section, he concludes his prayer:

Lastly, that knowledge now being discharged of that venom which the serpent infused into it, and which makes the mind to swell, we may not be wise above measure and sobriety, but cultivate truth in charity.[23]

If we wish, we can dismiss all this as rhetorical high-mindedness, supported by conventional piety. But to do so would require a wilful ignorance of the religious sensibility of English natural philosophers throughout the seventeenth century. It would also require us to imagine Francis Bacon, a man conscious of his talents from his earliest years, and determined to dedicate himself to the service of God and of man, spending so much of his life on a purely technocratic fantasy.

Taking this ethical and religious concern seriously, we note in the above passages that there is a scriptural reference in the descriptions of the corrupted state. The 'sin of our parents' is that of Adam and Eve, and the 'serpent' is their tempter. Indeed Bacon sketched a history of the stages of the Fall of Man, relating the corruption of philosophy as he saw it to the scriptural account. Concerning the Fall itself, Bacon is quite sure that this did not arise from man's desire for natural knowledge;[24] but just as the angels fell from lust of power, so man fell from lust of knowledge:[25] a knowledge of Good and Evil conceived as independent of God's will.[26] Bacon believed that the Fall of Adam was not complete and absolute (in agreement with those who traced the *prisca sapientia* to Noah, such as Newton and the Masonic tradition); for then,

the law was first imprinted in that remnant of light of nature which was left after the fall, being sufficient to accuse.[27]

Later the manner of revelation changed, to the written law, the prophets, and finally Christ. However, even at that first Fall, there was

the curse, which notwithstanding was no new creation, but a privation of part of the virtue of the first creation.[28]

Bacon does not hope for the original 'virtue' of nature's workings to be restored; man must forever earn his rewards.

In fact, there has been a second Fall; Wherefore our dominion over creatures is a second time forfeited, not undeservedly; and whereas after the fall of man some power over the resistance of creatures was still left to him—the power of subduing and managing them by true and solid arts—yet this too through our insolence, and because we desire to be like God and to follow the dictates of our own reason, we in great part lose.[29]

Bacon nowhere speaks explicitly of the time and character of this second Fall, but it is likely that he gave some support to a popular doctrine that it occurred with the building of the tower of Babel,[30] and also that traces of the true wisdom survived to the times of the development of Greek mythology.[31]

In the terms of this deeper analysis of the causes of the corrupted state of philosophy, the problem of providing a guarantee of successful reform is easily solved within the same framework. On this, Bacon is quite explicit. He made strong use of the injunction of Christ, 'Ye err, not knowing the Scriptures, nor the power of God';[32] from this distinction, he can interpret the former as revealing God's will, and the latter, His works as studied by natural philosophy. Moreover, Bacon provides an abundance of points to prove that God intended man to discover the nature of his Created world. First, He left his 'seals and imprints'[33] on things, as well as his 'footprints' or 'vestiges'. And these are the true Ideas of the divine, which are so different from the Idols of the human mind.[34] It is through God's grace that man will 'write an apocalypse or true vision of the footsteps of the Creator imprinted on his creatures'.[35] Moreover, these 'vestiges', although not patent to the common view, were intended to be discovered. His hiding of the 'characters and impressions of his providence',[36] as in the final causes of natural processes, makes His wisdom 'shine forth more admirably', as that of the master politician 'that can make other men the instruments of his ends and desires and yet never acquaint them with his purposes'.[37] We are assured from scripture that God did not wish to keep these evidences concealed, for as Solomon said, 'The glory of God is to conceal a thing; the glory of the king is to search it out'.[38] This concealment was not intended as a trial for man; rather,

> Even as though the divine nature took pleasure in the innocent and
> kindly sport of children playing at hide and seek, and vouchsafed of his
> kindness and goodness to admit the human spirit for his playfellow at
> that game.[39]

Thus we can be sure that the secrets of God's creation are meant for man to discover; and we can be equally sure that man's dominion over the natural world is a 'divine bequest', as in the passage from Aphorism 129 that I quoted earlier.[40] This is supported by Bacon's references to man's partaking of the Sabbath with God, as in one of his famous prayers:

> Wherefore if we labor in thy works with the sweat of our brows thou
> wilt make us partakers of thy vision and thy sabbath.[41]

It also appears in the passage from the *Masculine Birth of Time* from which I quoted earlier; there Bacon promises his 'son' that his 'chaste wedlock' with things themselves will produce

> a blessed race of Heroes or Supermen who will overcome the
> immeasurable helplessness and poverty of the human race, which cause
> it more destruction than all giants, monsters or tyrants, and will make
> you peaceful, happy, prosperous and secure.

We might also enquire whether Bacon offered some hint of the character of this promised knowledge; for here the theological conceptions may throw some light on what, if anything, Bacon meant by 'form'. First, we must not forget that Bacon's concern, as much as that of Descartes, was with a universal science including all the arts of human and social behaviour. Second, the knowledge desired was an unmediated contact with 'things themselves'. These are the creations of God; man should establish direct contact with them through contemplation of them; he considered himself as having 'submitted my mind to things';[42] and that 'commerce of the mind of man and things' is 'more precious than anything on earth'.[43] This union with things[44] is not merely an intellectual act, but is the key to the whole sacred endeavour of the material redemption of mankind. Thus in *The Masculine Birth of Time*, Bacon speaks from his 'inmost heart', saying, 'My dear, dear boy, what I propose is to unite you with *things themselves* in a chaste, holy and legal wedlock . . .', whose issue will be the redeeming Heroes or Supermen described above. Although in his writings on method, he promises only to take the human reason up to *prima philosophia* or *sapientia*, achieving the most fundamental and general axioms,[45] his conception of the reform extended further. Thus, in speaking of the ends of enquiry in the *On the Interpretation of Nature*, he dismisses the ignoble and vulgar purposes as elsewhere, and asserts:

> but it is a restitution and reinvesting (in great part) of man to the sovereignty and power (for whensoever he shall be able to call the creatures by their true names he shall again command them) which he had in his first state of creation.[46]

The completion of Bacon's programme for philosophy is then no less than the redemption of mankind, to the extent that is possible, from the consequences of the original Fall.[47]

It is clear that a goal of such cosmic significance could not be achieved merely by the establishment of a scientific research institution. The task of discovering God's works must proceed hand in hand with that of interpreting His will; otherwise it will surely be corrupted. Bacon nowhere says this; and indeed one optimistic passage indicates otherwise:

> Only let the human race recover that right over nature which belongs to it by divine bequest, and let power be given it; the exercise thereof will be governed by sound reason and true religion.[48]

However, we are justified in considering this as propaganda; for even in the Utopian *New Atlantis*, the sages of Salomon's House took no chances:

> And this we do also: we have consultations, which of the inventions and experiences which we have discovered shall be published, and which not; and all take an oath of secrecy, for the concealing of those which we think fit to keep secret: though some of those we do reveal sometime to the state, and some not.[49]

This caution, combined with Bacon's unflattering view of the intellectual and moral condition of the scholars of his own time, makes it certain that his was a task not to be accomplished by administrative means alone.

To carry out his programme, Bacon would need men whose wits were not only sharp, but also cleansed. These would necessarily be set off from the common, corrupted society of the time, either by their being already reformed, or by being ready to reform. How was Bacon to locate and recruit those few who were ready to embark on the great work in a spirit of humility, charity and innocence? On this, the evidence is that Bacon planned to operate on two levels, in a time-honoured fashion. For society at large, there was an exoteric doctrine, cast in the terms that could be generally appreciated, with hints of the deeper message. But there was also to be a brotherhood of 'true sons of science'.[50] Bacon publicly[50] invited membership in this; and so in a sense it was not esoteric. But it was for those few who had been able to reform, and on one important point Bacon's esoteric teaching would have been radically different from his public statements.

This relates to a problem where his assertions seem insincere or self-contradictory: the value, and future role, of the philosophy then dominant. Bacon is at pains to deny hostile intentions towards it:

> For I do not object to the use of this received philosophy, or others like it, for supplying matters for disputations or ornaments for discourse — for the professor's lecture and for the business of life.[51]

Later, he protests the sincerity of his professions of affection towards the 'received sciences', citing his published writings, including the *Advancement of Learning*, as evidence.[52] But he protests a bit too much; for his disclaimers of general utility for his own philosophy turn into an affirmation of its innate superiority:

> It does not lie in the way. It cannot be caught up in passage. It does not flatter the understanding by conformity with preconceived notions. Now will it come down to the apprehension of the vulgar except by its utility and effects.[53]

For a long time I considered this to be an unresolved contradiction in Bacon's own thought, considering that his beloved studies of letters and the law fell within the class of inane works. But a reading of the unpublished *Refutation of Philosophies* gave the clue; there, the sage, 'a man of peaceful and serene air, save that his face had become habituated to an expression of pity', spoke to his 'sons', and advised:

> Therefore keep your old philosophy. Use it when convenient. Keep one to deal with nature, and the other to deal with the populace. Every man of superior understanding in contact with inferiors wears a mask. If I may, as my habit is, speak freely among friends, then I advise you: Possess Lais but do not let her possess you.[54]

127

The reference is to a famous courtesan; the distinction was made in a reply by the philosopher Aristippus, to critics of his personal behaviour.

Through an appreciation of the essentially *moral* aspect of the reform proposed by Bacon, together with a text such as this one, we can resolve the question of the nature of his esoteric teaching. In his Note B to Ellis's preface to the *Novum Organum*,[55] Spedding reviewed the texts which seemed to call for an esoteric teaching. His conclusion was that Bacon proposed to withhold the publication of his Formula,

> 'not as a secret of too much value to be lightly revealed', but as a subject too abstruse to be handled successfully except by the fit and the few.

This is almost correct; but for 'abstruse' one should substitute 'holy'. Bacon was sure that his method would 'level men's wits', but those wits must *first have been purified*, or (at a later period) protected from the contamination of the false and impious philosophies.

We can now come to the final problem, that of establishing the ripeness of time, so that recruits will come forward in good heart. My interpretation of Bacon's solution to this problem might appear farfetched or paradoxical, were it not for the support of his published texts, and the coherence of the religious framework of his strategy for reform as I have developed it up to this point. Bacon's discussion of this in the *Novum Organum* occupies the section from Aphorism 92 to Aphorism 114, giving the arguments for Hope, with some rambles *en route*. In Aphorism 92 he states that the greatest obstacle to progress has been despair; and by examples of his successes, he may with gentleness prepare men's minds with hope. The introduction to the section on Hope, Aphorism 93, provides a religious and theological foundation. It opens with:

> The beginning is from God: for the business which is in hand, having the character of good so strongly impressed upon it, appears manifestly to proceed from God, who is the author of good, and the Father of Lights.[56]

Elsewhere Bacon makes a strong use of the term 'light' as a synonym for knowledge. The passage continues with a scriptural sanction for his programme for a gentle reform proceeding from small beginnings:

> Now in divine operations even the smallest beginnings lead of a certainty to their end. And as it was said of spiritual things, 'The Kingdom of God cometh not with observation', so is it in all the greater works of Divine Providence; everything glides on smoothly and noiselessly, and the work is fairly going on before men are aware that it has begun.[57]

One might interpret this as an answer to the query by a sceptical reader, whether Bacon had succeeded in putting any of his fine words into practice. (In the previous Aphorism, he promised a set of particulars, admittedly the strongest means of inspiring hope, for later parts of the Instauration: and for the sake of gentleness, offered only the plan of the work at this stage.

So far the claims for hope in his programme are rather general; but he concludes the aphorism with material that puts the present age in its true setting:

> Nor should the prophecy of Daniel be forgotten, touching the last ages of the world—'Many shall go to and fro, and knowledge shall be increased': clearly intimating that the thorough passage of the world (which now by so many distant voyages seems to be accomplished, or in the course of accomplishment), and the advancement of the sciences, are destined by fate, that is, by Divine Providence, to meet in the same age.[58]

In brief, Bacon believed that by his efforts he was helping to usher in the millennium. One quotation from a large book is but slender evidence for such a dramatic thesis; but supporting evidence is found on the frontispiece of the *Instauratio Magna* as published. For there, under the well-known picture of the ship clearing the twin pillars on its way to the open sea, is the motto, *multi pertransibunt et augebitur scientia.* Any reader familiar with scripture would recognize the text, from the apocalyptic Daniel 12, verse 4 which reads: 'But thou, O Daniel, shut up the words, and seal the book, even to the end of time; many shall run to and fro, and knowledge shall be increased'. Although the text itself has been questioned, and these connotations of Bacon's motto were doubtless lost on later generations (including those who chose the latter part for the motto of the University of Leeds), Bacon's readers would have been well aware of them. And in the context of thought of Bacon's time, a millennial belief supported by scripture is not at all surprising. Any great reformer must have the touch of the saviour about him; and through the seventeenth century, the Holy Writ was an accepted source of clues to the meaning of the revolutions of times.

Comments on Bacon's Strategy

It remains for me to deal with one outstanding problem in this interpretation of Bacon's strategy for reform; and then we can consider how this throws light on other aspects of Bacon's endeavour. The problem is that this interpretation apparently runs counter to Bacon's explicit statements of the separateness of theology and natural philosophy. The most extended account of the damage done by theologians and divines is in Aphorism 89 of the *Novum Organum*, Book I; there Bacon refers to the 'troublesome adversary and hard to deal with: namely, superstition, and the blind and immoderate zeal of religion'.[59] He then cites the story of the Greeks who were found guilty of impiety for giving natural explanations for thunder and for storms, and mentions the

Church Fathers who denied the earth's antipodes. He mentions also the defects of systematic theology, and then the fears of natural philosophy resulting from 'the simpleness of certain divines'. His defence of natural philosophy as the 'most faithful handmaid' of religion rests both on its power to dispel superstition, and on the text 'ye err in that ye know not the Scriptures and the powers of God'. None of this entails a secularization of the spirit of enquiry or of the conception of its ends; it is the sort of defence of natural philosophy against incompetent zealots which was continued in an apologetic tradition for science, at the hands of liberal churchmen, to the end of the nineteenth century.

There is one point where Bacon identifies a particular error in the mixture of the natural and the divine, which might seem to argue against the use of scripture in any investigation of nature:

> In this vanity some of the moderns have with extreme levity indulged so far as to attempt to found a system of natural philosophy on the first chapter of Genesis, on the book of Job, and other parts of the sacred writings: seeking for the dead among the living: which also makes the inhibition and repression of it the more important, because from this unwholesome mixture of things human and divine there arises not only a fantastic philosophy but also an heretical religion. Very meet is it therefore that we be sober-minded and give to faith that only which is faith's. [60]

Fortunately, the mention of Job makes the identification of the culprits easy, at least for those who know something of the history of alchemical philosophy. Bacon's target here is the school of Paracelsus, and the 'heretical religion' would have been some variety of sectarianism, radical both in religion and politics. [61] Hence Bacon would speak with unusual severity about its dangers, and advocate means of control out of keeping with his usual gentleness in political and religious affairs.

Indeed, any opposition between 'natural philosophy' and 'theology' in Bacon's thought is to some extent an artificial construct, since he deeply distrusted systematic theology itself. He considered that there were very strict limits on the powers and rights of the human mind to attempt to penetrate the divine mysteries. In the *De Augmentis* he discusses the proper use of natural theology to 'refute and convince Atheism, but not to establish religion'. For the world is the work of God and not His image. From His works we can demonstrate that He exists and governs: and in His works we can demonstrate the basic properties of God's presence, rule and benificence; and also 'reasonably elicit' other 'wonderful mysteries'.

> But on the other side, out of the contemplation of nature and elements of human knowledge to induce any conclusion of reason or even any strong persuasion concerning the mysteries of faith, yea, or to inspect and sift them too curiously and search out the manner of the mystery, is in my opinion not safe. [62]

Bacon elsewhere gives hints that the corruption of theology has resulted from the same abuses of reason as the corruption of natural philosophy;[63] and also that the path towards true knowledge is the same in both cases: experience and aphorisms rather than argument and systems.[64]

We can safely conclude, then, that Bacon's conception of human knowledge of the divine did not entail a separation in spirit, methods or ends between inquiry into God's will and His works. In fact, if we look a bit more closely into Bacon's personal religion, we find the two endeavours brought into close relation. If we try to classify Bacon in respect to the problems of rational theology, we would probably call him a fideist. But this would be to apply a foreign and inappropriate scheme to Bacon's thought. His religion, like his philosophy of nature, was concerned primarily with practical works, and less with niceties of doctrine.[65] We express his view of the world very simply: man's corruption resulted from vanity; and man's redemption will be achieved by charity. For Bacon this was the message of Christ: he observed that all Christ's miracles were of mercy, not of judgement; each one was designed to help ordinary human beings with their ordinary problems. Similarly, in his meditation on Hypocrites, subtitled 'I will have mercy and not sacrifice', he makes charity to be the touchstone of true religion. The meditation opens with:

> The ostentation of hypocrites is ever confined to the works of the first table of the law, which prescribes our duties to God. The reason is twofold: both because works of this class have a greater pomp of sanctity, and because they interfere less with their desires. The way to convict a hypocrite, therefore is to send him from the works of sacrifice to the works of mercy.

This penetrating observation is followed by one even more so:

> There are some however of a deeper and more inflated hypocrisy, who deceiving themselves, and fancying themselves worthy of a closer conversation with God, neglect the duties of charity towards their neighbour, as inferior matters.[66]

On charity itself, Bacon discussed the various circumstances in which it is ordinarily applied, to an enemy repentant or at least defeated.[67] None of these satisfied him; even the feeling that virtue is proceeding from one may be a form of pride. No, the 'summit and exaltation' of charity comes only

> if evil overtake your enemy from elsewhere, and you in the inmost recesses of your heart are grieved and distressed, and feel no touch of joy, as thinking that the day of your revenge and redress has come.

Such a Christ-like conception of charity, encompassing a complete forgiveness and a complete love, should be kept in mind when we see the term in its frequent occurrence in Bacon's exhortatory passages. Pity for the sufferings of mankind comes out repeatedly in his various prayers, and his picture of a sage is of 'a peaceful and serene air, save that his face had become habituated to the expression of pity'.[68]

Far from imagining a 'conflict between science and religion', Bacon saw the investigation of nature as a divine work. It not only served to reveal God's works, and to reform the intellect and soul of the enquirer, but also to imitate Christ in 'the relief of man's estate'. With this understanding of the connotations of his words, we may now see how Bacon's vision is encompassed in the final sentence of his prayer:

> Lastly, that knowledge being now discharged of the venom which the serpent infused into it, and which makes the mind of man to swell, we may not be wise above measure and sobriety, but cultivate truth in charity.[69]

With this interpretation of Bacon's conception of his task, we may be better equipped to approach the problem of his 'sources' and of the development of his ideas. It is well known that many of his aphorisms and illustrations are derivative from published sources; and a thorough search of the relevant sets of literature might well reveal Bacon to have been a sort of philosophical magpie, picking up ideas from everywhere and then publishing them, rearranged and slightly polished, as his own. But to condemn him for this would be to misconceive his task, which was not to do original research, but to plead for a cause. Also, the roots of his commitment, and his informal synthesis of ideas, could not be assembled from a set of index-cards. We know that from an early age he was aware of his talents, and was determined to devote them to the service of man and God. It is possible that his earliest endeavours were in a literary–humanistic direction, culling the literature of aphorisms and apothegms, and from them distilling 'axioms' on the nature of man. But this path was rejected, and by the age of thirty he had committed himself to finding the key in the study of nature. We simply do not know what person, or book, wrought this conversion. John Dee's departure from England probably came too early; and although Bruno was on hand during the crucial period,[70] he receives no mention whatever in Bacon's reflective writings, and his attack on institutional Christianity would be altogether too radical for Bacon's taste. Palissy the potter would probably have been only a self-educated workman for Bacon, not someone to provide him with his own particular version of the seventeenth century commitment to approaching God through Nature. The most likely source of Bacon's conversion seems to be some current of pietistic Paracelsian philosophy; there one would find the mixture of the themes of Christian charity and a manual interaction with the things of Nature. The sentiments of scepticism of official learning, pity for the sufferings of mankind, and dedication to a pure and holy reform that van Helmont shows in his autobiography[71] are strikingly similar to those of Bacon. This is not to assert any link of influence between the two; but to indicate that their common form of commitment may well have derived from a common source.[72] Bacon's vehement condemnation of Paracelsian scriptural natural philosophy is not conclusive evidence against such an early influence; it is commonplace in politics for a man to derive his permanent ideals from a radical source, and eventually come to see the ongoing tradition of that source as the worst enemy of his matured programme.

Finally, we may consider whether this reinterpretation of Bacon has any significance for our understanding of the development of science from his time up to the present. Accepting the theological framework of his strategy for reform, we can add yet another criticism of his work to the already considerable stock. In one respect he was wrong: not merely was the millennium not at hand in the early seventeenth century, but the growth of scientific knowledge and of the power of its applications neither required nor produced such a moral reform in society as he had considered essential. Even though ordinary life for ordinary people is more peaceful and humane by far in the advanced societies than it was in Bacon's time, the twentieth century wars of ideology and empire have produced barbarities that match anything achieved during the wars of religion of the times before and after Bacon's career. Also, between Bacon's time and our own, his concern for the reform of the sciences could recede into past history as a curiosity of bygone times. Over the generations, natural science achieved appropriate methods of inquiry and viable social institutions for its work, so that it could progress to ever greater triumphs.

But very recently, it has been impressed on us all that science lives not by PhDs alone. The political problems of the management of a large and complex scientific community, internally and in relation to its sources of financial support and recruitment, become ever more demanding; and the moral problems of responsibility for abhorrent applications of scientific results are likewise intensifying. This is not to say that the times are again ripe for a prophet with Bacon's particular message, or indeed for any prophet at all. But the moral commitment, and pity for mankind, that drove Bacon to make his contribution towards the advancement of learning can no longer be dismissed as irrelevant or peripheral to the real business of science. Even if his scientific achievements are negligible, his elaborated methodology a bore, and his theological framework obsolete, yet in his aphorisms he may still speak to us.

This essay was first published in *Science, Medicine and Society in the Renaissance (Walter Pagel Festschrift)* (ed. Allen G. Debus), New York, Science History Publications, a division of Neale Watson Academic Publications Inc., 1972, pp. 97–119. A first draft was read to seminars at Leeds and at Cambridge in 1966. Its ideas have been developed in the course of teaching the *Novum Organum* at the Rijksuniversiteit te Utrecht. I am particularly grateful to Mr van Drunen, then a student at Utrecht, and to Ir. H. Peters, of Boxtel, for their discussions of this aspect of Bacon and the materials which they made available to me.

References

1 For a vigorous counter-attack on this tendency, see Hesse, Mary B. 'Hermeticism and historiography: an apology for the internal history of science', *Minnesota Studies in the Philosophy of Science*, V (1971).

2 See Wiener, Norbert, *God & Golem, Inc.*, MIT Press, 1964, 50–1.

3 For a generally sceptical interpretation of the evidence for Descartes' involvement with the Rosicrucians, see Gouhier, H., *Les premières pensées de Descartes, contribution à l'histoire de l'anti-Renaissance*, Paris, 1958.

4 See 'Mr. Bacon in Praise of Knowledge', Bacon, *Works*, ed. Ellis, Spedding and Heath, London, VIII, 124.

5 Bacon, *Novum Organum* (1620), Book 1, Aphorism 95, in *Works*, IV, 92–3.

6 *Works*, IV, 79–80.

7 *Novum Organum*, Bk I, Aph. 74, in *Works*, IV, 74–5.

8 *Ibid.*, Aph. 110, in *Works*, IV, 99–100.

9 *Works*, III, 156–66.

10 It is a commentary on the historiography of science that the immediate ancestry of Bacon's 'Three Inventions' was discovered by Joseph Needham, in the course of tracing them back to China. A possible direct source for Bacon was le Roy, Louis. *Of the Interchangeable Course or Variety of Things in the Whole World*, English translation, 1594. I am indebted to Dr P. Rattansi for the information on le Roy and on Needham's work.

11 In his earlier writings, Bacon had no doubt that the discoveries were chance. Thus in the *Temporis Partus Masculus* he mentioned gunpowder as an example of a 'lucky hit': 'If gunpowder had been discovered, not by good luck but by good guidance, it would not have stood alone but been accompanied by a host of noble inventions of a kindred sort.' (Translation from Farrington, B., *The Philosophy of Francis Bacon*, Liverpool University Press, 1964, 71). By the time of the writing of the *Novum Organum*, he was more cautious. In arguing for the possibility of new discoveries, he admitted that most of the standard examples 'may seem to depend on certain properties of things themselves and nature, there is at any rate nothing in the art of printing which is not plain and obvious', *Novum Organum*, Bk 1, Aph. 110, in *Works*, IV, 100. His description of the process showed no acquaintance with the device of cast interchangeable type which distinguishes Western printing after Gutenberg from earlier methods of stamping an image in ink.

12 *Ibid*, Aph. 81, in *Works*, IV, 79.

13 *Ibid*, Aph. 129, in *Works*, IV, 144.

14 See 'Plan of the Work', *Works*, IV, 26–7, for both points together.

15 *Novum Organum*, Bk I, Aph. 68, in *Works*, IV, 69.

16 For an English translation, see Farrington, *op. cit.*, 59–72.

17 *Ibid.*, 70.

18 *Works*, IV, 33.

19 Tr. *Ibid.*, VII, 243.

20 *Works*, VII, 222.

21 *Ibid.*, V, 132

22 'The Great Instauration, Preface', in *Works*, IV, 19.

23 *Ibid.*, 20.

24 *Ibid.*, 21.

25 *Ibid.*, 20–1.

26 'Confession of Faith', Works, VII, 222.

27 *Idem.*

28 *Ibid.*, 221.

29 'Nat. & Exp. Hist'. *Works*, V, 132.

30 Ibid, 133.
31 For a full discussion, see Rossi, P., *Francis Bacon, From Magic to Science*, London, 1968, Ch. 3, 73–134.
32 See the *Meditationes Sacrae*, tr. in *Works*, VII, 252; and *Novum Organum*, Bk I, Aph. 89; *Works*, IV, 89.
33 This figure is used many times; see 'Plan of the Work', Works, IV, 33; and 'Nat. & Exp. Hist.', *Works*, V, 132.
34 *Novum Organum*, Bk I, Aph. 23; *Works*, IV, 51; and Aph. 124, *Works*, IV, 110.
35 'Mag. Inst. Plan', *Works*, IV, 33.
36 *De Aug.*, Bk III, 5; *Works*, IV, 365.
37 *Ibid.*, 364.
38 *Novum Organum*, 129; *Works*, IV, 114.
39 'Mag. Inst. Pref.', *Works*, IV, 20.
40 *Works*, IV, 115.
41 'Mag. Inst. Plan', *Works*, IV, 33.
42 *Novum Organum*, 129; *Works*, IV, 115.
43 *Ibid.*, Aph. 113; *Works, IV*, 102.
44 The importance of this contact with 'Things' in Bacon's philosophy has perhaps been obscured by the translators' practice of using a variety of terms for '*res*', including 'fact', 'particulars' or 'nature'. Indeed, one may say that most of the times such terms appear in an English translation, the original is '*res*'. It could be argued that the Latin term had extended connotations for Bacon, as it does in legal usage; but in every instance I have tested, the translation of '*res*' as 'thing' improves the sense.
45 *De Aug.*, Bk III, 1; *Works*, IV, 337.
46 *Works*, III, 222. See also *Novum Organum, Preface; Works*, IV, 20.
47 This is hinted at in the Proem of the Great Instauration; I translate the third phrase as: 'he (Bacon) thought that all trial should be made, whether that commerce between the Mind and Things (which is the most precious of anything on earth, or at least of earthly things), might be restored to its integrity, or at least brought to improvement'. See *Works*, I, 121 and IV, 7, for original and translation.
48 *Novum Organum*, Bk 1, Aph. 129; Works, IV, 115.
49 *Works*, III, 165.
50 *Novum Organum, Pref.; Works*, IV, 42.
51 *Loc. cit.*
52 *Novum Organum*, Bk 1, Aph. 128; *Works*, IV, 113.
53 *Novum Organum, Pref.; Works*, IV, 42.
54 Farrington, *op. cit.*, 108.
55 *Works*, 107–13.
56 *Works*, IV, 91.
57 *Ibid.*, 91–2.
58 *Ibid.*, 93.
59 Ibid., 87–9.
60 *Novum Organum*, Bk 1, Aph. 65; *Works*, IV, 66.
61 I am indebted to Ir. H. Peters for this important identification.
62 *De Aug.*, Bk III, 2; *Works*, IV, 341–2.
63 *Novum Organum*, Bk I, Aph. 89; *Works*, IV, 88 and *De Aug.*, Bk IX, 1; *Works*, V, 111–19.
64 'Advancement of learning', *Works*, III, 487–8; and *De Aug.*, Bk IX, 1; *Works*, V, 118.
65 Farrington relates this emphasis to an English tradition, extending back through More and Colet. See Farrington, *op. cit.*, 17.
66 *Meditationes Sacrae, Works*, VII, 249.

67 *Ibid.*, 245–6.
68 *The Refutation of Philosophies,* Farrington, op. cit., 104.
69 *Novum Organum, Pref.; Works,* IV, 20.
70 Farrington, *op. cit.,* 27.
71 See the opening pages of the *Oriatrike, or Physick Refined* (1662).
72 One of the few 'moderns' for whom Bacon shows any respect is Petrus Severinus, a moderate Paracelsian of Denmark.

Criticisms of Science:
From Past to Present

An Example from Classical Civilization

Although we shall soon see that the 'science' that was the object of criticism has been a complex and varied entity, the oldest example of detailed criticism known to me has a surprisingly modern tone. This is the comedy of Aristophanes, *The Clouds*, of around 420 BC. I shall discuss it at some length because of its usefulness in illustrating many of our concerns. A brief quotation will indicate the general style:

> *Student*: What would you say then if you heard another,
>   Our master's own?
> *Strepsiades*: Oh, come, do tell me that.
> *Student*: Why, Chaerophon was asking him in turn,
>   Which theory did he sanction; that the gnats
>   Hummed through their mouth, or backwards, through their tails?
> *Strepsiades*: Aye, and what said your master of the gnat?
> *Student*: He answered thus: the entrail of the gnat
>   Is small: and through the narrow pipe the wind
>   Rushes with violence straight towards the tail;
>   There, close against the pipe, the hollow rump
>   Receives the wind, and whistles to the blast.
> *Strepsiades*: So then the rump is trumpet to the gnats!
>   O happy, happy in your entrail learning!
>   Full surely need he fear nor debts nor duns
>   Who knows about the entrails of the gnats.

At one level we can see in the character of Strepsiades a precursor of those modern legislators who occasionally regale their colleagues with lists of ridiculous titles of research projects on which the taxpayer's money is being spent. Certainly the problem of justifying research whose only goal is 'positive' factual knowledge is one that defies easy solution. It is clear from the dialogue as well

137

as from the context that mere 'positive' knowledge of fleas is only ancillary to other goals. Strepsiades is a rustic who has come to Athens to learn how to argue with the 'wrong logic' in the law courts, and thereby escape the debts that his wastrel son has incurred. He has been directed to this school of 'Socrates' as a likely source of instruction. He is willing to put up with all these irrelevant facts as the price he must pay for mastering the techniques that will enable him to solve his practical problems. For the students and 'Socrates', however, such facts are serious business; they lead to the philosophical study of nature, and the achievement of wisdom. The discipline illustrated in the main body of the play is meteorology; the Gods are not abolished but the phenomena of thunder and rain are 'explained' by coarse jokes about digestive functions.

Thus Aristophanes blended the voices of the Sophists, who hired themselves out to teach debating skills, with those of the 'physiologues', who produced 'disenchanted' explanations of natural phenomena; then he named their representative 'Socrates'. It is likely that this was both inaccurate and unfair, but then Aristophanes was a writer of critical comedies, and in this one the moral is plain. The end comes when the son of Strepsiades displays a superior mastery of the 'wrong logic', to the extent that he is justified in beating up his father; the latter then burns down the school with its inhabitants. The chorus approves, as 'Socrates' and his group have blasphemed the gods. In this little drama the 'positive' facts derive all their significance from their ideological function; and this is seen as clearly by the 'scientists' as by their enemies. Only later do we find spokesmen for science claiming that embattled scientists (such as Galileo) should have both the privileges of an ideological combatant on the right side, and also the immunities of an encapsulated scholar.

The circumstances producing this early criticism of 'science' are worth mentioning. Athens was embroiled in the serious Peloponnesian War, having been led by Pericles through a cycle of patriotism, interstate co-operation and ultimately imperialism. The essence of the free Athenian polity, immortalized in Pericles' late oration, might well have been corrupted and destroyed before anyone noticed it was there. At the court of Pericles were 'freethinkers', including the philosopher Anaxagoras, who was eventually tried for impiety. Certainly there was plausibility in Aristophanes' implicit accusation that the 'demythologizing' of nature and of the city had led to a corruption of the people. The relation of the historical Socrates to all this is beyond my present concerns (Ferguson 1971).

We gain some idea of the rapidity of the change of cosmology in fifth century Athens when we consider the tragedy *Prometheus Bound*, by Aeschylus, only a half-century earlier. There Prometheus lists all his gifts to mankind: they are all techniques, with no 'pure' or philosophical science to be seen. What is startling to a modern reader, and perhaps embarrassing to some, is that the really advanced 'sciences' were those of prognostication by magical means. From our modern viewpoint we can perhaps imagine the intellectual and spiritual disturbance which the denigration and destruction of the old cosmology must have caused more easily than could our predecessors in scholarship. In his classic work on Aeschylus, George Thomson (1941) omits the major part of Prometheus' speech which deals with magic; then he comments on 'the bold naturalism of the account'.

There is also a criticism of 'science' built into the Prometheus legend: the gods are jealous of man's powers. Whether this is simply one of the less enlightened responses of the Greek deities, or whether this reflects a deep fear of uncontrolled knowledge, like the Garden of Eden story, is matter for speculation. Of the prehistory of this sort of 'science criticism' I can offer only one fragment: for the early Hebrews, iron was an unclean substance and not to be brought into a holy place, because of its associations. Thus, a loathing of the evil effects of natural knowledge applied to technical problems can be traced back very far indeed.

Criticism in the Scientific Revolution

Although 'science' is an essentially complicated and confused term, I am here concerned with the cluster of activities and styles that are dominant at the present time. For brevity I can omit descriptions of debates over occult arts and scholasticism from the Medieval and Renaissance periods. However, the Scientific Revolution of the seventeenth century is so directly ancestral to our own situation, that a review of debates then can be helpful for perspective on ourselves.

The prophets of the scientific revolution had a commitment to a positive dream for a reformed natural knowledge; but not surprisingly, they were more articulate in their criticisms of the existing science and learning. From the criticisms which each of them made we may gain some insights into what he considered to be central to his own programme. Bacon's critique was the most broad-ranging, and also the most related to practice. He considered all the different sorts of men claiming to advance knowledge, and found them all wanting in their methods, attitudes and ethics. Although the professed men of knowledge were guilty of just about every one of the seven deadly sins, it was, in my opinion, pride that Bacon found most monstrous. There is little doubt that he saw himself as the inaugurator of a brotherhood of pure reformers of knowledge and then of mankind; the millenarian connotations of *Et Augebitur Scientia* would not have been lost on his readers (Ravetz 1971). Descartes probably also entertained some ambitions of a messianic character, and his interest in the shadow brotherhood of Rosicrucians is difficult to deny (Arnold 1958). But his lasting impulse to reform came from his experiences as an adolescent schoolboy. Having believed that books could reveal the Good and True, he truned in his disillusion on the entire syllabus, reserving special scorn for philosophy and theology, and allowing only mathematics a partial exception (Descartes 1638). By contrast to these two, Galileo seems to have been concerned mainly with natural philosophy, and his brief, disconnected, critical analyses were made mainly in the context of polemical debate.

It is now generally recognized that there were three, not two, sides in the philosophical struggles of the early seventeenth century; against the 'mechanists' were arrayed Aristotelians with an 'organic' world view, and 'alchemists' with a 'magic' world view. Of course, there were factions and conflicts within each camp, and each exerted an influence on the other two (Kearney 1971). The debate between the two 'losing' sides is not well chronicled; van Helmont's sufferings at the hands of the Inquisition are nearly forgotten (Bonelli and Shea 1975). Nor do we have editions of counter-criticisms by Aristotelians (of the various sorts) to the 'atomists'. Fortunately, we do possess published documents from a great debate on the other front: between Paracelsians and Galileans, roughly speaking, in Civil War England. The occasion was an attempt by more radical educational reformers to include universities in their plans. The attack was led by John Webster, and in a war of pamphlets the defence was made by Seth Ward and John Wilkins. Webster denounced the universities for their supposed conservatism; in their reply the academics cast reflections on his competence, and denounced his alchemical recommendations as antithetical to all Bacon's precepts. But they had to admit that Bacon did advocate experiments as a way to learning, and that they refrained from forcing such things on their students, since the universities were still essentially élite finishing schools rather than centres for advancement of learning or diffusion of useful arts (Webster 1976).

With the decay into insignificance of its two rivals—outside Germany, at least—the school of the 'mechanical' philosophy of nature came to complete dominance by the end of the seventeenth century. But it had lost the prophetic zeal of its earliest proponents, and indeed in England, at least, experimental philosophy came to be regarded as a gentleman's eccentricity, at a time when manners and morals were the prime concern of the cultivated classes. In spite of—or perhaps because of—the near deification of Newton in early eighteenth century England, there was no corps of really talented men to continue his work. A savage satire of scientific academicians and industrial innovators was at the heart of the story of Gulliver's voyage to Laputa as told by Jonathan Swift. An equally pungent sociological analysis of scientific dogmatism was made by the philosopher George Berkeley in the course of his debate over the concealed obscurities at the foundation of the calculus (Ravetz 1971, pp. 219–23). But systematic and socially effective criticism of the dominant styles of science was by this time becoming exceedingly difficult, as 'reason' became the touchstone for all decisions in polite European society.

The Romantic Challenge and Its Descendants

It is useful to remember how deeply split was the Enlightenment movement on the question of science. All factions agreed on the necessity of doing away with the corrupt tyranny of the Church. But not all shared the faith of d'Alembert and Condorcet that a Newtonian type of science, both natural and social, would itself bring reason and justice to human affairs. In particular, Rousseau and his followers, combining Arcadian, romantic and populist elements, raised a significant challenge to orthodox science during the revolution, appearing as forerunners of the cultural revolutionaries of recent times (Gillispie 1959).

The flourishing of romantic poetry in England also had its scientific aspects. Blake's contempt for atomism and 'single vision' is well known to today's counter-culture, and Coleridge's enthusiastic study of *Naturphilosophie* (Knight 1972) was more plausible than we now realize, given the exciting and chaotic state of chemistry and biology at the time. But the movement was short-lived; and the English combination of utility and inductivism kept their science rather more practical and less speculative and sensitive than in Germany.

Germany was, of course, the home and source of romanticism, particularly in science. Swedenborg, the engineer-turned-psychic, provided elements of continuity with earlier enchanted philosophies of nature. To the acute embarrassment of German men of science for a century afterwards, the great poet Goethe considered his work on optics as important as any other he did. Romanticism, in *Naturphilosophie*, had an ontological basis of opposition to the hard experimental science that was to replace it, a commitment to some sort of existence 'beyond reductionism'. Future historical studies may find a surprising number of people of such tendencies among known critical or eccentric scientists. Thus G.T. Fechner, the founder of psychophysics, was led to his classic empirical studies by the need to corroborate his panpsychical philosophy, as exemplified in 'Nanna, or the soul life of plants' (Jaynes 1972). Also we now find that A.R. Wallace broke with the Darwinian theory of the descent of man from apes because of the intensity of his spiritualist experiences (Kottler 1974). A direct link to the present-day counter-culture is provided by Rudolf Steiner, who combined Goethe with theosophy; and in spite of the apparent isolation of his established followers in 'anthroposophy', he indirectly provided inspiration and insights for the romantics of today.

A link to another contemporary focus of criticism can be found in Max Scheler, the brilliant though eccentric German philosopher of the earlier twentieth century. He did not merely mourn the passing of the 'organic' *Gemeinschaft* world in the well-known German style; he also examined modern science as the characteristic production of a peculiar, alienated consciousness (Staude 1967). Much of the later 'cultural' historical materialism — as, for example, the neglected essay by Christopher Caudwell, *Crisis in Physics* (1939) — seems to contain echoes of Scheler's analysis, though of course without his particular judgement on the phenomenon.

The ontological criticism of modern materialistic scientism has flourished throughout the century, though until quite recently, at least, kept on the sidelines. The biological sciences have produced descendants of vitalism in 'holism'; this developed into the concept of 'levels of organization', as characterized in Whitehead's 'organismic' philosophy, with continuous extensions to mysticism in Bergson—gloriously misunderstood by Bertrand Russell in his essay *Mysticism and Logic*—and in Teilhard de Chardin. From physics came a more 'spiritualist' tendency, most notably seen in Crookes and Oliver Lodge; later Eddington, Jeans and Milne continued the criticism of materialistic science from a more Platonic point of view. E.A. Burtt was the first to analyse seventeenth century science as the product of a metaphysical shift; his classic book (1924) opens with a contrast between Dante's hymn to the Divine Light and the schoolboy Epicurean heroics of Bertrand Russell's 'A free man's worship'. It was to be nearly half a century before professional historians of science could become sufficiently critical of science to appreciate this work.

Modern Radical Criticisms of Science

Although social criticisms of science on behalf of the non-élite classes were made in earlier centuries, they have gained coherence only recently. The course of Marxist criticism of science may indicate some reasons for this delay. To a large extent, Marxists have wanted only to inherit and purify bourgeois culture, rather than to transform it.

Lenin's vigorous book on philosophy of science (1909) accepted the facts and values of science as unproblematic; indeed, his version of materialism involved commitment to an impersonal, external world and cohered well with a scientism just a shade above the vulgar. It appears that the German Marxists of the 1920s, the first generation of Marxists who really enjoyed a collectivity of educated and academically employed scholars, were rather involved in debates with Kant, Weber and Freud. Marcuse and Mannheim reflected these concerns. Attacks on 'rational' service itself were then the property of a mystical, pre-Nazi Right (Forman 1971). Hence it was only in the 1930s that Marxist criticisms of science, mainly in England, emerged with intellectual force. This important movement has been studied by Werskey (1975) from several approaches, generally more social than doctrinal. There seems to be a common theme in all the criticisms, namely that science could produce peace and plenty for all—as well as culturally valuable knowledge from pure research—were it not for the 'fetters' imposed by a corrupt and destructive capitalist system. The most eloquent statement of this faith was in J.D. Bernal's *The Social Function of Science* (1939). The mixture of humanitarian, technocratic and reductionist—Faustian motives in Bernal's thought has not yet been fully explored, although B. Easlea (1973) has given some preliminary hints. The use of the Soviet Union as a shining example of the future became increasingly difficult as Stalin's regime became more oppressive; but it was only after the war that a major scientific scandal, the Lysenko episode, really upset the Marxist scientific community and provoked defections on a scientific issue.

In spite of a now lengthy experience of criticism in the West and practice in the East, the Marxist socialist criticism of science has not yet succeeded in articulating a coherent positive alternative. Although the slogan of 'socialist science' has been raised several times in the Soviet Union, it has usually been so entangled with crude and opportunistic campaigns within science as to gain no genuine credibility. The disillusion of J.D. Bernal with Soviet science, though only to be inferred from hints in his writings (Ravetz 1972), is likely to have been as severe as that of Max Born (Thompson 1953) or Kapitsa (Roszak 1969, 1972) with non-political 'industrialized' science. Indeed, the very possibility of a distinctively 'socialist' science now seems to be an open question for those who have the greatest personal commitment to the idea. Thus the avowedly radical British Society for Social Responsibility in Science once organized a conference to inquire: 'Is there a socialist science?' The outcome was far from conclusive.

A different dimension of radical criticism of modern science and technology can be traced back to the ethical and aesthetic writings of Victorians such as John Ruskin and William Morris. Though their ideas were neither stable nor always internally cohesive, they gave a reminder that the industrial system does more than exploit, it blights. Neither aspect is purely derivative of the other. A literary expression of this view was developed by D.H. Lawrence; the critical school of F.R. Leavis developed it further, and this at least as much as Marxism served as a basis for the political radicalization of a generation of English intellectuals (Thompson 1953). On the more overtly political side, the Ruskin influence — mixed with communitarian ideals and the studies of Kropotkin in social philosophy — has worked through many channels including that of Gandhi to the 'intermediate technology' of Schumacher (1973). Based on 'Buddhist economics', it invokes the increasingly powerful slogan, 'Small is Beautiful'.

Although the 'ethical' approach does not involve an enriched cosmology or enhanced experience for its criticism of science, its themes are shared by many approaches which do. The novelist Aldous Huxley emerged as an important critic of science with his *Brave New World*, which described a science-based utopia where happiness was enforced, and civilization was trivialized and debased. In the 1930s he became a pacifist communitarian consciousness-enhancing prophet; and by the 1950s his experiences with Eastern religion had prepared him for psychedelics. He then became a link to the Leary group, and thereby helped form the synthesis of the 'Politics of Ecstasy' which was so important for a brief period in the 1960s. This movement, identified and named by Theodore Roszak as 'the counter-culture' (1969), made cosmology and inner experience the 'base' in reality while the political–technical complex, the superstructure, was rotting away in our own time. A more anti-Marxist radicalism would be hard to imagine. Perhaps it was inevitable that the attempt to unite Marxism with a variety of romanticisms dating from the Freudian Revolution of the 1920s, inspired by Marcuse's *One Dimensional Man* (1964), should have had such a brief, though intense, career.

This review of radical critiques of science from the outside would be incomplete without one embarrassing example. Liberal intellectuals tend to assume that all radical popular criticisms of science, as of other élite social institutions, must be from the Left. Philosophically reactionary populism is, if not a contradiction in terms, then at least an anomaly to be explained away. Yet the strength and persistence of the biblical fundamentalist attack on the teaching of Darwinian evolution in the United States should be a warning against scientific complacency (Grabiner and Miller 1974). Those responsible for this movement feel themselves excluded from a fair share of intellectual influence, just as do Marxist radicals. The more sophisticated defenders of biblical 'literalism' can argue in a very Lakatosian way about administrative suppression of their research program when it only *seemed* to be undergoing a degenerate phase; certainly neither side of the debate can rigorously prove the truth of its assumptions. Heavy-handed political tactics by scientist-politicians against 'creationist' propaganda have proved counter-productive, just as in the Velikovsky affair (which, although more bizarre in details, has not involved an overt challenge on the principles of scientific evidence). The issues of *Pensée*, published for a time by students in Portland, Oregon, showed a reasonable debate on scientific problems between Velikovsky and his critics (see also Gillette 1974). Even if the 'reactionary' criticisms of science are of a character with occasional chauvinistic denials by oppressed ethnic and cultural minorities of the originality or value of Western science, these criticisms should serve as a reminder that the dominant style in science, however great its intellectual power and social benefits, can yet be a tool of cultural oppression in many directions.

Science Policy Studies: From Publicity to Politics

A noteworthy feature of the present period is that sharply critical analyses of the scientific endeavour are made by established scholars, whose general radicalism may be mild or even non-existent. This respectable, 'inside' criticism of science reflects the new self-awareness of science, and the loss of its earlier assurance. Looking back on pronouncements of earlier spokesmen of science, we are impressed by their propagandist character. The 'man of science' was, for such as T.H. Huxley (1893), von Helmholtz (1893) or Karl Pearson (1892), a paragon of the best intellectual and moral virtues.

The earliest writings in a self-conscious tradition of sociology of science presupposed and reinforced this assumption. Thus Robert K. Merton, whose first work was historical studies of possible social influences on science, produced (1942) a theoretical eulogy for the idealistic scientist who shares an 'ethos' involving 'four norms' of behaviour. Such an image was consensus right through the early post-war period; such diverse figures as Polanyi, Popper, Bernal and Vannevar Bush could all agree that what science mainly needed was more latitude for doing its own thing. In itself, science was so innately good that there were no inherent problems of government that might endanger its progress. From earlier centuries through the post-war decade, science policy studies were in essence little more thant science publicity pronouncements. The only critical voices from within established science were those of eccentrics like Leo Szilard (1961) and Norbert Wiener (1964).

Science policy analysis as such can therefore be said to begin with two studies whose limited, descriptive appearance belies their fundamental significance. Derek Price's fantastic straight-line, semi-log graph of growth (1963) did more than show a continuity with the past: it tolled a bell for the future. Those commentators who predicted that eventually we would need to give PhDs to dogs and cats were only partly ridiculous. Price showed that a situation of unequal growth-rates in scientific demand and societal supply could persist unchanged for only a limited length of time. If the supply of resources could not increase beyond all expectation, the demands of science would need to moderate. In his rigorous, boldly quantitative way, Price exposed one of the fundamental contradictions of 'big' science: that quantitative growth, previously so necessary for vitality, must stop soon. Indeed, one could define 'big' science as that whose claim on resources is so large as to be politically significant, and which is thereby constrained by general social priorities.

A neat contrast to Price's study was that of Alvin Weinberg on 'Criteria of scientific choice' (1967). Instead of impersonal statistics on quantitative growth, we have wise reflections on qualitative choice. For the affluent, post-war, big-science Americans, it was bad enough to remind the world that choices — and rejections — are necessary. But by challenging the absolute value of 'pure science', by including social concerns as legitimate components of any decision on investment in science, he seemed to be betraying the autonomy of the scientific endeavour. Emotive pleading aside, Weinberg's study did prepare for the exposure of an even more basic contradiction in 'big' science: the total confusion of the disparate goals of scientific research and of the appropriate social roles of scientists. We shall return to this later.

My own contribution to science policy studies began shortly after; in late 1964 my article on the Mohole scandal appeared (Ravetz 1964). In it I tried to define corruption in science, importing the norms of social behaviour appropriate to politics, business enterprise, or speculative technology. This led to the floating of a publicity stunt that quickly became a gigantic project, with inadequate study of goals, feasibility or costs. Around the same time I began to work up the ideas embodied in my book of 1971; and a problem posed by Derek Price's study became crucial at that early stage. What, after all, is the difference between 'little science' and 'big science' as social activities? All the indicators are continuous; how — in terms of Marxist dialectic — does quantity pass into quality? I recall that the question, phrased without the Marxist terminology, of course, was put by Jack Morrell. The answer to this question was suggested by another part of Marxism: a change in the capital-intensity of scientific research. The old craftsmen-producers who offered their finished products on a market of quality assessment are replaced by managers who must convince an investing agency to provide heavy capital for a future project. Much else follows from this, and is made coherent by it; thus I came to the idea of the 'industrialization of science', and passed on from Marxism to other sources of insight.

Around the same time, Jean-Jacques Salomon saw the present period as one of techno-positivism, of the *savant* or aristocratic scholar being replaced by the *scientifique* or scientific worker (1973). In this insight he had been anticipated in 1960 by John Ziman, who had used the English cricket class distinction between amateur 'gentlemen' and paid 'players'; that is to say, between a 'vocation' and a 'career'. In his book, Salomon went on to identify the most cruel contradiction of all: that the noble ideals of the traditional scientific endeavour had rested on an illusion of innocence. Science, for so long the destroyer of ideologies, was revealed as a variety of false consciousness. How to preserve the ethics of a *savant* in the new disenchanted age is a problem Salomon left to the reader.

For the first really consistent, many-sided, Marxist analysis and criticism of science in this present period, we are indebted to Hilary and Steven Rose. After exploring the historical background in their book (1969), they moved to the attack in 1970 with their essay on the myth of the neutrality of science (Fuller 1971). With a host of suggestive examples, they showed how both scientific *choice* and scientific *concepts* are ideologically and politically influenced in various degrees. The political lessons of this may seem straightforward, but the Roses saw some tricky ethical problems, such as: Was Einstein guilty of the bomb? To save something of the functions of the discredited theory of the neutrality of science, they distinguished between a Kuhnian paradigm, subject to ethical judgements, and puzzle-solving within it, the last preserve of ethical neutrality. Whether this analysis would hold indefinitely may be doubted. Subsequently they have extended their analysis to describe the 'incorporation' of science in the bourgeois (and also the Soviet) state, wherein science functions as a means both of material production and of social control, while itself experiencing the social and political stratification and alienation of any techno-bureaucratic enterprise. The 'myth' of 'pure' science has been maintained only by a concentration of attention on the exploits of the academic élite; but this is now weakening, and the various titles implying some separation or opposition between 'science' and 'society' are themselves mystifying and obsolete. Although their analysis provokes queries and criticisms at many points, the Roses have had considerable success in their sustained endeavour to achieve a Marxist critique of modern science, all the time preserving the standards of civilized debate. (See Rose and Rose 1976.)

The formal sociology of science gradually emerged from the influence of Mertonism. Stuart Blume (1974) studied power in the scientific establishment, and found that it is but imperfectly correlated with scientific attainment. Rather, power—realized through the equivalent of patronage, or the allocation of research funds—derives to a strong degree from contacts in the bureaucracies that feed science. This arrangement is, of course, self-reinforcing. There was at least one large-scale empirical study, on some 400 scientists, to see whether they subscribed to, or had even heard of, Merton's 'four norms'

(Ellis 1972); the answer was disconcerting then but hardly needs stating now. An investigation of the scientists working on the first moon-rocks (Mitroff 1974) showed a fine mixture of traditional idealism with tough American realism; as one scientist said, if a result isn't worth being stolen it isn't worth producing.

By the mid-1970s the stream of 'critical policy' studies became a flood. We now face the problem of having too many approaches to the phenomenon and no inclusive theory for them all. Complementary to my theory of 'industrial-zation' is Harvey Wheeler's description of the 'bureaucratization' of science (1975). Where I saw the corruptions of 'entrepreneurial' science, he sees the onset of mediocrity and trivialization of research, paralleling the tendencies of high-technology consumer industries like pharmaceuticals and automobiles. Though this too had been anticipated by Leo Szilard long ago, it was then only an inspired guess (1961). Wheeler relates the present process to the current deceleration of growth, and anticipates a rapid ossification of the scientific enterprise. One solution, though more directed at the 'Andromeda Strain' problems of DNA research, is external political control through the 'consti-tutionalization of science'.

We can hardly expect the proposed critical alternatives to established science to be more coherent than the parallel movements in politics. But it is significant that in the realm of ideas, science lacks strong and confident defenses against these attacks. An idea which Dean Harvey Brooks proposed in 1975 indicates the state of ideology of established science; he suggested that American science could be rejuvenated by our making it the focus of another great national endeavour, providing a unifying purpose for the nation! Though this might well come to pass some time in the future, it is, in the wake of the moon-race and Vietnam, a forlorn hope. More symptomatic of the current atmosphere is a volume of essays produced at the University of Michigan in connection with the quincentenary of the birth of Copernicus. The title is *Science and Society: Past, Present and Future* (Steneck 1975). In it the social and human relevance of science is exemplified by a quote from the mother of an American black child; a visiting scientist met her on an educational aid project. She said:

'But you never show your white faces around here. You never say "I'm sorry. I'm sorry for what's happening. I'm sorry that we got our white folks walking on the moon while you black folks are falling on your beds sick with hunger and your stomachs rotting. I'm sorry that your boy is an epileptic . . ." Everything in the name of science. But any way you cut it, you're the master, we're the dogs, and I just got to wait and see whether a seizure some day will take my boy away from me . . .' (p. 227).

Doubts among the Scholars

The ideological motivations and functions of the various scholarly disciplines that study the natural sciences have had a shadowy history. On the one hand, the glorification or defence of science in general, or loyal praise for the founding fathers of some particular specialty, were quite legitimate concerns of the (usually amateur) philosophers and historians of science until recently. But since they nearly all shared in the defining assumption of our science, that it is simple truth, having no connection with ideology, they could not rise to self-awareness about their own efforts. Only now, given the combination of professional self-consciousness among some scholars, with the current mood of disenchantment with science, can a truly critical analysis of the past and of the present be achieved. This means that the way is now open for a genuine history and sociology of science; for until such reflective disciplines have some critical distance from their object, they cannot produce anything more than anecdote, chronicle or hagiography.

I deal with contemporary critical currents in other essays in this volume, and so there is no need for great detail here. Let it suffice that until the present century, the problem of error in science had a similarly shadowy existence among philosophers and spokesmen for science. Of course, all proclaimed the open and self-critical character of science. But nowhere was the problem of error in genuine science dealt with seriously. This is because the overriding ideological function of science was to show how science always got it right. Historians could nearly always explain the falsification of established scientific theories through myths of the failings of the side that was ultimately proven wrong.

Among traditional historians the adherents of phlogiston (a reagent in a theory of combustion) had 'ignored' the problem of negative weight; those of caloric (which is still measured in elementary physics experiments) had 'ignored' the cannon-boring experiment of Count von Rumford; and so on. Such stories required a considerable simplification and distortion of the historical record; on the case where a great scientist was simply wrong, as Newton on the corpuscular theory of light, the story was fudged. Incomplete knowledge at the time was never a sufficient excuse for honest scientific error; otherwise our own incomplete knowledge might be leading us astray. The possibility of honest, competent scientists being in error, the spectre of false-hood resulting from the application of scientific method, had never been seriously confronted.

Confirmation of this thesis of mine comes from the example of Popper (1963), who recognized the possibility of error with great boldness; and who indeed defined genuine science by its falsifiability. But his great example was the legendary Einstein, who (it might be imagined) earned the right to possess truth, by sincerely admitting that his theory might be false. Popper's whole logic is devoted to showing how his scheme of science is fundamentally different from those of the verificationists, in spite of its concentration on theories that *pass* tests rather than fail them.

But once the rot had set in, nothing could stop it. With the loss of the faith that science possesses, to a unique degree, the True, and following on from that the Good, successive philosophers occupied ever more radical positions. The end of the epistemological tradition was accomplished by Paul Feyerabend. But a year before his last salvo, *Science in a Free Society* (1978), there appeared the first popular work in the new direction, where science has been studied for philosophical purposes as 'just another' social activity. This was *Laboratory Life* (1977), by Latour and Woolgar, a somewhat self-mocking anthropological essay on those strange creatures and their 'inscriptions'; we might call it the school of 'the scientist as fuzzy-wuzzy'. The members of the Science Studies Unit at Edinburgh University, notably Barry Barnes (see 1974, 1977) and David Bloor (see 1976, 1983), had been the pioneers in advocating a version of relativism with their 'strong programme in the sociology of knowledge', but their style and background were those of the traditional scholars; and their paradoxical theses never caught on with the public in the same way as the tales of the anthropologists and ethno-methodologists.

Even the historians of science are now sharing the general spirit of rebellion. Whiggery (referring to the 'Whig interpretation' of history as the story of progress) is now nearly a term of abuse among the more sophisticated professionals; they know that the events of the past were quite other than the brave precursors of the glorious present. One historian has argued, though on dubious evidence, that Newton 'fudged' his data on several crucial occasions (Westfall 1973). Also, the ideological sensitivity of genuine history, breaking the propaganda image of the Good Scientist and the teaching image of Cumulating Facts, has been advanced in a paper entitled 'Should the history of science be X-rated?' (Brush 1974). Indeed, the history of science is now reaching the point of maturity, where it need not stay at the level of muckraking or demystifying exercises.

Personal Interpretation

We have lived long enough with the new atmosphere of criticism of science to be able to grow out of our emotional reactions to it, and to begin to appreciate its meaning for the future of science. We all know that science is intimately linked to society, that science cannot be perfect in an imperfect society, and yet the future of science cannot simply be reduced to that of society. But we still lack a unifying theme to encompass the ongoing technical, social and ideological changes in science. I would like to make a tentative offering in that direction.

The clue to a deep problem is the ambiguities in the term 'science'. Does it mean 'pure' or 'basic', or 'applied' or 'mission-oriented', or even 'R & D', or a bit of all of them in varying proportions at various times and places? The different names refer to very different activities, each with their own internal and external goals and ideologies. To let 'science' cover the whole lot, invoking only the technical puzzle-solving common to them all, leaves out some of the most important elements of science of the past and present. To distinguish among the various sorts of science, producing species of hyphenated scientists, might seem more conducive to clarity. But then we find that the categories blend into each other at so many points that paragraphs of explanation would be needed to establish each demarcation. So we can make a first conclusion: the complex multiplicity of roles and the consequent ambiguity of self-consciousness are now essential structural features of science.

Other social institutions doubtless have the same property; whether science suffers to an exceptional degree could be explored in a disciplined study. But, another feature of the situation of science aggravates its tensions and contradictions. Considering the many roles performed by scientists, we notice that one is almost always absent: that of the consultant professional, who acts on behalf of a client and takes personal responsibility for his decisions. The scientist may produce internally motivated results like a *savant* or scholar; or he may solve technically motivated problems in a corporate enterprise as a *scientifique* or research worker. Only rarely can he do what an independent engineer or physician does as a routine: solve problems and take decisions whose quality is soon tested by the welfare of a client. Now we know that the learned professions have plenty of problems of their own. But to a great extent these arise from a failure to honour a public trust that is embodied in a multitude of particular cases. The scientific community cannot even claim to have such a problem. There are no institutions for qualifying a scientist as a professional or — more significant — for disqualifying him or her.

In this feature of the social structure of science, we can see the sources of the strongly enforced alienation of scientists: from society; from the fruits of their work; from any effective sense of responsibility. Individually cut off from social decisions and their consequences, either by personal remoteness (such as academics) or subservience (such as research employees), they have neither the experience nor the opportunity to do anything to control the engine of total change that they are still fabricating. Even the engineer who insists that it's his duty only to follow orders is at a higher level of awareness, for he at least sees the problem, and can choose a policy. The community of science is then in a position of creating great power while being deprived of the responsibility for its use. This is a new twist on the old formula for corruption. It may help to explain the essential confusion, in practice and ideology, which has been revealed by the recent critical studies of science.

Clearly this is not a healthy situation. Yet it is built into the style of research, as is evidenced both by the necessary autonomy of some (not easily defined) portions of it, and by its externally directed applications, without which science would receive only small social support. Considered as a problem, it is one that cannot be solved like a puzzle in social administration or education. Indeed, considered as a threatening challenge, it might well be classed as a 'contradiction'. Will it be a driving contradiction, forcing a restructuring of goals, ideas and institutions? Or will it be a crippling contradiction, where established interests cling to their bits of power and security, preventing any change before catastrophe strikes? Only time will tell. But I hope that we have here a useful element in the enormous task of understanding, criticism and action which will accompany the formulation of new science policy studies.

This essay was first published in *Science, Technology and Society. A Cross-Disciplinary Perspective* (eds I. Spiegel-Rösing and D.J. Price), London and Beverley Hills, Sage Publications, 1977, pp. 71–89.

References

Aristophanes (423 BC) *The Clouds*, tr. Benjamin B. Rogers, Bell, London, 1916.

Arnold, P. (1958) *Histoire des Rose-Croix*, Paris.

Barnes, B. (ed.) (1972) *Sociology of Science: Selected Readings*, Penguin.

Barnes, B. (1974) *Scientific Knowledge and Sociological Theory*, Routledge, London.

Barnes, B. (1977) *Interests and the Growth of Knowledge*, Routledge, London.

Bernal, J.D. (1939) *The Social Function of Science*, Routledge, London.

Bloor, D. (1976) *Knowledge and Social Imagery*, Routledge, London.

Bloor, D. (1983) *Wittgenstein: A Social Theory of Knowledge*, Macmillan, London.

Blume, S.S. (1974) *Towards a Political Sociology of Science*, The Free Press, New York.

Bonelli, M.R. and Shea, W.R. (eds) (1975) *Reason, Experiment and Mysticism in the Scientific Revolution*, Science History Publications, New York.

Brooks, H. (1975) 'Can science be re-directed?', lecture at CNAM, Paris, December 1975.

Brush, S.G. (1974) 'Should the history of science be X-rated?', *Science* **183**, 1164–82.

Burtt, E.A. (1924) *The Metaphysical Foundations of Modern Physical Science*, Kegan Paul, London.

Clagett, M. (1959) *Critical Problems in the History of Science*, University of Wisconsin Press.

Debus, A. (ed.) (1971) *Science, Medicine and Society in the Renaissance* (W. Pagel Festschrift), Science History Publications, New York.

Descartes, R. (1638) *Discours de la Méthode*, deuxième partie.

Easlea, B. (1973) *Liberation and the Aims of Science*, Chatto and Windus, London.

Ellis, N.D. (1972) 'The occupation of science', in Barnes (1972), pp. 188–205.

Ferguson, J. (1971) *Socrates*, The Open University, Milton Keynes.

Feyerabend, P. (1978) *Science in a Free Society*, New Left Books, London.

Forman, P. (1971) 'Weimar culture, causality and quantum theory 1918–1923: adaptation in German physicists and mathematicians to a hostile intellectual environment', *Historical Studies in the Physical Sciences* **3**, 1–116.

Fuller, W. (ed.) (1971) *The Social Impact of Modern Biology*, Routledge, London.

Gillette, R. (1974) 'Velikovsky: AAAS forum for a mild collision', *Science* **183**, 1059–62.

Gillispie, C.C. (1959) 'The *Encyclopedia* and the Jacobin philosophy of science: A study in ideas and consequences', in Clagett (1959), pp. 255–89.

Grabiner, J.V. and Miller, P.D. (1974) 'Effects of the Scopes trial', *Science* **185**, 832–7.

Helmholtz, H. von (1893) 'On the relation of natural science to science in general', in

Popular Lectures on Scientific Subjects (ed. M. Kline), Dover Publications, New York, 1962, pp. 1—28.

Huxley, A. (1932) *Brave New World*, Chatto and Windus, London.

Huxley, T.H. (1893) 'On the advisableness of improving natural knowledge', in *Methods and Results*, Macmillan, London pp. 1—28.

Jaynes, J. (1972) 'Fechner, Gustav Theodor', *Dictionary of Scientific Biography*, Scribner, New York, Vol. IV, pp. 556—9.

Kearney, H. (1971) *Science and Change, 1500—1800*, Weidenfeld, London.

Knight, D. (1972) 'Chemistry, physiology and materialism in the Romantic period', *Durham University Journal* **64**, 139—45.

Kottler, M.J. (1974) 'Alfred Russel Wallace, the origin of man and spiritualism', *Isis* **65**, 145—92.

Latour, B. and Woolgar, S. (1977) *Laboratory Life: The Social Construction of Scientific Facts*, Sage, Beverley Hills and London.

Lenin, V.I. (1909) *Materialism and Empirio-Criticism* (tr. D. Kvetko). In *Collected Works*, Vol. 13, Laurence, London, 1930.

Marcuse, H. (1964) *One Dimensional Man*, Beacon Press, Boston.

Merton, R.K. (1942) 'The institutional imperatives of science', reprinted in *Social Theory and Social Structure*, The Free Press, New York, 1967.

Mitroff, I. (1974) *The Subjective Side of Science*, Elsevier, Amsterdam.

Pearson, K. (1892) *The Grammar of Science*, Scott, London.

Popper, K.R. (1963) *Conjectures and Refutations*, Routledge, London.

Price, D.J. (1963) *Little Science, Big Science*, Columbia University Press, New York.

Ravetz, J.R. (1964) 'The Mohole scandal', *The Guardian* 27 October.

Ravetz, J.R. (1971) *Scientific Knowledge and Its Social Problems*, Oxford University Press.

Ravetz, J.R. (1972) review of *Science in History* by J.D. Bernal, in *Technology and Culture* **13**, 664—6.

Rose, H. and Rose, S. (1969) *Science and Society*, Allen Lane, London.

Rose, H. and Rose, S. (1976) 'The incorporation of science' in their *The Political Economy of Science*, Macmillan, London.

Roszak, T. (1969) *The Making of a Counter-Culture*, Doubleday, New York.

Roszak, T. (1972) *Where the Wasteland Ends*, Doubleday, New York.

Salomon, J.J. (1973) *Science and Politics*, Macmillan, London.

Schumacher, E.F. (1973) *Small Is Beautiful*, Abacus, London.

Staude, J.R. (1967) *Max Scheler, an Intellectual Portrait*, The Free Press, New York.

Steneck, H.H. (ed.) (1975) *Science and Society: Past, Present and Future*, University of Michigan Press.

Szilard, L. (1961) *The Voice of the Dolphins and Other Stories*, Simon & Schuster, New York.

Thompson, D. (1953) *Science in Perspective: Passages of Contemporary Writing*, John Murray, London.

Thomson, G. (1941) *Aeschylus and Athens*, Routledge, London.

Webster, C. (1976) *The Great Instauration: Science, Medicine and Reform, 1626—1660*, Duckworth, London.

Weinberg, A.M. (1967) 'Criteria of scientific choice', in *Reflections on Big Science*, Pergamon, Oxford.

Werskey, G. (1975) 'Making socialists of scientists: whose side is history on?', *Radical Science Journal* (London) **2/3**, 13—50.

Westfall, S. (1973) 'Newton and the fudge factor', *Science* **179**, 751—8.

Wheeler, H. (1975) 'Science's slippery slope', *The Center Magazine*, Santa Barbara, California, January/February, 1975, pp. 64—72.

Wiener, N. (1964) *God and Golem, Inc.*, MIT Press, Cambridge, Mass.

Ziman, J. (1960) 'Scientists: gentlemen or players?', *The Listener* **68**, 599—607.

The Marxist Vision of J.D. Bernal

The idea of 'progress', which more than any other single element defines modern European civilization, became associated with science only rather recently, in the eighteenth century. Before then all human affairs were conceived largely in religious terms, even science; and the rise of a purely secular idea of science, as the embodiment of progress, occurred in Britain only in Victorian times. The present century has seen repeated blows to the assumption of progress, though up to now it has proved remarkably hardy, always adapting its content to changing circumstances. My own dialogue with the ideas of J.D. Bernal, as the leading representative of a humanistic Marxist vision of science, has developed through my witnessing of the tragedy of his lifelong commitment to a faith in science as progress.

If we consider the fortunes of the idea of progress during this century, we are impressed by the frequency with which people could experience disillusion. 'Losing faith' is supposed to be a problem that afflicts the religious; but on reflection we see that belief in progress and science is also vulnerable in its own way. Much of the creative thinking about science in this century can be interpreted as a struggle to retain faith; and I shall use this idea to analyse J.D. Bernal and the significance of his work. The fact that Bernal was a Marxist and personally committed to the Communist movement serves here to emphasize the conflicts he experienced. Although the guilt suffered for association with Stalinism is different from that for the atomic bomb, at root they are manifestations of the same rationalistic optimism gone wrong.

I can view Bernal's endeavour with particular sympathy, coming a generation after him and starting early in life with a political commitment roughly where he was then. In my case it was relatively easy to disengage myself from the constraints of political commitment and of intellectual style in which he was eventually trapped. My private debate with Marxism began in my early teens, when I sensed a shallowness in the writings of Marxist philosophers who were clearly dedicated human beings and sometimes also distinguished scientists. It was further shaped by my political development then and into the

1950s, whereby I formed my own assessment of socialism as it was then being produced in Eastern and Central Europe. Somewhat later, when I came into the history of science, an urgent item on my personal agenda was to see what, if anything, could be done with Marxism as a source of insights. In this connection I studied Bernal's work, and even had the good fortune to meet him once for a private conversation.

I came to see Bernal as a tragic figure, one whose life had been so compromised and corrupted by the struggle to retain his faith that by the end he could not really make sense of it. But I had already discovered that that sort of 'failure' is not at all the same as life wasted. When occasions presented themselves, I welcomed the opportunity to work out my thoughts on Bernal. One such came in an invitation to contribute a chapter on Bernal as an historian of science, to a proposed commemorative volume. When this did not materialize, the essay was available for a special issue of the journal *Isis*, marking the fiftieth anniversary of the Second International Congress of the History of Science. On that occasion, a delegation of Soviet intellectuals thrust the Marxist interpretation of the history of science before the world, and thereby changed the lives of a number of brilliant young English scientists. As it appeared in *Isis*, my essay was followed by a critical appraisal by Richard S. Westfall.

The following year I had an invitation to lecture from the Science Policy Foundation, whose Director, Maurice Goldsmith, was a (not uncritical) follower of Bernal in his social vision of science. The proposed titled was 'The social functions of science'; and I adapted that to a review of Bernal's classic *The Social Function of Science*,[1] whose third edition had appeared just forty years previously. It was, I admit, a rather thin excuse for speaking of the past rather than of the present and future; but the lecture was well received, and points from the discussion were incorporated into the published text.

J.D. BERNAL AND THE SOCIAL FUNCTIONS OF SCIENCE

Regardless of its insufficiency as the solution to a personal quest, Bernal's historical writing provided edification and inspiration to readers in many lands. His direct influence on the construction of socialist policies, in Britain and elsewhere, came through his personal contacts and his essays on contemporary science. A collection of these was published as *The Social Function of Science*.[1] It went through three editions in the early war years in Britain, a testimony to its popularity and significance.

Re-reading it after many years was as exciting for me as its first discovery. In this book I could see a really distinguished mind at work. How effortlessly could Bernal identify, classify, analyse and solve problems! With a magnificent sweep, his surveys run through the history, sociology, political critique and the future of science. His was a coherent vision, one deriving from a great tradition of progresive thought about science which first matured in the mid-eighteenth century but was, I think, enriched and deepened by Bernal's own intense concern for science and democracy.

Reflecting on the forty years since that edition, we can see how in many ways his vision has been realized. We have had a planning of science, and also the applications of science to human welfare. These have truly relieved ordinary people of discomfort, pain, deprivation and squalor to a degree which might have been unimaginable to people who didn't have Bernal's optimistic faith in science. In Norbert Wiener's terms, science has made possible 'the human use of human beings'. We may, with Bernal, speak of the next phase, a 'scientific—technological revolution'. Through all problems and criticism, let us never lose sight of those positive achievements.

Beyond Bernal

Recently there has developed a sense that the problems are rather deeper than those which Bernal could see. Although he identified many infirmities and abuses of science in his time, there are new problems which one feels could not have been analysed in his framework of ideas. Perhaps the best example of such a problem is given by the accusation made by Lord Zuckerman, who was a younger contemporary of Bernal's.

Zuckerman has gone on public record accusing particular kinds of scientist of being 'the alchemists of the arms race'.[2] His model of the nuclear arms race is one where teams of scientists, not in universities but in defence establishments, dream up devices based on the application of known physical principles. Then, acting like denizens of bureaucracies anywhere, they try to aggrandize their own little empires by selling their devices in the normal bureaucratic way to their superiors.

But these devices happen to be not increased education provision or welfare programmes, but weapons of mass destruction. Thus, these scientists produce the impetus for weapons development. This impetus goes right through the system and results in politicians believing that there is a *need* on strategic grounds for such and such a weapons system to be available in a few years' time. The weapons system is then ordered and the scientists on the 'other side' then say with increasing plausibility 'Ah, this system that we are developing is just what *our* side will need to counter that system which *theirs* is now deploying!' So Zuckerman has blamed such scientists as being among the prime movers in the arms race. Zuckerman is a man who speaks from knowledge and experience, as a former governmental scientific adviser. Yet he feels that there is a deep moral corruption in some sectors of science, by which this particular phenomenon is produced.

There are other cases, which I will discuss in passing, where we have grounds for unease about the behaviour of scientists in the social side of their work, and in the management of the applications of science. I reflected on all of this as I looked at Bernal's book, and I had a wondrous feeling of puzzlement. Because as I read the book it was all so coherent, so convincing, so self-contained that it was impossible to see where he got it wrong. This was a striking phenomenon, of the type that can present the historian with the occasion for framing and studying a significant problem. For when a deep and coherent set of ideas about the future turn out to be inaccurate, the error will lie less in particular details than in something basic. So I found myself conducting an historical exercise just to see how Bernal could have missed those things which have now become quite crucial problems in the management of science and technology, given the depth of his understanding and his personal shrewdness about the society of science.

Bernal's vision, and its limitations, may thus provide us with clues for the development of an enriched appreciation of the social functions of science, appropriate to our time which are even more complex and problematic than his own.

A Way Forward

I try to do this by constructing some simple charts of the process of science; and by their successive elaboration to trace the development of insights into the problem. For the first version, we have the basic model for 'autonomous' science; from the research activity flow results leading to the True and also the Good.

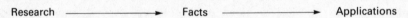

We enrich that fairly quickly by looking at the motivations for the research. We start off with curiosity driving the scientist. You can say that the scientist has curiosity, he does research, and gets some facts which satisfy his curiosity. Of course we know that one set of facts throws up more problems, leading to more curiosity, and the process iterates. On the other hand, there is social need. A perceived social need can stimulate research which produces the relevant facts; the facts then provide the basis for an application, and thus the need is satisfied. In diagrammatic form, this is shown as:

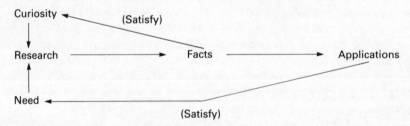

It was part of Bernal's greatness that he saw that science needs *both*

motivations. Pure curiosity leads to 'ivory tower' science, with only haphazard applications to human needs, while excessive concentration on applications can lead to the trivialization of research. But the combination of the two, first proclaimed by Francis Bacon in his call for experiments 'of fruit *and* of light', provides the stimuli for a balanced and healthy science.

We are already in a position to analyse how things can go wrong. First there is the old, simpler explanation of how things can go wrong: scientific curiosity is blocked by 'dogma and superstition'. The appreciation of this as a barrier goes back at least to the Enlightenment; it was recognized through the nineteenth century. In those times, the main agency of 'dogma and superstition' was the institutions of religion. In that epoch the struggle of science against the stifling influence of institutionalized religion was, as Bernal saw, part of the struggle for human freedom in general.

By the time we come to the twentieth century, when science is closely involved with industry, and where finally the applications of science are of great practical importance, a new kind of problem arises: the cycle leading to and from human needs can be interrupted, or distorted, or destroyed by secular institutions. I think Bernal was original in achieving this appreciation, for it requires a radical political and social viewpoint, unlike that of the traditional 'rationalists'. As Bernal pointed out, applications of science can be blocked or distorted by commercial greed. It may be that this was more obvious during the time of the Depression than now; Bernal quotes a case where large firms simply buy up patents so as to prevent that competition which, through innovation, would threaten their investments. This has been less obvious since the Second World War; but the distortion of technology into anti-social directions has been well documented.

Another 'abuse' of science is applications which are themselves deformed and evil; the worst is war. Instead of being an application serving social need, these harm and frustrate social need. War-science is little studied by sociologists of science, and not at all by philosophers of science. This uniform silence of the academics only heightens our appreciation of Bernal's clarity of vision. For such science, now estimated to absorb something like half the corps of 'scientists' world-wide, deforms and corrupts science and technology alike. Conducted in secret, largely beyond the control of legislatures, it distorts the direction of R & D, and (even in the USA) starves less glamorous sectors of science and of industry.

We are now in a position to enrich the original, somewhat simplistic analysis, and to depict the problems as Bernal saw them. I have tried to lay out the elements so that the obstacles to the completion of the cycles are clearly seen as external to science itself.

I should say that Bernal himself saw and described all such things as they occurred in his own time. His conclusion was simple: this is what you must expect when you have an unjust and inefficient social order kept going by greed and warfare. Change the social order, and you will be able to change science. And he indicated here and there in his book, writing in the mid-1930s, that there were signs that in the USSR, these problems were beginning to be solved. I comment on some of those examples below.

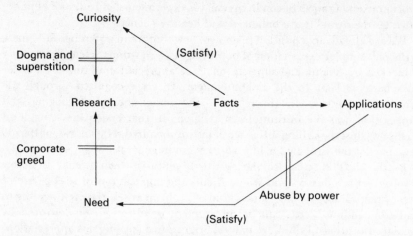

By using my model a little more, we can see ways in which the process can be further elaborated. I hope thereby to see the kinds of problems which Bernal himself would have appreciated, had he been living and working a bit later, when the evolution of our kind of science had proceeded further.

Unrealism

The first new problem I can point to is in fact quite old; it was discussed by Jonathan Swift in his Voyage to Laputa in *Gulliver's Travels*. For a long period of optimism it was forgotten by proponents of science. But now we find that one may identify a social need, call for research whose facts will provide relevant applications, get it done, and then discover that the research is ineffective. There is a promise which cannot be fulfilled; more than that there is a promise in which great investment has been made, which still cannot be fulfilled. Perhaps the easiest example to cite is the American war on cancer: Richard Nixon said, 'if Jack Kennedy can get a man to the moon, I can cure cancer'. He decided to throw money at the cancer problem as Kennedy had decided to throw money at the space problem. Kennedy had won—they got a man to the moon and back; but Nixon failed—cancer was not cured.

We may then think of all the many problems which the proponents of social science believed it could solve; one must remember that Bernal was part of the movement for the extension of the scientific method into all spheres of life. We can now see that in some way or other the characteristics of social problems, even problems of poverty and disease, do not easily yield to that style of attack, based on the physical sciences, which people confidently believed they would. My best example here is a very simple one; those who created the British

National Health Service imagined that it would be a self-reducing government department. Once we caught up with the arrears of ill-health, due to past poverty and neglect, there would be less and less need of a health service! It is fair to say that we did catch up in many respects, but the problem did not go away. We can say that we now have problems at a higher level of effectiveness for humanity: but expensive problems, there still are.

Ecology

Ineffective science leads at worst to disappointed hopes; but we must now face new kinds of problem resulting from the very power of science-based technology. It is possible to make applications of science which have very great effects indeed, some of which are intended but others quite unintended. And these latter may be adverse or even catastrophic.

I think it important that this category of *blunders* in science was not recognized by Bernal and indeed was recognized by hardly anyone of his generation. For this I quote from one paragraph of his book, on page 379, describing the dreams of a science-based society.

> There are large tasks still for mankind to undertake — the ultimate conquest of space, of disease, and death, most of all their own ways of living together. We get a kind of foretaste of this activity by the work of the Soviet Union in the conquest of the Arctic. With a fully organised world society such tasks could be pushed far further. It will no longer be a question of adapting man to the world but the world to man. For instance, the present Arctic with its wastes of tundra, glacier, and sea-ice is a legacy of the geological accident of the Ice Age. It will disappear in time, leaving the world a much pleasanter place, but there is no reason why man should not hasten the process. By an intelligent diversion of warm ocean-currents together with some means of colouring snow so that the sun could melt it, it might be possible to keep the Arctic ice-free for one summer, and that one year might tip the balance and permanently change the climate of the northern hemisphere.

It thus appears, with the wisdom of hindsight, that Bernal and his generation were utterly lacking in 'ecological' sensitivity. This is by no means a criticism of scientists in Bernal's field or of his political persuasion. Even those who were out there coping with the environment were possessed of a 'magic bullet' mentality, as Kenneth Mellanby recorded in *Pesticides and Pollution*: in the 1950s the applied entomologists expected that soon there would be poisons that would kill the nasty bugs and leave the nice ones.[3]

Thus Bernal and his contemporaries, and indeed his predecessors, were the victims of what we can now see as an illusion, from which we only now are recovering. That is, that the consciously benevolent applications of science cannot do harm. This assumption, or rather faith, has a long history, back indeed to the seventeenth century. We can see it in Francis Bacon, who really believed that magic and the idea of 'powers too great to be revealed' were not merely sinful, because you were getting something for nothing, but also implausible, because things do not really happen like that.[4] As the vision of the world (for European peoples) lost its quality of enchantment, it became common sense that science was really safe — effects could only be proportionate to their (material) causes. The concepts of a trigger reaction, of a non-linear, synergistic reaction, of a complex and unstable ecological *system*, were effectively absent from mainline scientific thinking, including that of Bernal, until well into the post-war period. In the absence of such concepts one cannot imagine blunders, and one cannot imagine some things with which we are now confronted as urgent problems of survival.

Ethics

Finally, I come to the third major problem which is not to be found in Bernal's book — the consequences of the human frailties of scientists. Bernal certainly knew of the imperfections of the community of science; and in the book he discusses various organizational problems with great shrewdness and insight. But as to the scientists themselves, he maintained a commitment of extraordinary intensity. The very last paragraph of the book (a *most* significant location) consists of a *credo* of Science as Communism. Thus

> Already we have in the practice of science the prototype for all human common action. The task which the scientists have undertaken — the understanding and control of nature and of man himself — is merely the conscious expression of the task of human society. The methods by which this task is attempted, however imperfectly they are realized, are the methods by which humanity is most likely to secure its own future. In its endeavour, science is communism. In science men have learned consciously to subordinate themselves to a common purpose without losing the individuality of their achievements. Each one knows that his work depends on that of his predecessors and colleagues, and that it can only reach its fruition through the work of his successors. In science men collaborate not because they are forced to by superior authority or because they blindly follow some chosen leader, but because they realize that only in this willing collaboration can each man find his goal. Not orders, but advice, determines action. Each man knows that only by advice, honestly and disinterestedly given, can his work succeed, because such advice expresses as near as may be the inexorable logic of the material world, stubborn fact. Facts cannot be forced to our desires, and freedom comes by admitting this necessity and not by pretending to ignore it.

These are things that have been learned painfully and incompletely in the pursuit of science. Only in the wider tasks of humanity will their full use be found.

So science is the model of the classless society, and scientists themselves are somehow purified by the activity of research. Here again, Bernal follows the prophetic vision of Francis Bacon very closely. Bacon himself had a Utopian vision of what could be done by men of science. His theory for it was cast in theological terms, although he did appreciate its social aspect sufficiently to write the prophetic *New Atlantis*. With Bernal the vision was cast in secular terms, but still motivated by the highest idealism.

Francis Bacon had already worried about the problem of avoiding the production of evil by the powers of science. His own solution to the problem was, in my paraphrase, 'it needs good men to do good science'; of course this is a pun on the word 'good'. For Bacon had seen how easy it is to do rotten, shoddy or selfish scholarship or research. He deduced that it requires people of a superior moral stature even to start effective work; and then by that very activity they would be further purified.[5]

Bernal shared this idealistic ethical vision. He has many deep and penetrating discussions of the organization of science, its ailments, how they can be cured. He said very shrewd and penetrating things about democracy and authority in laboratories; but still he was basically quite idealistic about the society of science.

One confirming clue to this idealism may be seen in the contemporary works of the sociologist Robert K. Merton. In his classic early papers on science, he included a 'norm' of 'communism' (or alternatively 'communalism'), which enjoined the free sharing of results. Much later Merton came to recognize, and to grapple with, the social and ethical problems resulting from the quite real relations of property that are embodied in scientific results. Such a 'property' is rather subtle, and can be overlooked by someone who is not desirous of the vulgar rewards of fame and power. But the many disputes over priority and authorship that have disfigured the life of science show that even the greatest of scientists are not immune to such considerations.

In fact, it is easy and natural to draw parallels between the individualistic conception of the achievement of new, atomic 'facts' and the capitalist social order in which such a view took root in early modern Europe. The property inhering in an authenticated scientific result is more subtle than real-estate but it is equally profitable. It draws 'rent' through the prestige derived from citations. Bernal's ignoring of this (now obvious) aspect of science under capitalism seems to reflect a personal determination to imagine science as the unconditioned agent that will yield the Truth of nature and the Good for mankind.

Now that we are aware of the property relation, which conditions and partly motivates the work of individual scientists, we can see how the community of science necessarily reflects (though it does *not* precisely copy) the structures of property and power of the wider society in which it is embedded. Bernal's vision of an essentially classless, communistic science, only waiting for society to catch up with it for its full potential to be realized, must be recognized as rather more Utopian than Marxist in its socialism.

Institutionalized Conflicts

Thus our third new problem, after ineffective research and blundering technology, is the imperfections in the social institution of science. How are they realized? I cannot give an analysis here; a few examples must suffice. One has already been shown — Lord Zuckerman's analysis of the role of scientists as promoters of the nuclear arms race. Some might object that such people, working in secret on technology, rather than the acquisition of new knowledge, are not really 'scientists'. This becomes a matter of definition; but those who would restrict the honorific term to those who pursue old-fashioned independent, inapplicable research are really more in the spirit of Polanyi than of Bernal.

Another manifestation of the problem (which I owe to Sir Alex King's mention in the discussion after the original lecture) is 'bureaucracy'. Large-scale projects require organizations that are also large-scale, but which are in addition complex and which possess a tendency to take on a life of their own. Those who have never experienced this phenomenon may find it hard to imagine how people can completely lose sight of the original 'mission' of an institution, concentrating solely on immediate problems of position, prestige and patronage. But it happens, with deadly regularity; and institutions devoted to 'research' are as susceptible as any other. Lack of awareness of this problem has been responsible for the disappointment of very many hopes in the post-war period, from those of a new international order in science, to those of a new social order in particular countries.

Finally, I mentioned problems of 'quality control' in science and technology, again problems which might have been inconceivable as *systematic* problems to a dedicated scientist of Bernal's generation. This is a large topic, which I discussed, perhaps prematurely, in my book of 1971.[6] Now we see the sprinkling of cases, which may be more notorious than significant, of outright fraud in science. More significant for me at present are analogous problems in technology. To cite only one salient example: we should ponder the significance of the fact that it took a *student* to discover that the niobium used as an alloy in the steel of PWR pressure-vessels has such intense and long-lasting radiation that the decommissioning of such reactors will be enormously more difficult and expensive than previously assumed.[7] Where were the scientific experts who should have checked on such a possibility during the previous decades? Working for a bureaucracy that preferred not to know, is the answer.

Conclusion

We can now make the final full elaboration of the earlier model. It is relatively easy to locate 'ineffective research' and 'blundering applications'. But 'imperfect institutions' have such pervasive effects, that we must simply put them somewhere as a reminder.

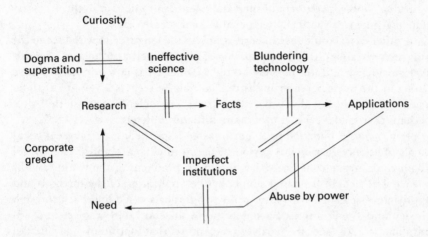

Applying the spirit of Bernal himself, it is possible to explain the emergence of such new problems by the changes in science itself, and we must never forget that they appear alongside the brilliant successes of science and its applications. In my own book I remarked on the ways that science has become capital-intensive, so that decisions on research represent an investment of resources rather than a preference by a lone craftsman. Consequent to this, the community changes to large, hierarchically organized laboratories; and with the interpenetration of science and industry, the 'society' of science cannot survive as an uncontaminated haven of non-material values.

But I would not like to leave the matter there, as if it could be simply 'reduced' to a 'material' base. I think attitudes and commitments are important too. Among those which I think made science particularly vulnerable to the stresses and temptations of post-war 'big science' was an optimism, bordering on hubris, concerning the powers of the applications of science for human benefit. But there was another belief, less obvious but equally fundamental, with which I shall conclude.

This faith is that the community of science cannot get things seriously wrong. Of course individual research is partly speculative and always corrigible. Of course the march of progress renders old theories obsolete. But—and this was the working experience of academic scientists—all change was *progressive*; errors and mistakes were winnowed out by honest criticism, and new theories generally include and explain their predecessors. The idea that science could collectively get something wrong for a long enough period for it to be significant simply lay outside Bernal's framework of possibilities.

Of course it becomes a matter of degree; if blunders in technology are revealed, by whatever means, within one or two decades, does not that prove the self-correcting nature of the scientific process? In a sense, yes. But for practical purposes, the time-lag (increased by the bureaucratization of science) may be uncomfortably long. It may be long either in the lifespan of an individual whose investment of time and talent is nullified, or in the necessary response-time to a maturing technical or ecological crisis.

In either case, confidence in corrections 'in the long run' may reduce to the only such certainty, which is the ending of life. The self-assurance of scientists that outsiders could not possibly be right, which (it is now admitted) was so strong in the nuclear power industry, can now be seen as a variety of pride. Science was traditionally believed to provide a defence against this vice; perhaps that made its onset even more difficult to detect.

Bernal's *Social Function of Science* was perhaps the last of the great testaments of science in which a person of broad intelligence and philosophical depth could argue coherently that the social problems of the world, and of science itself, could be solved simply by the application of the methods and approach of science. With him, a line of prophets extending back through Huxley and Condorcet to Bacon, came to an end. With respect and admiration, we re-read it, partly to recapture that optimism and human commitment, and also to gain clues as to how our own times present challenges which require new insights on fundamentals. As a scientist, Bernal would, I am sure, have considered this too as progress.

J.D. BERNAL'S HISTORY OF SCIENCE

J.D. Bernal was one of that small group of brilliant British radical scientists whose vision of a Marxist science of society, based partly on a new history of science, was shaped by the Soviet contribution of 1931. The most significant products of his vision were the monumental *Science in History* and the more specialized *Science and Industry in the Nineteenth Century*.[9] The latter work is a thoughtful and careful exploratory essay, almost as by a scholar for scholars. The broad sweep of *Science in History* and its continuing popularity, wide diffusion, and ideological significance make it the work by which Bernal's Marxist endeavour is to be assessed. I shall concentrate on it here.

Bernal was fortunate not only in having an encyclopaedic mind, but also in living in a social milieu that did not automatically relegate those who exercised broad interests outside research to the status of eccentrics. The achievement of *Science in History* is not at all reduced, but is better understood, when we recall the analogous works by J.B.S. Haldane, Lancelot Hogben and Joseph

Needham.[10] We can look on Bernal and his colleagues as late participants in a tradition of 'philosophy of nature', before specialization and fragmentation had finally conquered science, leaving only 'popularization' as the link between reflective research scientists and the lay public.

Science in History may be analysed for its contribution to the history of science and used as evidence for the evolution of Bernal's thinking on basic problems. My conclusion is that the book has made a disappointingly small contribution to the history of science; that this is because while essentially it was motivated by post-war problems, it attempted pre-war solutions; and that Bernal's historical work suffered particularly from its origins in the Cold War period, when even the ecumenical Joseph Needham was isolated and strident. Bernal's lack of success is a reminder that the theoretical maturing required for an effective Marxist analysis of science in modern societies is even now a hope rather than an achievement. This negative assessment is not at all a personal judgement on Bernal or on the commitment that produced his historical work. It could be argued that every great thinker fails, in part, on her or his life's project; but the incidental achievements are a permanent enrichment for humankind.

By Bernal's account in the preface to the book, the occasion of its composition was an invitation to give a series of lectures in 1948. Before then his historical concerns, though long-standing, had been insufficiently urgent to go beyond private notes or the sort of brief synoptic account that appeared in his 1939 *Social Function of Science*. When *Science in History* was finally complete, he admitted (perhaps too modestly): 'It is only now that I am beginning to understand what are the problems of the place of science in history'.[11] Although (as I shall argue later) the work was conceptually and politically obsolescent by the time it appeared, its magnificent scope and coherent outlook yielded an excellent publication career. It ran through four editions in England alone, between 1955 and 1969, as well as through two in the United States. There were translations into some fourteen foreign languages, covering all the socialist countries and all major culture areas. By a strange irony, the last edition came out in four illustrated paperback volumes, marketed in the 1970s in England and the United States to a readership to whom Bernal's commitments and concern must have been utterly remote.[12]

Science in History is really two books in one binding. The first five parts take the story from the Paleolithic to the Victorian age. This historical material was little altered through successive editions, though a series of notes at the back of the third edition (the only one with substantial revisions) record Bernal's reactions to new discoveries and to critical reviews. The massive sixth part, comprising nearly half the bulk of the book, deals with 'science in our time'. It draws mainly on Bernal's own experience, scientific and political, and it was extensively reworked, for scientific and political reasons, between editions. At first a cold-war tract in praise of socialism and its works, it later became a quite balanced essay in socialist apologetics. The concluding seventh part was allowed to remain substantially intact from its first version.

Professional historians of science, even those who disagreed deeply with Bernal, admired his daring and his vision in attempting to write a global and synthetic history.[13] But they were wrong to compare his work to their own rather limited excursions in synthesis. The model for Bernal was not that of the specialist historians, who at their best could tell only the history of progress of scientific ideas. Rather, the tradition of histories of the progress of knowledge, arts and culture, starting with Condorcet and extending to H.W. van Loon and H.G. Wells, should be seen as the source and inspiration for Bernal's work.[14] Themes, assumptions and even materials were available for him there, particularly in the relation of intellectual and cultural progress to its social and material context. And he could make a significant enrichment to the theoretical setting of these works through his own version of Marxism. It was not only that he could provide a plausible real cause for progress more substantial than an instinct for achieving the Enlightenment values of reason and liberty. With his scheme he could offer a certain measure of historical imagination by seeing the past as more than a story of gradually decreasing error and negativity. He assumed that progress depends on the needs of a ruling class, which at the beginning of its rule desires to improve human knowledge and power, becoming stagnant and reactionary only towards the end. Thus even the bourgeoisie is not totally or simply bad; rather it has outlived its historical usefulness. In this mode of explanation, Bernal could assert that ancient priesthoods promoted magic rather than rational enquiry 'when the early temple establishment decayed, and the priests became increasingly dependent on the offerings of the faithful'.[15]

Bernal's explanatory framework, which looked beyond the content of scientific ideas to the broader interests of relevant producers and consumers of those ideas, helps explain the lack of contact between him and established historians of science. The latter generally dealt with 'scientific ideas', at their best in a broad and sympathetic way (as did Charles Singer and W.P.D. Wightman), at their worst in a narrow, dogmatic or precious way (as did Alexandre Koyré).[16] The bad influence of Koyré should not be underestimated. In his 'idealist' reinterpretation of Galileo, he denied Galileo not merely a social context but even his experiments! When he achieved eminence in America, he insisted on a totally superficial interpretation of the scientific revolution as a choice between particular styles of geometrical and mechanical thought.[17] Anything suggestive of social influences on science or scientists Koyré dismissed as 'Marxist'.[18] Thus a generation of young historians of science, who might well have been receptive to Bernal's 'externalist' approach if not to his conclusions, was kept firmly in abstracted intellectual history.

Were that the whole story one could view, and judge, *Science in History* as a production in a great tradition of amateur philosophical popularization, related only indirectly to the narrow, frequently pedantic professional research in the field. But the weakness, indeed the tragedy of the work, lies in Bernal's neglect of post-war Marxist thought in the history of science, which was then being developed by a lively group including S.F.Mason.[19] The lack of contact between Bernal and these people poses an important problem and in itself provides a clue to the character of *Science in History*, for one of the main functions of the book, whether or not consciously intended by the author, was to reinforce the faith of those who were already committed to a Marxist interpretation of the world. They saw the majestic sweep of the survey, combined with a multitude of convincing and detailed facts and further enhanced by the scientific eminence of the author. All this could provide a powerful argument in support of a commitment to Marxism as the truly scientific philosophy of our age. It really works: here is human history explained in Marxist terms. In this respect the achievement of *Science in History* is genuine. A look at one later work in a non-Marxist rationalist tradition, *The Ascent of Man* by Jacob Bronowski, shows how much more real explanation can be accomplished within a Marxist perspective.[20] But for those who were already questioning the adequacy of pre-war Marxism (as I was in the 1960s), the book was not particularly inspiring or reassuring.

The historical section of the book (as opposed to the political Part VI) had three quite discrete divisions, with very different problems and style. The earlier part of the history, before the Renaissance, moves rapidly and with a sure touch through the standard material. While convinced of the ultimately decisive role of the economic foundation and equally certain of the distinction between real science and false paths to knowing, Bernal is by no means mechanistic or unimaginative in his interpretations. He even spares Christianity some of the blame assigned to it by Gibbon. He sees the Decline as a cyclical process, reflecting the inability of classical civilization to solve the contradictions basic to its characteristic social relations of production. In all this section one sees Bernal's mind performing at its best: reworking a mass of material into a synthesis that is plausible and coherent. Its only failing is that it solves somewhat too much, leaving nothing for puzzlement and wonder, in all that vast spectacle of growth and decline. But it is a matter of taste whether or not 'the Greek miracle' should be left partly as such, or totally reduced to natural causes; and Bernal's audience would certainly prefer historical science to mystery.

Jumping over to the other successful sections, we can admire Bernal's reviews of the technical aspects of contemporary science. It is well to remember that his was not merely an encyclopaedic intellect; his profound achievement in applying physical methods to the elucidation of living systems required scientific insight of a rare order. So in this section we have surveys of twentieth century science that should become historical sources in their own right. His account of physics is noteworthy in this respect.

The weaknesses of Bernal's approach become most apparent in the middle part of the story: the creation of modern European science from the sixteenth century onwards. In broad outline his story is quite plausible. First, it was nascent capitalism in the later Middle Ages that enabled the developing productive forces (including science) to escape the stagnation suffered previously in the Chinese and the Islamic cultures. Then there were the three distinct phases, terminating in 1540, 1650, 1690, which he calls Renaissance, Wars of Religion, and Restoration. These involved, respectively, progress in 'uses of science', the 'first great triumphs of the new observational, experimental approach', and their consolidation after 'the overthrow of the feudal–classical theories in the previous hundred years'. As the developments described in the narrative move further from the sphere of production more exclusively into that of thought, the plausibility of the reduction to the economic foundation weakens drastically. Several crucial problems are glossed over: the role of a specifically capitalist class in fostering science; the use of science and scientists as agents of social oppression; and the causes of the 'disenchantment' of the world of Nature.

Bernal's neglect of the first issue, the support given science by a specifically capitalist class, derives from his neglect of political aspects of power in favour of its economic aspects, a neglect shared by traditional Marxist historians. Bernal (always sensitive to complexity and paradox) remarks at the beginning of his discussion of the middle period that it has no convenient name; and so he labels it with the surprisingly un-Marxist 'Wars of Religion'. He does not mention that political historians have discussed a phenomenon of absolutism, where the state, whose power was then concentrated in the crown, asserted itself against other institutions. Because of their preference for economic at the expense of political explanations, Marxists have tended to search for the relations of 'science' with 'the bourgeoisie' rather than with the state. But the latter relations were vital, first in France and then in Central and Eastern Europe, and available in the latter case for adaptation to the needs of socialism. 'Capitalist' and 'statist' post-feudal social contexts each had their contribution to make. Evidence for the importance of the latter is provided by these words of Galileo:

> It is impossible to obtain wages from a republic, however splendid and generous it may be, without having duties attached. For to have anything from the public one must satisfy the public and not any one individual; and so long as I am capable of lecturing and serving, no one in the republic can exempt me from duty while I receive pay. In brief, I can hope to enjoy these benefits only from an absolute ruler.[21]

Thus he decided to return to ducal Florence from republican Venice, in spite of the benefits and security he enjoyed there.

There is no explicit sign that Bernal sensed how inadequate the classical (economic rather than political) Marxist framework was on this period. Perhaps quite unself-consciously he used a crucial term with damaging equivocation, to enable his essential point to be stated: 'The new experimental philosophers, or scientists as we would now call them, ... appeared more as individual members of the new bourgeoisie, largely lawyers . . .; doctors . . .; a few minor nobles . . .; churchmen . . . and even one or two brilliant recruits from the lower orders . . .'.[22] To be sure such people belonged to cities; but we must remark that none were in roles related to the bourgeoisie as defined by Marx. I do not mean to criticize Bernal personally for this gap at the centre of his story, but rather to show how here his Marxist framework does not carry him through, either to fruitful solutions or even to interesting problems.

On the second problem, science as a means of oppression, the Marxist tradition at least allows for its recognition, while for the rationalists it is a pure embarrassment. The genocidal horrors practised by European imperialism on its conquered lands (what we now call the Third World), involving the technologies of warfare, of primary-products exploitation and of various addictive poisons, did not interest Bernal greatly. Closer to home, the relation of Paracelsian alchemy to radical politics was already becoming familiar to Marxist historians of the English Civil War period. But Bernal did not consider these contradictions within a class-linked natural science, as well as the incidental costs of the advance of a class in its 'progressive' phase, to be historically significant once the ultimate goal has been fixed. The result of this approach is that Bernal's history is externalist-whig, differing only in detail from the internalist-whig style of the historians of science dominant in his time.

Finally, the really big problem of the seventeenth century is the exceptionally rapid rate then of the 'disenchantment' of nature. As a whole, this was a complex process extending through many centuries of European history. If one's unit of time is a quarter millennium, then it is clear that 'rationality' and 'capitalism' rise simultaneously. But on a finer scale the correlations become very difficult to maintain. Although he had no doubts that the ancient pseudo-sciences were nonsense, Bernal was not uncharitable toward them. He even recognized, in connection with Paracelsus, that '. . . owing to the intrinsic complexity of chemistry, it was this intuitive and mythical approach rather than the rational mechanical one that was to be most successful in advancing chemistry until its revolution in the eighteenth century'. This bold statement puts the scientific revolution in an unusual perspective. For if chemistry was so complex, then *a fortiori* so would be biology, medicine, and most of craft production. Hence we may say that for the greater part of science as it affected life, the 'mechanical' approach was as counter-intuitive as the supposed motions of the earth. Also, it was largely unsuccessful; as Bernal remarks, 'In fact, the only parts of the external world where their methods succeeded were those already cultivated by the Greeks.'[23]

The rise of the 'scientific' world view in the seventeenth century was therefore *not* a reflection on the successful practice of 'disenchanted' science. Rather, even by Bernal's account it would seem to be something that was, in Lenin's phrase, *von Aussen hineingetragenes*. Perhaps it came from the rise of the bourgeoisie and its world view (on which Max Scheler and Christopher Caudwell speculated[24]), but it is doubtful whether the appropriate sort of bourgeoisie was then rising with sufficient strength to do the job. Further, there is the awkward fact that the progressive 'corpuscular' philosophy was introduced to Protestant bourgeois England as an import from Catholic Absolutist France by such Royalist emigrés as Walter Charlton and Thomas Hobbes. Thus neither 'scientists' nor 'bourgeois' provide the basis for an adequate 'rational' explanation of the diffusion of the scientific world view as it actually happened in the seventeenth century. This has remained a puzzle and a source of contention among historians to this day; but it passed unrecognized by Bernal in spite of his sharp perception of particular points.

For a rationalist history of science written in the heroic 1930s, such criticisms as these would have been quite inappropriate. Although Hessen and his colleagues in 1931 were by our standards naive and simplistic, they were pioneers, throwing speculative bridges across the gap between 'science' and 'society'. But by the 1950s there had been some development. The surge of left-wing and Marxist thinking in the wartime and early post-war period produced a few people seriously concerned with the social history of science. They tended to be isolated both from their technocratic comrades of the Old Left and (later) from the mainly Leavisite radicals of the New Left; both these were uncritical about science, the former in accepting it, the latter in rejecting it. However, the new Marxist scholars were there, and a monument to their achievement is S.F. Mason's *Main Currents of Scientific Thought.* Had its rich insights been cultivated and developed, our critical understanding of the past and the present of science would have been greatly accelerated. In particular, I believe that the Leeds group of scholars in the 1960s could have made an even more powerful synthesis of the intellectual and social aspects of seventeenth century English natural philosophy. But it was not to be. Mason and Lilley were academically isolated, and neglected by Bernal, whose sources outside the pre-war Marxists seemed to be the leading academic historians. Only by accepting the assessments of the latter group could he state the paradox (needless because it was incorrect) that the scientific innovators 'from Copernicus to Newton, were the most conservative in their religious and philosophical outlook'.[25]

In some respects this is a cautionary tale. Bernal was not the first, nor the last, of those who when they eventually discover the unravelled perplexities of their present situation turn to past history for the answer. Rarely do they reflect that history, though capable of fruitful study by amateurs, is nonetheless a discipline requiring respect. There, as anywhere else, enquiry is not so much discovering facts as solving problems. And if the problem is neither clearly defined initially nor encouraged to grow in dialogue with the evidence, the result will be flat. This seems to have been the case with Bernal, in spite of all the qualities of *Science in History* that enabled it to compete for a popular audience with the best of the professional historians' work. One sign of his failure to grow as a historian is his dropping of historical studies once the first edition of the book was complete. The later editions show only slight evidence of continued interest in the subject: very occasional textual changes, and the notes on scattered topics added at the end. The contrast with the material on contemporary society, almost entirely rewritten, is striking.

In fact Bernal did not stop reflecting or trying new approaches to the problems of science. From the history of science he turned to 'the science of science'. Given his later awareness of the virtual absence of worthwhile social science in the socialist countries and his generally low opinion of its state under capitalism,[26] this would seem to be a rather weak reed to clutch. It is as if Natural Science, previously the great motor of progress, subject only to the needs of the Developing Forces of Production, were now to be guided into its final consummation of the Scientific–Technological Revolution by a few practitioners of the most mechanically materialist, ideologically blind, statistical social science. This is a far cry from the problem-situation that motivated the original work on the book: 'the troubles of the times, and the inescapable connection between them and the advance of science' and the task 'to release the new forces of science for welfare rather than destruction . . .'.[27]

The full story of the evolution of Bernal's practical and philosophical thought in the post-war period is not my concern here. In my review of the fourth (illustrated) edition, I remarked that Bernal then had apparently less hope for solving mankind's problems and also less faith in the socialist nations.[28] I may speculate that until the threat of nuclear annihilation became real (that is, some time *after* Hiroshima) Bernal could see no *essential* problem in the advance of science, which he had always believed would lead by logical necessity both to material plenty and to social rationality. His reflections on the new problems of science were conditioned by the sharp polarization of politics in the early 1950s; for his accounts of contemporary science he could not afford the luxury of objectivity or even of public fraternal criticism. Perhaps even the ongoing English Marxist speculations about the political history of science, however orthodox their authors, were also fraught with dangers for Bernal as the leading Western spokesman for an embattled socialist camp.

All these particular circumstances may have done no more than give precise shape to Bernal's endeavours. Joseph Needham could move through his vast encyclopaedic study towards a statement of his own combination of radicalism and mysticism, for that is what he had believed in all along. Bernal started as a prophet of a disenchanted magic, where men's reason would accomplish all imaginable good things.[29] In the 1930s his faith in reason was enriched by a keen social conscience, and he turned to history only when the realization of his dreams seemed threatened, following the Second World War. He then slowly learned that for all its intrinsic interest, history spoke only in riddles: the past presented paradoxes wherever it was closely scrutinized, and it also offered little reassurance or guidance for the novel problems of the present. So Bernal moved on, or back, to a technocratic style of approach, in the 'science of science'.

Since Bernal's time there has arisen in the West a new current of social and institutional history of science, now growing rapidly in strength and sophistication. It would be a kind tribute to Bernal's memory to describe it as a development from his work, but unfortunately that would be true only in a minor part. For the new studies of this kind are far from Marxist in their orientation, but rather partake of the new, tough, demystifying attitude to science. At one main centre, Pennsylvania, the focus is on institutional history and power politics; at another, Edinburgh, it is on the spuriousness of 'objectivity' and on 'the strength of social interests'. My appreciation of Marxism, in particular dialectical materialism, is enhanced by study of these newer works. For I believe that Marxism could provide a considerable enrichment to the present practice of social history. However, professedly Marxist history of science is now practised in the West on a very small scale. The Roses' social history of modern science, *Science and Society*, came at the end to confront the contradiction of the evils created by the science of today. One of the authors, while still supporting Marxist materialism against the subjectivists and mystics, has moved to a position that would have stunned Bernal: she feels that scientific research may now be too tainted to be an honest occupation.[30]

This consideration of Bernal may seem an epitaph on his endeavour, reducing it to error and futility. But history, unlike Bernal's sort of science, has a meaningful place for tragedy.[31] Another way of describing the seventeenth century would show how the great prophets and philosophers of the age, including Bacon, Galileo, Descartes, Harvey and Newton, ended their careers with the failure of their life's project—and some in deep disillusion as well. Bernal's historical work, with all the limits resulting from its circumstances, has a touch of greatness about it. Should Marxist scholarship become revitalized at some future time, a grateful and critical appreciation of that work will be an important foundation for further progress.

The first part of this chapter, 'J.D. Bernal and the social functions of science', was adapted from an essay first published under the title 'The social functions of science: A commemoration of J.D. Bernal's vision', *Science and Public Policy*, October 1982. The second part of the chapter, 'J.D. Bernal's history of science', was first published under the title 'Bernal's Marxist version of history', *ISIS* 1981, **72**, 393–402.

References

1. J.D. Bernal, *The Social Function of Science* (3rd ed., London: Routledge, 1942).
2. Zuckerman, Lord, *Nuclear Illusion and Reality* (London: Viking, 1982).
3. Mellanby, Kenneth, *Pesticides and Pollution* (London: Collins, 1967), p. 122.
4. Bacon, Francis, *De augmentis scientiarum*, 1620, trans. in *Works* (Ed. Ellis and Spedding), Vol. IV, Bk 3, Ch. 5, p. 367–368.
5. J.R. Ravetz, 'Francis Bacon and the reform of philosophy', 1972, see this volume.
6. J.R. Ravetz, 'Quality control in science', *Scientific Knowledge and Its Social Problems* (Oxford University Press, 1971), Ch. 10.
7. Norman, Colin, 'A long term problem for the nuclear industry. Worn-out

reactors may remain radioactive too long to entomb. A student discovered what the experts missed', *Science*, 1982, **215**, 376–379.

8. N.I. Bukharin, *et al.* (1931) *Science at the Cross Roads: Papers Presented to the International Congress of the History of Science and Technology held in London, June 29 to July 3, 1931, by the Delegates of the USSR* (London: Kniga, 1931; 2nd ed. London: Frank Cass, 1971).

9. J.D. Bernal, *Science in History* (London: Watts, 1954); J.D. Bernal, *Science and Industry in the Nineteenth Century* (London: Routledge & Kegan Paul, 1953).

10. See G. Werskey, *The Visible College* (London: Allen Lane, 1978).

11. Bernal, *Science in History* (1954), p. vii.

12. 2nd and 3rd eds: London: Watts, 1957, 1965. Paperback (4th) ed: London: Watts/Penguin, 1969; Cambridge, Mass.: MIT Press, 1971.

13. L. Pearce Williams, review of *Science in History*, *Isis*, 1957, **48**, 471–473.

14. Condorcet, *Esquisse d'un tableau historique des progrès de l'esprit humain* (Paris, 1794); H.W. van Loon, *The Story of Mankind* (London: Harrap, 1922; with 27 reprints to 1961); H.G. Wells, *The Outline of History, Being a Plain History of Life and Mankind* (London, 1920).

15. Bernal, *Science in History*, p. 90.

16. Charles Singer, *A Short History of Science* (Oxford Univ. Press, 1941); W.P.D. Wightman, *The Growth of Scientific Ideas* (Edinburgh/London: Oliver and Boyd, 1950).

17. A. Koyré, 'Galileo and Plato', *Journal of the History of Ideas*, 1943, 4, 400–428.

18. Henry Guerlac, 'Some historical assumptions about the history of science', in A.C. Crombie, ed., *Scientific Change* (London: Heinemann, 1963), pp. 797–812, on p. 810.

19. S. Lilley, *Men, Machines and History* (London: Cobbett Press, 1948); S.F. Mason, *A History of the Sciences: Main Currents of Scientific Thought* (London: Routledge & Kegan Paul, 1953).

20. Jacob Bronowski, *The Ascent of Man* (London: BBC, 1974).

21. Galileo (letter of 1610) quoted in Stillman Drake, *Discoveries and Opinions of Galileo* (New York: Doubleday, 1957), p. 65.

22. Bernal, *Science in History*, pp. 287–288.

23. *Ibid.*, pp. 273, 350.

24. Christopher Caudwell, *The Crisis in Physics* (London: John Lane, 1939), Ch. 2, 'The world as machine'.

25. Bernal, *Science in History* (1965), p. 350 (not in 1st ed.).

26. *Ibid.*, pp. 870–872, 833–834, 840–842.

27. Bernal, *Science in History* (1954), p. vii.

28. J. R. Ravetz, rev. of *Science in History* (1971), *Technology and Culture*, 1972, **13**, 664–666.

29. J.D. Bernal, *The World, The Flesh and the Devil* (1st ed. 1929; London: Cape, 1970); see the discussion in Brian Easlea, *Liberation and the Aims of Science* (London: Chatto and Windus, 1973).

30. Hilary and Steven Rose, *Science and Society* (London: Penguin, 1969); Hilary Rose, 'Hyper-reflexivity: A new danger for the counter-movements', in Helga Nowotny and Hilary Rose, *Counter-movements in the Sciences* (Dordrecht: D. Reidel, 1979).

31. J.R. Ravetz, 'Tragedy in the history of science', in Mikuláš Teich and Robert Young, *Changing Perspectives in the History of Science* (London: Heinemann, 1975).

3
A NEW AWARENESS

As the realities of science have changed, so our awareness struggles to keep pace. Some spokesmen for science try to pretend, or even to hope, that a bit more 'public understanding' will bring back some bygone times of serene prosperity. Angry young men among scholars are intent on demystifying all pretensions of science to be anything other than just another game, or business. A public, becoming increasingly concerned about threats to their well-being, and even more that of their children, repeatedly sees official experts exposed on television as determined to reassure, at all costs. All this is a long way away from the traditional image of science as being a sort of 'fountain of facts', to which all could come to collect what they needed for the solution of their problems. In my earlier book I reviewed all these problems as they appeared at that time, and then devoted myself to an analysis of the production of scientific knowledge of the traditional sort. Without such a basis, I felt, I could not make an effective systematic analysis of what happens to science when it is deprived of its traditional intellectual structures and political protection. The essays in this section represent my attempts to formulate a new understanding; at present they are all partial insights, for the reality is complex and ever-changing. But together they provide some elements which will necessarily be incorporated into any new synthesis.

The first essay here records my solving of an intellectual problem that had been with me since my undergraduate days. It concerns the philosophy of science, which in spite of its academic character is quite influential as an authoritative source for more popular conceptions of science. When I studied this as an undergraduate, it struck me that what was being described had little relation to 'science' as I was learning or understanding it. Yet the authors were clearly intelligent men, committed to some sort of understanding and truth. But what sort? Years later, through my friendship with the late Imre Lakatos, I came to renew the question, and then discovered the answer. Basically, these philosophers (those of the 'logical positivist' school, and their critics such as Popper) were not so much concerned with what working scientists do, as with Science as a symbol of the True and with it the Good. The peculiarities of their doctrines, and the character of their debates, then began to come clear. In those terms I could understand the great debates in philosophy of science of the 1960s, particularly the roles of Lakatos and Feyerabend; in them the ideological commitment was explicit. I could then develop the argument through successive drafts of an essay. But for a long time the philosophy of Thomas Kuhn withstood my analysis; and this was a severe weakness since his work has been so influential. But when I had the opportunity to lecture at length on this history, at Fudan University (Shanghai) and Wuhan University, in China, the final pieces of the puzzle fitted together.

More recently my focus has moved from scientists and science to the society in which they function; and the issues of commitment, and success and failure are also present on this larger scale. In this case the easiest way into the problem is through quality control. In the years since the publication of my book, this has become recognized as a serious problem, both in science and technology. In the former case, there are the well-known scandals of plagiarism, and worse, of cover-up by sponsoring institutions, mainly in the USA. For the latter, there is the Japanese challenge; through their focus on industrial quality control, they have taken the lead, now approaching a commanding position, in a wide range of industries. Is there something about modern Western societies that inhibits the maintenance of quality control? If so, the cyclical theories of rise and decline of civilizations, first articulated by the Muslim historian Ibn Khaldun, may become relevant; then it was luxurious living among the élite classes that led to a decline in national vigour; now the mild pleasures of consumerism are available to most, and serve as a model to all. Some might wish to interpret this essay as 'conservative', advocating the reversal of a trend which in America is described as going from the work ethic to the shirk ethic. But I do not think the trend is so simple, and less that it can be simply reversed. I am concerned to observe and analyse it, so that whatever is done about it is not the sort of reaction that only makes things worse.

The pleasures of consumerism may be mild in comparison to those of the extravagant luxuries of the rich of yesteryear; but there are now so many consumers that their combined impact on the planet threatens us all. Participating in a conference on the Gaia Hypothesis provided me with the occasion to reflect on how our science-based powers of destruction affect our approach to the traditional questions of the philosophy of science, or indeed of philosophy in general. Issues that have hitherto been explored mainly through the medium of philosophical science fiction are now appropriate for serious analysis. What emerged clearly for me was that not merely man's relationship with nature is now in question (are we some sort of pathogen that might destroy its planetary host?), but of humanity itself (are we something of a failed experiment?). Also, our scientific knowledge, if judged by the Darwinian criteria of success through survival into the future, becomes of a paradoxical status since by its means there may easily be such disruption of our habitat that civilization, and with it science, is injured or destroyed. All this may seem gloomy; but then many great earlier theories of man and the universe have served to modify our conceited view of ourselves; so perhaps Gaia, with these philosophical glosses, will help us towards a necessary humility.

This can be enhanced by a reminder of how our scientific knowledge, under modern conditions, does not protect us against ignorance and even fantasies. The delusion that we are so protected may be one of the more serious defects of our culture. In the brief concluding piece for the section (first produced for a Japanese anthology and then reprinted by Zia Sardar) I review the different ways in which our science can, and does, go wrong.

Ideological Commitments in the Philosophy of Science

To outward appearances the academic discipline of 'the philosophy of science' has in recent times been an austere and abstract study. Its concerns have been with one major problem, to the near exclusion of all others. The truth-claims of completed scientific knowledge have been considered to be the only area of really worthwhile philosophical enquiry. The process of discovery, or the ethical problems of research or of applications, have traditionally been relegated to the status of non-problems or at best peripheral ones. Even now, as these other sorts of problems gain in interest among philosophers, the absence of a coherent framework of ideas for constructive study inhibits their development; while epistemology, the theory of scientific knowledge, still dominates teaching because it at least provides materials that can be taught.[1]

Furthermore, the sort of science considered worthy of study is very special. So special, in fact, that it might not even exist. The main tradition in the philosophy of science, including its variants and critics, has been devoted to considerations of matured 'exact' sciences, which combine quantitative experiments and mathematical laws to give the most assured knowledge to which humankind can attain. Other sorts of disciplines are deemed 'immature'; and their main assigned task is to find ways to approach or achieve the proper state. The obvious paradigm case for a genuine science is physics, whose solidity is attested by its triumphs both in theory and in application. It has been noticed that the theoretical end of physics has been in a state of continuous conceptual turmoil and revolution for nearly all of this century, and so its own credentials as a steady, perfected matured science are not beyond criticism. Imre Lakatos recognized this in a revealing footnote in one of his later papers, where he remarked:

> This [when a tradition degenerates] seems to be the case in modern particle physics, or according to some philosophers and physicists even in the Copenhagen school of quantum physics.[2]

However, practitioners and defenders of this philosophical tradition can argue that even if this philosophy-of-science describes no actual science it tells what any *genuine* science must be like. Its claims to special and unique status as a philosophical enquiry are not therefore dependent on whether its objects of study are precisely reflected in the imperfect world of human experience.

Such a conception of itself is quite legitimate for an academic discipline, particularly a philosophical enquiry. We do not ask geometers to go about measuring the earth, so we should allow philosophers-of-science a corresponding freedom to develop their own autonomous discipline. It is unfortunate that some people so misinterpret the field as to try to glean insight from it about the status and methods of confessedly immature descriptive sciences;[3] but that cannot be the responsibility of the philosophers. The philosophical task of showing how assured human knowledge can in principle be obtained in some sorts of natural science, is one that takes priority over merely practical concerns.

If all the foregoing argument for purity seems as reasonable as I have tried to make it, we are well prepared for an historical paradox. This is, that the founders and most of the main protagonists in the development of twentieth century philosophy of science have been deeply committed to causes directly involving humanity; and their doctrines of the philosophy of science were shaped with those broader ends consciously in view. The reason that 'science' in this tradition seems unlike ordinary practice is not because of its being a purified object of abstract conceptual analysis, but because of its being a symbol of the Good and the True in a certain ideologically engaged tradition of philosophical polemic. If, as I believe, it is time to move on beyond the insights and scholarly problems of that tradition, we should appreciate its sources of commitment so as to make an accurate and sympathetic assessment of its permanent achievements. Also, we will be better able to understand its particular weaknesses and thereby to remedy them in our own studies.

The Vienna Circle: Proclaiming the True in Science

The focal point of the coherent tradition of philosophy of science was Vienna, of the 1920s and earlier 1930s. There flourished the Vienna Circle, a grouping of philosophers and other scholars that included Karl Popper on its periphery. While Popper's writings, philosophical and autobiographical, are clear on his deep and abiding political commitment, the better-known English-language writings of the members of the Circle do not overtly depict such an influence. Yet the connection was there; the school's founder and greatest philosopher, Mortiz Schlick, was assassinated in 1936. And Schlick was truly a martyr; his was a cause that extended back to the Enlightenment of the eighteenth century: a struggle against 'dogma and metaphysics' (the intellectual tools of reactionary clerical forces) and the invocation of 'science' as the unique way to truth and human improvement.

181

A manifesto issued by the Vienna Circle itself in 1929 makes all this quite plain.

> The increase of metaphysical and theologizing leanings which shows itself today in many associations and sects, in books and journals, in talks and university lectures, seems to be based on the fierce social and economic struggles of the present: one group of combatants, holding fast to traditional social forms, cultivates traditional attitudes of metaphysics and theology whose content has long since been superseded; while the other group, especially in central Europe, faces modern times, rejects these views and takes its stand on the ground of empirical science. This development is connected with that of the modern process of production which is becoming ever more rigorously mechanized and leaves ever less room for metaphysical ideas. It is also connected with the disappointment of broad masses of people with the attitude to those who preach traditional metaphysical and theological doctrines. So it is that in many countries the masses now reject these doctrines much more consciously than ever before, and along with their socialist attitudes tend to lean towards a down-to-earth empiricist view. In previous times, *materialism* was the expression of this view; meanwhile, however, modern empiricism has shed a number of inadequacies and has taken a strong shape in the *scientific world-conception*.
>
> Thus, the scientific world-conception is close to the life of the present. Certainly it is threatened with hard struggles and hostility. Nevertheless there are many who do not despair but, in view of the present sociological situation, look forward with hope to the course of events to come. Of course not every single adherent of the scientific world-conception will be a fighter. Some, glad of solitude, will lead a withdrawn existence on the icy slopes of logic; some may even disdain mingling with the masses and regret the 'trivialized' form that these matters inevitably take on spreading. However, their achievements too will take a place among the historic developments. We witness the spirit of the scientific world-conception penetrating in growing measure the forms of personal and public life, in education, upbringing, architecture, and the shaping of economic and social life according to rational principles. *The scientific world-conception serves life, and life receives it.*[4]

In support of this interpretation we have the personal testimony of the Norwegian social philosopher Arne Naess. He recalled:

> The Vienna Circle was a nucleus of a movement for 'rationality' and against certain forms of metaphysics which at the time were closely allied with fascism and national socialism. It had all the missionary zeal of a movement, and it was touching but also somewhat alarming to

watch Otto Neurath embrace aloof and aristocratic Polish logicians of various philosophical affiliations and proclaim, 'We agree! You are one of us! If Neurath sensed that one was *somehow* on the right side, one was identified as a sort of logical positivist. Protestations were of little use and disagreements were conceived as due only to 'unhappy formulations' (*unglückliche Formulierungen*) and there was always a remedy for that.[5]

There is a stylistic feature of the Vienna Circle's studies which supports the interpretation of their being prophets in analysts' clothing. For their vision of science was quite deliberately abstracted from the processes of a personal creation and historical development; and in this regard they were more extreme in their demarcations than their great predecessor, Ernst Mach. For in his own critical studies, as of mechanics,[6] Mach allowed for the maturing of a discipline through several phases, the earlier, anthropomorphic ones as important and valid in their own way as those which were appropriate to a more perfected state. The Vienna Circle showed no interest in such origins or their vestiges, being concerned solely with the establishment of the credentials of statements in fully matured sciences.

Why this aspect of the Vienna Circle's programme has not been made prominent is a matter beyond my present purposes to explain fully. Let it suffice that with the rise of Nazism in central Europe, the surviving members of the school dispersed to the Anglo-American cultural area. There, the ideological battles were in a totally different style and on different issues. It was only natural for the positive content of the scholarly work to be emphasized and its ideological commitments (themselves severely shaken by the defeat of the anti-Nazi forces) left in discreet obscurity.

There they remained, through the lifetimes of the founders of the school and the careers of their pupils. But in the present period, there is a renewed ideological relevance to the philosophy of science, related not so much to struggles against the traditional Right as to attacks from the new Left. Hence it is relevant and illuminating to see how, beneath the dry formalisms of the logical-positivist writers, there was an intense commitment to a political cause.

Popper: Rescuing the Good in Science

In the case of Sir Karl Popper, one of the deepest and most influential philosophers of science of our time, the clues to ideological commitment are available in his best-known work. In a classic autobiographical essay, he describes how he came to conceive of the criterion of *falsifiability* in the demarcation of genuine science from its spurious imitations. Even allowing for the inevitable rationalization in the recollection of an event after a lapse of nearly four decades, the story has all the intensity and drama of a genuine conversion experience.[7] Put simply, in 1919 the young Popper was a radical student who was inspired by four great thinkers who styled themselves as 'scientists': Karl Marx, Sigmund Freud, Alfred Adler (the personality psychologist) and Albert Einstein. After the defeat of the Central Powers in 1918, the way seemed open for the forces of scientific rationalism to achieve their goals in society as well as in nature. But things began to go wrong: failures and complications in the political struggle, doubts and confusions in the intellectual debate.

Popper began to sense that the pretensions to 'scientific' status (meaning, of course, embodying the good and the true) of socialism and psychology were not correct. Yet by the accepted criteria of the time, they were indubitably scientific. An adherent of Marx or of Freud could display numerous confirmations of their theories (very close to the principle of 'verification' that was at the heart of the Vienna Circle positivism). And Adler relied on the inductive evidence of his clinical experience for the development of his theories. Perhaps one of the most fateful moments in the philosophical thought of the century occurred when Popper queried one of Adler's instant diagnoses, and was assured of the psychologist's 'thousand-fold experience' of such cases. Popper reports that he could not help saying 'And with this case, I suppose, your experience has become thousand-and-one-fold.'[8] This could be read as a sarcastic little joke; but actually it sends a searchlight beam into the weak centre of straightforward inductive reasoning. (It should be recalled that even when statistics are collected in an apparently inductive fashion in a controlled scientific experiment, the logic of the exercise, which should be reflected in all the techniques, is that of the testing of an hypothesis and *not* the confirmation of an inductive generalization.)

Popper makes one little remark on the background to these incidents, that calls out for historical investigation. This is, that he and his friends *already* knew that science is not infallibly true, and that scientists can err; hence a genuine demarcation of real science from the spurious would have to be independent of truth. Now, where these young radicals could have learned this lesson, is an intriguing and perhaps quite important question; I recommend it.

Popper's story is given added point by his example of astrology, as being no worse, methodologically, than the sciences which he had come to suspect. Now, this was not an example of an ancient and discredited pseudo-science chosen for its rhetorical effect. With the collapse of traditional authority in central Europe after the defeat of 1918, all sorts of fringe activities flourished wildly. Astrology was prominent among them, and supported self-appointed professors, institutes and learned journals. To such radical intellectuals as Popper, it could well have been the most vicious of the aberrations, because of its pretensions to the status of an empirical science. Hence to show that by the criteria of the Vienna Circle, the superstition of astrology could not be excluded, was to indicate the intellectual bankruptcy of the school.

Another implicit criticism in Popper's account concerns the dogmatism of the would-be sciences of man and society; and this would strike another blow at positivism's claims to be defeating the traditional enemies of reason. He describes how the practitioners of such fields, as the followers of Freud and Marx, use the doctrines in a particularly insidious fashion to protect themselves from criticism. The Marxist critical of the Party is deemed 'petty bourgeois'; the patient sceptical of Freud's interpretations is diagnosed as 'deeply neurotic' and so on. Thus immunized against criticism, and fortified by their 'confirmations', these essentially speculative, non-scientific studies could become really pernicious dogmatic pseudo-sciences. We notice that this defensive device is the same as that of traditional theology, which includes doctrines whereby all dissent is proved to be heresy. (I am grateful to Dr R. Sinsheimer, then at the University of California, Santa Cruz, for this observation.)

Thus, as I reconstruct Popper's problem-situation from his text, he had already given up Truth, and then found that the positivistic criteria admit both superstition and dogma. How to find an example by which *real* science can be demarcated from the suspect fields of Marxism and psychology, as well as the more patent pseudo-sciences? Einstein's bold theory of general relativity, and, more, his dramatic challenge to the astronomers to test it in the eclipse of 1919, provided that experience. For Einstein had argued mathematically that Sir Isaac Newton had been *wrong*, on a fundamental point of his system of the world. And now he was calmly inviting the scientists to test his claim, to determine whether he was greater than Newton—or himself only the author of a misconceived theory. *That* was real science—not fake confirmations, but bold conjectures ruthlessly put to the test. Popper concluded that what made a theory scientific was not that it was verifiable, but that it was falsifiable. But the heart of his insight was that what made a man a real scientist and not a fraud was the *moral* quality of daring to be shown to be wrong.

This is a very deep insight into the essentials of our science and indeed of our modern European civilization. If there is any doubt as to Popper's political commitment in its genesis and development, that can be removed by acquaintance with his influential works in political philosophy, such as *The Open Society and Its Enemies* and *The Poverty of Historicism*. The achievement had its own cost, reflected in Popper's use of the 'falsifiability' principle in the philosophy of science. For Popper was not content to leave it as an essentially ethical principle of genuine scientific behaviour; he needed to adapt it to function as a principle of epistemology and of method.[9] Severe problems were then encountered, for it turned out to be exceedingly difficult to demonstrate how knowledge could increase as a result of applying tests designed to falsify hypotheses: if such a test was successful we gained only the knowledge that some particular statement is false; while if it was unsuccessful we learned only that the statement was not yet proved false. As a principle of method, the projection of bold, very general hypotheses is not even a good caricature of the way scientists work. And, as an historic joke of the sort frequently associated with Einstein, the astronomical observations he suggested would not have been admitted by himself as a refutation of his theory even if they had gone against it.[10]

The contemporary student derives from Popper's work a sense of urgency and commitment, unlike in the case of the technical writings of the Vienna Circle philosophers. It is not made clear what the urgency is precisely about, since the scheme of 'science' portrayed there is obviously unlike the practice of either the ordinary or the great scientists. But with the help of the autobiographical essay and the political writings, we can appreciate the kinship of Popper to the Vienna Circle, both participating in the tradition of central European rationalism, in which 'science' was not so much a particular social activity as a Cause. However, we should recall the strong difference between them. Whereas the Vienna Circle proclaimed the good news of Science in a thoroughly traditional Enlightenment way, Popper jettisoned the True of science in order to rescue the Good. Post-Popperian philosophy of science may be seen as a test of whether even this desperate measure would suffice for the ideological defence of Science in the later, troubled years of the twentieth century.

In the history of ideas, time does not run at all smoothly. The matured programme of the Vienna Circle was developed after the revolution in 'atomic' physics was well under way, and also after the insolubility of the 'foundations crisis' of mathematics had been proved by the most rigorous of mathematical arguments. Hence its confidence in the security and intelligibility of matured exact natural science was betrayed by events even before it became the basis of a programme. With Popper, time played other tricks: his insights of 1919 waited some fifteen years before appearing fully in print; and by the early 1930s the German-language market for politically liberal philosophy of science was drying up rapidly. So he spent long years in New Zealand preparing his *political* philosophy, on whose basis he came to London. Only in the later 1950s, nearly forty years after the initial enlightening experience, did his philosophy of science begin to affect English-language academic opinion.[11] It is a true mark of its quality that it was still fresh and stimulating; the long reign of the Vienna Circle philosophers and their associates and students was at last being challenged. Popper also had the pleasure of seeing a school develop around himself. But, inevitably, there soon appeared a threatening and in some respects sinister rival philosophy: that of Thomas S. Kuhn. The response to this engaged him, and even more his brilliant protégé Imre Lakatos, through the 1960s.

Kuhn: Kicking Open Pandora's Box

Kuhn appeared on the philosophical scene in 1962; he was already recognized as a brilliant historian of the mathematical and physical sciences. His book *The Structure of Scientific Revolutions*[12] was an instant success. Although some philosophers of science felt that his ideas were incomplete in their novelty, originality and clarity of expression, there was no denying the popularity of the book or its lasting influence. The enormous influence of

Kuhn's work is due not merely to the depth of his insights. More, he seems to be describing science the way it really is, and doing so with a mastery that comes only from matured historical knowledge and reflective personal experience. His scientists are neither the impeccable truth-gatherers of the positivist tradition, nor the heroic conjecturalists of Popper, nor yet the paradox-generators of Lakatos. They are, normally, just ordinary people, concerned only to solve research puzzles within an unquestioned framework of concepts and methods. Kuhn's own experience of science was in post-war America, where ideological struggles were very muted and science was well on the way to becoming a big business. His account, reaching its audience when a rapidly expanded world of science and science education had lost most of its earlier sense of adventure and commitment, reads like the plain unvarnished truth. Because of this close relation to a new, disenchanted common sense of science, its ideological significance is more difficult to discern and also more devastating.

According to Kuhn, scientific progress alternates between 'normal' and 'revolutionary' phases, in which (respectively) scientists make piecemeal advances, or choose between rival grand systems. By this account, it appears that normal science is boring, and revolutionary science incomprehensible. He offers no methods or criteria for helping scientists decide in a revolutionary situation. Hence the genuine 'progress' of science (so vital for its traditional ideological message) becomes impossible to account for, and hence to guarantee, in both 'revolutionary' and 'normal' science alike. Indeed, Kuhn eventually reflected on the way that ultimate purposes are implicit in our idea of scientific 'progress', and wondered whether we couldn't dispense with it in the evolution of human knowledge just as we have done in the evolution of species.[13] With disarming candour, he describes normal scientific work as 'the strenuous and devoted effort to force Nature into the conceptual boxes provided by professional education'.[14]

Having casually dropped the True, he equally lightheartedly dismissed the Good of science. In his general account of the argument of his book he describes the response of established scientists to the crisis that precedes a revolution is such unflattering terms as the following:

> Normal science, for example, often suppresses fundamental novelties
> because they are necessarily subversive of its basic commitments . . .
> when . . . the profession can no longer evade anomalies that subvert
> the existing tradition of scientific practice — then begin at last the extra-
> ordinary investigations that lead the profession at last to a new set of
> commitments, a new basis for the practice of science.[15]

Popper did well to entitle his own criticism of Kuhn as 'Normal science and its dangers'.[16]

The most striking evidence as to what was *not* worrying Kuhn comes from an exchange of the mid-1960s, when the mischievous Paul Feyerabend observed that Kuhn's idea of 'normal science' as 'puzzle-solving within paradigms' provided no means of distinguishing between scientific research and other activities, even including organized crime.[17] The point of this remark was that the association of science with any sort of ethical consideration (either in goals or in methods) was completely obliterated on Kuhn's model. Kuhn's response was simply to remark that he never claimed his model to apply exclusively to science.[18] And there the matter rested.

Kuhn's work is an illuminating example of the way in which a doctrine can have ideological consequences in near independence of the concerns and commitments of the author. It could be and was used for a denial of an objective, universal basis of scientific knowledge, for several purposes. On the one hand, it seemed to offer a behaviouristic criterion for the genuineness of a scientific field: one where debate on fundamentals is suppressed, and all work proceeds as puzzle-solving within a dogmatic framework. For insecure scientists in fields of human behaviour, this offered a justification of arbitrarily imposed Departmental conformity. But rebellious researchers and revolutionary students could utilize the relativity of 'paradigms' to struggle for a substitution of their favoured dogma against the officially sanctioned one. Both sorts of move are destructive of the open dialogue which is the essence of Western liberal democracy, of which 'science' had for generations been taken by its advocates as the great exemplar. Hence for those with any sensitivity to ideology, Kuhn's doctrines were a menace. All his colleagues distinguished Kuhn's doctrine from Kuhn himself; personally he is rather liberal in his politics, rather conservative in his philosophy of science, and not at all interested in ideology. Amidst all that central European intensity, he stands out as the American who just described it all the way it seemed to him, and then was amazed at the fuss made about it. Or is he? It is hard to imagine such an impact being made on the inherited image of science by some sort of accident. Is there more to Kuhn's message than meets the casual reader's eye?

Of course there is, and it shows in the repeated irony, sometimes quite savage, that appears in odd words and phrases in the text. When he remarks that a scientific training is more narrow and rigid than any except orthodox theology, or that the official disciplinary histories of science are like those of *1984*[19] we need not assume that the analogies are unintentional. A more coherent set of clues is provided at the very beginning of the book, where he compares existing histories to tourist brochures or language texts, by which we have been 'misled in fundamental ways'.[20] These are, briefly, in the assumption that scientific progress is linear and cumulative; and that incorrect scientific theories are patently absurd. Kuhn seems to have believed such things right through his education, until he helped teach a course for non-scientists which involved reviewing old theories like Aristotelian mechanics, phlogistic chemistry and caloric theory of heat. To his 'complete surprise, that exposure to out-of-date scientific theory and practice radically undermined' his basic conceptions.

In a later autobiographical commentary[21] Kuhn actually described how it happened: 'My moment of enlightenment [*sic*] began in 1947, when I was asked to interrupt my current physics project for a time in order to prepare a set of lectures on the origins of seventeenth century mechanics . . .'. Kuhn's first reading of Aristotle agreed with the consensus view; but perhaps with a keener historian's insight than he then realized, he asked, 'but was it conceivable that his errors had been so blatant?' Thus we have the problem; and then the epiphany:

> One memorable (and very hot) summer day those perplexities suddenly vanished. I all at once perceived the connected rudiments of an alternate way of reading the texts with which I had been struggling . . .

Thus we have a record of Kuhn's moment of enlightenment, analogous to Popper's of 1919 if not so dramatically retailed. But why should this produce the anger reflected in the irony? It seems most likely to me that at some stage Kuhn realized that he had been the victim of a deception; and we can identify the source of the deception in a root contradiction in the old, received ideology of science. This had two elements: that science is always true, and also always progressive. To explain those cases where progress seemed to have occurred at the price of exposing error, the old-time historian's technique was simple: to show that no *real* scientist could have believed that stuff. Kuhn discovered, by seeing the reasonableness of the discarded and discredited scientific theories, that the history he had trustingly imbibed was to some significant extent a pack of lies. Hence his anger, and also hence his extreme reaction, leading to the rhetorical flourishes about the 'arbitrariness' of what is believed in science at any time. The True of science had been betrayed in its falsified history; and so the Good is also compromised. All this is a speculative reconstruction on my part; but it at least explains the stylistic features of Kuhn's text and also the intensity that made it so readable and so significant for the ideology of science.

Lakatos: The Dialectical Defence of Reason and Freedom

It was as ideology that Imre Lakatos read Kuhn's philosophy; and from its first appearance he devoted his main efforts to combating both its philosophical errors and its political implications. This challenge provided a renewed practical focus for Lakatos' work; otherwise he might have been too exclusively concerned with the technical debates between the Popper school and its old and new opponents. Because of his tragically early death Lakatos achieved only a modest bulk of publications; and his various papers are either difficult or controversial or both. But by his intensity, brilliance and wit, he kept alive the spirit of Popperian committed philosophy. Through it all, he was quite clear about his own ideological engagements. Indeed, much of the stimulus and support for this present essay of mine was derived from him.

From his student days onwards, Lakatos had been, successively: a member of the anti-Nazi underground; a Communist Party activist; a bureaucrat in the Hungarian State cultural apparatus; a minor victim of the Stalinist purges of the early 1950s; a candidate for a treason trial, whose name happened not to be reached; a non-rehabilitated (therefore document-less) ex-prisoner in pre-liberalized Hungary; a rehabilitated person, student and member of the Petöfi circle during the Hungarian 'spring' of 1955 and 1956; a refugee after the Russian intervention of 1956; a research student at Cambridge, England, completing a thesis on the philosophy of mathematics; eventually a member of the Popper group at the London School of Economics (LSE); and finally an embattled opponent of the 'new left' student revolutionaries who concentrated on the LSE in 1968.

As Lakatos made clear in his published writing[22] the issue was plain: the defence of reason against its enemies, who (as Popper saw before him) could come equally well from the Left as from the old Right. But, working so much later than Popper and endowed with greater political and philosophical subtlety, he could appreciate those defects in Popper's system which required remedying. This apologetic work, undertaken directly as a response to the challenge of Kuhn, occupied the last years of his life and was of doubtful success. His earliest work, undertaken before he came under the direct influence of Popper, is more original and probably more significant. Its ideological commitments are not so open, but are thereby all the more worthwhile to explore.

Proofs and Refutations[23] is an essay in the philosophy of mathematics, in my opinion the first really new move in that field in the twentieth century. Previously philosophers and mathematicians had attempted to resolve the 'foundations crisis' in terms of mathematics being a fixed and rigid intellectual structure, consisting of clear concepts linked by unambiguous rules of inference. The various foundational programmes were devoted to exposing that structure in such a way as to eliminate the paradoxes and anomalies that had been discovered there. Lakatos saw a very different problem: as a preliminary to any genuine philosophy of mathematics, we must explore the dialectic of development both of mathematical concepts and a criteria of rigorous proof. For these are both historically conditioned, and any philosophy that ignores this fact perpetuates the bad tradition of dogmatism in mathematical thinking. His method was as radical an innovation as his doctrine: he expounded his philosophy through a classroom discussion of terrifyingly clever schoolboys, dissecting their hapless teacher's proof of a classic result in topology, the Euler Polyhedron Theorem.

The roots of Lakatos' philosophy of mathematics are clear: the strong Hungarian tradition of problem-solving mathematics, raised to an art and philosophy by G. Polya[24]; and a playful Hegelian style of dialectic, derived from a Marxism purified of its political content. His commitment was not so clear at the time of first publication of *Proofs and Refutations*; but it may be inferred from his life's work. One may imagine that the demonstration of the falsity of rigid and dogmatic thinking in mathematics, the most abstract of all sciences, could be applied *a fortiori* to the 'science of society' under which Marxist socialism was supposed to be constructed.

It could be that Lakatos's philosophy of mathematics was among the more significant intellectual achievements of the Petöfi Circle of the Hungarian Spring of 1955/6. There is even a conjecture that his criticism of 'proof' was born as a survival strategy under conditions of interrogation in Stalinist Hungary.[25] We recall the game played in Koestler's *Darkness at Noon*, where Rubashov had to admit guilt on any crime which he might *logically* have committed. In that game it mattered not that the accusations were, in the non-political factual sense, false. We may imagine that for a more experienced interrogaté, the prime task was to prevent the interrogator convincing him that 'confession' was a personal duty that could be rigorously derived from the objective needs of Party and Revolution. Denying the cogency of even a mathematical proof could then provide an escape hatch from the rigours of Stalinist political logic.

The affinity in spirit and commitment between Popper and Lakatos is plain. They came together not long after Lakatos settled in England, and they then jointly met the challenge of the ideological consequences of Kuhn's apparently non-ideological analysis of science in his *Structure of Scientific Revolutions* (1962). The great monument of their endeavour is the report[26] on a symposium held in 1965, in which Kuhn and all the other leading philosophers of science participated. Lakatos's own published contribution was under revision for some years afterwards, and so it stands as a fully matured expression of his views. He recognized that the versions of methodology that can be read out of Popper's writings are all too naive to stand scrutiny; there could be no 'instant rationality' in scientific choice. His task was to construct a 'heuristic' that would allow both for the complexity of the cognitive problems (where testing of theories could be neither immediate nor decisive) and for the human qualities of scientists (rightly unwilling to throw away years of work at the sight of the first unresolved problem) while yet preserving the ethical and political commitments of Popper. His philosophical keenness led him into further problems (conveniently overlooked by most of his contemporaries) including the relations between the history and the philosophy of science, and also the location of the ultimate warrant for correctness of philosophical accounts of science (he put it in the successful practice, as distinct from the theorizing, of the élite scientists). The resulting edifice of ideas, further enriched by Lakatos's delight in polemic and paradox, was impressive but unwieldy. It was also very vulnerable to criticism in respect both of its historical reconstructions and its philosophical generalizations. And Lakatos, like Popper, failed to face up to the political consequences of his philosophical critique: if the dominant self-consciousness of science, as enforced by its élites, has indeed been false, reactionary and dogmatic (this is clear from his account of mathematics), what do we conclude about science as a social institution? Can it really be the embodiment of that rationality and intellectual integrity which we know to be at the core of a liberal, democratic, 'open' society? Thus the Good of Science is no easier to defend, once it has become problematic, than the True.

Lakatos did not engage in his philosophical exercises for their own sake. While he was elaborating on his synthesis of Popperian idealism and Kuhnian pragmatics, he was also engaged in a political struggle with antagonists he considered as vicious and as dangerous as the Stalinist thought-police of Hungary. The rebellious students of the London School of Economics in 1968 were, in retrospect, a small and ineffective minority. But during their flourishing, they disrupted a distinguished educational institution, and announced their intention to capture it and much else beside. Even the native English academic staff at the LSE were caught up in violent struggles, ideological, institutional and personal. For Lakatos, it was the Red Fascists on the march again, and he reacted as if back in Budapest. This struggle convinced him that his version of Popperian liberal philosophy of science was central to the defence of civilization, and so gave his work a compelling intensity. But it took a heavy toll of his energies, and left him exhausted and ill.

It is conceivable to me that Lakatos eventually recognized that the great flexibility he had built into his model of rational scientific behaviour, for the sake of realism, had effectively undermined his political commitment and career. The crucial point is of time-scale; as he said, 'to give a stern "refutable interpretation" to a fledgling version of a programme is a dangerous methodological cruelty . . . [it] may take decades of theoretical work to arrive at the first novel facts and still more time to arrive at *interestingly testable* versions . . .'[27]. *Decades* of protection from critical judgement, even for an abstract scientific theory? How long then, for a new social system? By this criterion, the Soviet intervention of 1956 was quite possibly 'historically necessary' to protect the fledgling socialism of Hungary, scarcely a single decade away from war and Fascism. Thus Lakatos's lifelong exile was perhaps the result of a methodological error in the overly stern assessment of a fledgling version of a social development programme.

Only an intimate biography could tell whether Lakatos was aware of this latent contradiction. But since his methodological reflections were always guided by his political commitments, the practical implications of his strong denial of 'instant rationality' could not be hidden forever. What we do know is that one of the few comradely friends he retained from his earlier days in England exposed other crucial contradictions in his intellectual system, and effectively made himself rather than Lakatos the authority to be followed. This was Paul Feyerabend, in whose book *Against Method*, dedicated to Lakatos, the ideological aspects of the modern philosophy of science are taken to the ultimate in paradox and confusion.

Paul Feyerabend and the End of Classical Viennese Philosophy of Science

Feyerabend is certainly the most confusing and paradoxical figure in the philosophy of science of that period. It is not at all easy to decide whether he is a court jester, Zen master, or Fascist. The first, because he still operates within the community of philosophy of science, engaging successfully in highly technical debates on problems within the dominant style. In this respect, he is more one of the club than even Lakatos ever was, to say nothing to Kuhn, whose real commitment is to interpretative history rather than exemplified philosophy. Conventional philosophers of science cannot dismiss him, for he is capable of publishing a fully expert and illuminating — or wounding — study of problems or persons at any time. Yet in what seems to be another incarnation, he has written wild and destructive criticisms of the whole programme of philosophy of science, that is explaining and justifying the methods whereby (idealized) scientists gain new knowledge. Some might hope to contain his influence by not taking the critical diatribes too seriously, and treating him as a court jester, who says impossible things as useful reminders of the human frailties to which even philosophers are subject.

Careful consideration of his arguments shows that they are not so easily reduced to jokes. If philosophy of science has any pretensions to help us understand the activity of science, then his studies of the behaviour of great scientists are troubling indeed. For he shows by example that for any explicit rule of method enunciated by philosophers of science, there is an important occasion on which it was broken by some great scientist. In his *Against Method*[28] he goes far towards demonstrating that Galileo was a precursor of Feyerabend, treating all the rules, including that of simple accuracy (or honesty) in recording observations, with fine anarchistic playfulness. The epoch-making description of the surface of the moon that Galileo saw through his telescope, reported in the *Starry Messenger*, gives prominent and important reference to a feature (a large round crater on the line bisecting the lunar disc)[29] which can be made at all plausible only by the most skilful selection of modern lunar photographs[30]. And Galileo's struggle for the Copernican system can be considered 'scientific' only because he happened to be right; otherwise he broke every rule of the game.

Now, this is the sort of thing that can easily 'blow the mind' of a student for whom (like so many) the authority of science is as absolute as theology ever was in the Middle Ages. After such an experience of shock and disillusion, the student may be ready to awaken to the truth that there is no truth to awaken to. In his role of awakener, Feyerabend may be considered as a Zen master. But the analogy is very imperfect: a traditional Zen master operated in an I—thou relation, so that the searcher would be genuinely enlightened and not destroyed. Providing an anonymous reading public with an exhibition of a batch of sacred images being sprayed by a philosophical machine-gun is a very different activity indeed.

For this reason, and another as well, Feyerabend may come under suspicion of being in effect (though certainly not in intention) a Fascist.[31] For what he offers to replace the old ideal of philosophy of science is confused and uncon-structive. It is along the lines of allowing everyone to 'do his own thing' freed from the constraints of convention or of social or logical propriety. Those who recall the connections of Nazi German-Folk ideology and religion with earlier currents of Romantic and anti-mechanical philosophies are justifiably troubled by Feyerabend even more than by the other counter-culture prophets. Feyerabend's prescriptions may be all very well after the anarchist Utopia has been achieved; but in the short run it may mean destroying the intellectual barriers to the victory of arbitrary will and brute force in intellectual and hence social matters.

Feyerabend could reply to such an accusation with the rejoinder that for most of the world's peoples, aside from the mainly white, mainly male, mainly middle-class beneficiaries of high culture, that is precisely the unspeakable state of affairs already; and that this is both concealed and sanctioned by our dominant ideas of Science and Method. In his defence, in *Science in a Free Society* he describes the experiences in California which led to his conversion. Adopting a playful Feyerabendian style for the rational reconstruction of Feyerabend, we may take two episodes from the book, and combine them to imagine an 'epiphany of the yellow pencils' for his illumination.[32] These latter were the topic (along with black ravens) of the paradox which formed a principal concern of philosophers of science during the otherwise turbulent decade of the 1960s. So we may imagine Feyerabend at Berkeley during all the campaigns, teaching classical philosophy of science, including the paradox named above, when he became aware of his surroundings. These were first, a class of Californian 1960s types, including ethnic minority people whom he was expected to prepare for 'the wonderful chance to participate in the white man's manias'. Exemplifying these was (I imagine) the tear-gas that drifted into the classroom as the police broke up yet another student demonstration. Furthermore, having been abandoned by the best of the orthodox medical science that the University of California could provide, he was in the process of being saved by several unorthodox practitioners. This quintessentially 1960s combination completed the process of his disillusion with the official representatives of rationality and freedom, that had been growing for many years; and so he rejected the yellow pencils in favour of a radical democracy in all culture, including science. Thus enlightened, he turned on all scientific orthodoxies with the fierce delight displayed in *Against Method*.

Feyerabend is best understood in the context of the counter-culture which flourished most abundantly in California. His criticisms make sense when related to those of Ivan Illich and the other prophets of a new age. His political case against scientific medicine is supported by the chronicle of oppression and mutilation of subject peoples (including the whole female sex) at the hands of the certified experts.[33] Indeed, the only conclusive answer to his critique is the classic of a departing reactionary: 'Après moi, le deluge'—so that all but the most fanatical revolutionaries realize in retrospect the benefits of a rule of law that had at least been consistent, however harsh and unjust. There is a practical answer, of course, and that is to let time elapse and see what has happened to the message of the 1960s, and to the world which then for a moment seemed nearly in an apocalyptic state.

In Feyerabend's polemics, the ideological motivation for the philosophy of science finally became fully explicit. This was because he was accusing the dominant Viennese tradition of complicity in the betrayal of the ideals for which it had historically claimed to stand. Their idea of rationality had showed itself a tool of class and cultural imperialists; he would then demonstrate the incapacity of such a rationality as an instrument of learning about the world. Though in the last resort Feyerabend argued from within the philosophical tradition to which the Viennese adhered, his work was devastating to that tradition. After him came a variety of social science approaches to scientific knowledge, all of which argued that scientific knowledge is a social construct, of a lesser or greater degree of arbitrariness. Although there remained a few apologists trying to rescue something of 'objectivity', with Feyerabend came the end of classical Viennese philosophy of science.

If that tradition had been truly 'positive' like the science it proclaimed, and had tough and resilient roots in a real understanding of its practice, it would not, I believe, have been so vulnerable to the assault of its critics. But, as I have shown here, the image of 'science' that was invoked in that programme was itself the product of an ideology, however unself-consciously applied: that science is uniquely the bearer of the True and hence also of the Good, in opposition to religion and other forms of knowing. When that image lost its plausibility, through changes in the ideological and institutional context of science, the technical articulations made by previous philosophers of science were discovered to be hollow and brittle. Two profound but simplistic thinkers, one, Popper, an eccentric Viennese ex-radical and the other, Kuhn, an unsubtle American conservative, achieved the insights that demolished the foundations of the old scientistic faith; and then in spite of Lakatos's heroic efforts to construct a dialectical defence of reason and freedom, the whole edifice was brought down by Feyerabend's 'Dada' critique.

Conclusion: Where Do We Go From Here?

I do *not* wish to say that any philosophical system is only a tissue of rationalizations of an ideology, that enjoys some temporary plausibility. Although philosophy is very different in degree from the more 'positive' sciences that enjoy a more direct foundation in controlled experience, it too leaves behind a residue of achievement, in understanding rather more than in detailed knowledge, as each great movement or school passes through its cycle of growth and decay. But when all the signs point to a philosophical cycle nearing its end, it is time to see whether the world which was its passionate concern is still that which presents us with the problems that challenge and enrich us.

The ideology of the previous phase of philosophy of science was derived from a centuries-long battle with 'religion'. This lay not so much in the realm of individual faith, as in that of pretensions to exclusive knowledge, and of claims to political power partly on that basis. Now, in the later twentieth century, that old battle is over: the Christian Churches are in an excited and turbulent state that may indeed herald a great rebirth, but which certainly does not promise either the renewed obedience of the faithful or the deference of the secular powers. Instead, some at least of the clerical evils that motivated the endeavours of Enlightenment have now been inherited by the apparatus of anti-religious state power. And from science itself have come new evils, inconceivable once magic was discredited until the advent of the atomic bomb. So that those who still try to identify science with the humane, civilized values now find themselves in a confused night battle, where friend and foe are ever more difficult to distinguish.

My own retrospective assessment of the tradition would hinge on a distinction of three modes of discourse: heuristic, epistemology and ideology. The logical positivists ignored heuristic and so were vulnerable when it was introduced. Popper invoked it but in a very caricatured version. Kuhn might be said never to have grasped the distinction between an insightful heuristic and a rigorous epistemology. Feyerabend uses heuristic to destroy epistemology. Of all these philosophers, Lakatos best appreciated the difference, but was lacking in a sufficiently sensitive touch to keep their relations harmonious.

The old epistemological problems of science are, therefore, no longer fruitful for our understanding of that great creation of the human intellect. As they have become isolated from their roots in committed experience, they can provide no effective defence against the suicidal application of reason in Feyerabend's arguments. I suggest that they be given a rest, and that new critical insights be applied to the analysis of science, not in a spirit of angry demystification, but as a complement to progress already being made in the history and the sociology of science. There, studies of the actual conditions and constraints on scientific work are providing a picture that is rapidly being enriched, of how science can have both successes and failures, and virtues and vices, without being the subject of one simplistic verdict on the degree of its adherence to the Good and the True.

The speculative and analytical styles of enquiry appropriate to philosophy could find an immediate rich harvest in the many areas of ethics that impinge on scientific and science-based work. For epistemology, there are the peculiarly challenging and urgent problems of 'trans-science', where the questions may look like ordinary experimental topics, but where the technical answers lie beyond the limits of feasibility. The philosophy of the mathematical sciences could be rejuvenated by deeper analysis of their *in*exactness in practice, as distinct from their perfection in an ideologically loaded theory. The criteria of demarcation of science from pseudo-science, essentially untouched from Descartes until Popper, could do with more scrutiny. For example, there are the policy-relevant disciplines dependent on mathematical models where the uncertainties in the inputs must be suppressed lest the outputs become indeterminate. Such GIGO-sciences (for Garbage In, Garbage Out) have a role in statecraft analogous to that of classical astrology.

Must we admit them as scientific in spite of their vacuity, merely because their underlying metaphysic follows Descartes and Hobbes? Even the field of ontology, long since relegated to the most obscure corner of metaphysics, takes on a new relevance. When both visible prodigious phenomena and inward states of enhanced consciousness are, continuously since the 1960s, on the agenda of debate, the concepts of reality decreed in the early seventeenth century may no longer be taken as unproblematical. These are only a few problems shaped in terms with which I am familiar; as philosophers enlarge their image of science from an idealized physics, to medicine, technology, and the fields of 'regulatory science', the problems are profuse in their challenge.

I would not be so naive as to call for an end to ideology in the philosophy of science. The new problems will have their own ideological motivations too; that is necessary and healthy. But we can look forward to the closing of a chapter in the philosophy of science in which the persistent rule of a particular ideology was, in its later stages, all the more damaging because it was unrecognized. That is why I have done this survey in the interests of an enriched understanding of our past, so that we may better shape our future.

Adapted from an essay that was first given as a lecture to the Department of Sociology at Leeds University in 1977, then, as revised, published (in German translation) in *Versuchungen* (essays on the work of Paul Feyerabend) (ed. H.-P. Duerr), Frankfurt, Suhrkamp Verlag, 1980, and further revised and republished, in *Radical Philosophy* 25, 1984.

References

1. See, for an example of a recent textbook, A. Chalmers, *What Is This Thing Called Science?* (Open University Press; 1978).
2. I. Lakatos, 'History of science and its rational reconstructions', in *The Methodology of Scientific Research Programmes* (Cambridge; 1978), p. 137.
3. D. Harvey, *Explanation in Geography* (London, Arnold; 1969) is a good example of such an attempt; the author subsequently turned to politically radical interpretations of urban geography.
4. Vienna Circle, *The Scientific Conception of the World (1929)* (pamphlet) (Reidel; 1973) also in M. Neurath and R.S. Cohen (eds) *Otto Neurath: Empiricism and Sociology* (Reidel; 1973).
5. A. Naess, *The Pluralist and Possibilist Aspect of the Scientific Enterprise* (London, Allen and Unwin; 1972), p. 135.
6. E. Mach, *The Science of Mechanics* (1883, many translations and editions).
7. K. Popper, 'Conjectures and refutations', in *Conjectures and Refutations: The Growth of Scientific Knowledge* (London, Routledge; 1963), p. 36.
8. Ibid., p. 35.
9. K.R. Popper, 'Back to the pre-Socratics', in *Conjectures and Refutations* is a very attractive attempt to show how Popperian method and ethics were responsible for 'the Greek miracle' in natural philosophy.
10. G. Holton, 'Mach, Einstein, and the search for reality', in *Thematic Origins of Modern Thought* (Harvard; 1973), p. 236.
11. K.R. Popper, *The Logic of Scientific Discovery* (London, Hutchinson; 1959).

12. T.S. Kuhn, *The Structure of Scientific Revolutions* (Chicago; 1962).
13. Ibid., p. 170.
14. Ibid., p. 5.
15. Ibid., pp. 5–6.
16. K. Popper, 'Normal science and its dangers', in I. Lakatos and A. Musgrave (eds) *Criticism and the Growth of Knowledge* (Cambridge; 1970).
17. P. Feyerabend, 'Consolations for the specialist', in Lakatos and Musgrave op. cit., pp. 200–1.
18. T.S. Kuhn, 'Reflections on my critics', in Lakatos and Musgrave, op. cit. p. 245.
19. Kuhn, op. cit. (ref. 12), pp. 166, 167.
20. Ibid., p. 1.
21. T.S. Kuhn, *The Essential Tension* (University of Chicago Press; 1977), Preface p. xi.
22. I. Lakatos, 'Introduction. Science and pseudoscience', in *The Methodology of Scientific Research Programmes* (op. cit.).
23. I. Lakatos, *Proofs and Refutations. The Logic of Mathematical Discovery* (Cambridge; 1976).
24. G. Polya, *Mathematics and Plausible Reasoning* (2 vols) (Oxford and Princeton; 1954).
25. J.G. Goodfield, personal communication.
26. Lakatos and Musgrave, op. cit.
27. I. Lakatos, op. cit. (ref. 2), p. 151.
28. P. Feyerabend, *Against Method* (London, New Left Books; 1975).
29. Galileo, *The Starry Messenger* (1610), second drawing of the moon, with crater compared to Bohemia; see S. Drake, *The Discoveries and Opinions of Galileo* (New York, Doubleday Anchor; 1957), p. 35.
30. S. Drake, *Galileo at Work, His Scientific Biography* (University of Chicago Press; 1978), p. 145.
31. See E. Gellner, 'Beyond truth and falsehood', *British Journal for the Philosophy of Science* 26 (1975) 231–43. Feyerabend's reply, 'Logic, literacy and Professor Gellner', ibid. 27 (1976) pp. 382–91, where he denies being a Fascist by claiming court-jester and Zen master status. The reply is reprinted with modifications in *Science in a Free Society* (London, New Left Books; 1978), pp. 141–53.
32. Ibid., pp. 118, 137.
33. Ibid., p. 175. For partial confirmation of one of his accusations see *Science* 204 (22 June 1979), pp. 284–5: 'There is no scientific evidence that a radical mastectomy gives any better results than a modified one for early breast cancers, according to the consensus meeting held on 5 June at the National Institutes of Health'.

Quality in Consumerist Civilization:
Ibn Khaldun Revisited

Some cultures make good plumbing; some others, good space-rockets.

Who would lay down his life for General Motors; or indeed for General Westmoreland?

In the nineteenth century it was the capitalists' commercial goods, as Marx observed, that battered down the Chinese Walls of the traditional closed societies. Now we may speak of a more sophisticated stage of the process, whereby not merely cheap necessities but cheap luxuries are increasingly available to all the world, and much desired by it. Old patterns of authority have long been under erosion; now old life-styles and values follow, all swept aside by consumerism.

Those who are concerned for values that are in any way 'alternative' to consumerism, be they ecological, socialist or religious, may watch with horror as young adults the world over increasingly find all life's meaning conveyed on the colour TV screen. Movements for realizing something of more genuine value seem regularly to degenerate either into fashion or into fanaticism, or at best to remain isolated on a political or cultural fringe. The triumph of materialism, after centuries of struggle on the philosophical and then political planes, now seems to be accomplished through the commodities of modern affluent living or its reasonable facsimiles.

But in this century of its success, the heartland of material progress, the Occident, does not seem to be enjoying the fruits of its victories. A variety of malaises afflict it; its optimism and confidence have given way to confusion and drift. Some reasons for this condition are quite obvious; thus the real victor in the struggle for the affection of the global consumer is Japan, one of the recent barbarians, now even more menacing to America in peace than in war. But there is more; on top of economic stagnation, ecological crises and terrifying financial instability, there is a sense of loss of power at the real centre. Military might and high-technology leadership (closely related through electronics, space and nuclear energy) are now both compromised, partly by external competition and also by internal decay. At this point in history, if you want to put a payload into space, you do best to go to China, or perhaps to Russia. American rockets are, it seems, no better than American cars. And Star Wars approaches the ultimate in ruinous absurdity.

Does all this mean that the 'unbound Prometheus' of hitherto dynamic Occidental technology is now revealed as a giant with feet of clay, at least in the culture of its origin? Has the triumph of the soft values of consumerism been achieved by the loss of the hard values of national strength? If so, then it is most important for the phenomenon to be understood. This might not make any difference in the short run; but an historical perspective might be crucial for understanding and effective action, should the present unstable balance of influence and power between different national cultures eventually become disrupted or deranged.

Old Cycles of Empire, and their Social Cement

We all know the cycle articulated by Ibn Khaldun, starting with barbarian (perhaps 'hybrid'?) vigour, through stable prosperity, and finally corruption and decay from luxury. The story is at least as old as Saul, David and Solomon. Some empires repeated the cycle almost like clockwork, notably the Chinese. Others went through the process only a few times locally, and then succumbed to a global onslaught; such was the story of the Islamic communities.

About a half-millennium ago, a fateful shift occurred. The new barbarians did not come on horseback, ready to be tamed by the good things of palace life. Rather, they came in strange boats, bringing successively guns, Bibles, various poisons and diseases, and eventually things to sell and money to invest. World-wide they encountered no traditional culture in a vigorous phase, capable of resisting or of adapting creatively. It took a few centuries from the first easy conquests; but eventually all were penetrated and possessed, and became attached to the Occidental civilized world.

So the rise of the Occident was correlated with the enfeeblement of all the others. Was there a simple confluence of Ibn Khaldun cycles all over; or was there some larger, long-term shift affecting them all? On this I can, of course, only speculate. But we recall that what finally shattered the Inca civilization was not the Spanish invaders themselves, but the Great Inca's confession to his people that El Dorado, the Sun King, was nothing but a staged spectacle. The magic had already died; the land was a spiritual corpse waiting for the vultures. Similarly, the Aztecs, waiting for fair-skinned gods on winged vessels. China survived longer, with another cycle to go through; Japan shut the door and decayed quietly behind it until 1854. What of Islam? There the barbarians, with all their religious fervour, had already effectively destroyed that stable community that is the essence of Islam as a social possession of mankind.

The personal, visual experience of the monuments of those ancient civilizations is a great education in the relativity of cultures and also of technology. Vast social endeavours, and artistic craftsmanship of the highest pitch of excellence, were poured into edifices and furnishings designed for the glorification or perhaps even deification of a single individual. Such enterprises, often accomplished through the improverishment or enslavement of the masses, nearly defy explanation to the Occidental utilitarian mind. Was it only will, or caprice, or a desire to frighten or impress, that motivated the decisions for their construction? If so, that would represent a social practice, stable over many centuries, in which, regularly, very much was taken from society and nothing was given in return. Then the social structures apparently survived and were perpetuated and reproduced in spite of having no functions, only dysfunctions. To be sure, the oppression and exploitation could approach the absolute point; but then there could be uprisings, and at least in China, these would be a signal that the Heavenly mandate had been forfeited, and it was time for a change. The Ibn Khaldun cycle had completed one round.

Let us consider the possibility that that sort of production, with its characteristic excellence of technology, did have a social function, through which it provided a general benefit. This was obviously not on the material plane, unless all this extravagance was perennially accepted as necessary for the military and civil benefits of strong, stable government. It would be misleading to describe the monuments and their furnishings as 'symbolic', as if a dictionary of individual meanings would be necessary for their appreciation. Rather, perhaps that industry of rulership was organized around magic, in the sense of religious beliefs and experiences, adapted to the exercise of worldly power.

Experiences? Here the secular humanist (regardless of his or her profession of faith) starts nervously. Am I now invoking mysticism, superstition or perhaps psychedelia as the social cement for that highly developed technological form that dominated great civilizations for millennia? Let us not quibble about words; we can think of the *affect* that is now produced weakly and intermittently by the modern paraphernalia of patriotism: flags, songs, monuments, even some monarchs. As an intermediate case, we may recall the quasi-religious character of great or absolute rulers in recent times: the Czar, Stalin or Mao; or even (to some extent) F.D. Roosevelt and (for a time) Woodrow Wilson. In another age, with another consciousness, the systematically enriched subjective experience of participants, achieved through various technologies, some imaginable to us and some not, was the 'utility' of that charisma-industry. If we accept this thesis, then those other civilizations become at least comprehensible; otherwise they can only fill us with cosmic dismay, by their stupendous waste and abuse of human labour and talent.

We can speculate further: suppose that, however deformed or corrupted it may have become or been, this sort of charisma-industry did more than merely secure the passive obedience of the exploited masses. Perhaps, when it worked well, it combined the sacred and the secular, the sensory and the trans-sensory, so that (at least for those who were not totally excluded from its benefits) it provided an occasion and a motive for people to do and give of their very best, their labour and even their lives. In this way we can explain the otherwise incredible level of artistry routinely achieved in these productions. In our culture, it is hard to imagine such work being forced out of suffering slaves. Perhaps the religious/political matrix of belief, however much it violates *our* principles of equity and human realization, functioned to just that end.

This would have been the stable background to all the local cycles of dynasties. The successful barbarian conquerors (who came in anyway when the previous rulers had lost their charisma) could easily be recruited to the apparatus of social control accomplished through shared experience, and (as classically in China), the perturbations of life would soon diminish.

The Last Half-Millennium: The New Game

As I have indicated, whatever degree of effectiveness and stability the charisma-industry may have achieved at different times and places, it has universally been in decline for some centuries. The empire of the Occident has broken the old matrix; it denies and then ignores the shared subjective realities on which the old system depended. Marx well expresses the new consciousness when he assumes the non-existence of such realities, and then tries to explain the whole history of production and of technology on straight Benthamite lines. In the political sphere, we learn from the American Declaration of Independence that people have the inalienable rights of 'life, liberty, and the pursuit of happiness', and that governments are no more than practical instruments for the securing of those rights.

We should recall that this democratic manifesto was articulated rather late in the full cycle of expansion of the Occident. Previously there had been an important period of 'absolutism', as in Spain and France. But a glance at history shows that in comparison to the real thing, European absolutism was temporary and feeble. The Sun King, Louis XIV, named after the Incas by Campanella, enjoyed scarcely a pretence of truly divine sanction, and still less of authentic participatory experience with his nation.

At first this destruction of the old realities, already enfeebled, was a great liberation in a multitude of ways. Material production could now be used for widespread personal enrichment through the production and sale of materially useful goods for an open market. Innovation quickened, so that by the nineteenth century the productivity of the textile mills would have seemed quite magical in any other culture. With higher productivity, and with the fetters of economic and political constraints completely shattered, the broad masses could, over a few generations, come to participate in increased wealth, in decent conditions of work and living, so eventually in citizenship as well.

So, finally, with most paid labour mild in exertion and duration, with more people possessing leisure to enjoy and also some means with which to make it enjoyable, we have arrived at the matured consumerist culture. First America in the 1950s, then other countries, in their own times and fashions, achieved this universal easy life-style, best symbolized perhaps by colour TV and Coke. (I had previously thought that the suburban house and car were essential; but given present trends rather more than a fifth of the world's people will soon be entering consumerism without them.) Who would dare to denigrate the mild pleasures, the absence of pressures to dehumanize one's fellows, and the many opportunities for real benevolence and solidarity which such a culture enables and occasionally fosters? Let anyone imagine and design a feasible alternative that genuinely promises the masses, now including women as well as men, a better existence than consumerism, however thin and precarious it still is for most of the world.

Yet, as I observed at the beginning of this essay, there is now a darker side to the picture. While its values suffuse through the whole world, the heartland of consumerism suffers this peculiar loss of strength. Perhaps, while consumerism is the highest point of social evolution now attainable, it is *also* merely the means to a shallow and artificial substitute experience of reality and meaning. Certainly, the revolt of the first-generation affluent youth of the 1960s was based partly on just that issue. Also, being based on the presumption that happiness can and should be pursued successfully, consumerism has no vocabulary for comprehending the complementary aspect of human existence, including struggle, evil, pain and death. In this respect, however pleasant and liberating it may be, it may also be incapable of performing the vital social functions of belief based on a shared deep experience. Thus consumerism might mark (and contribute to) the onset of a downward phase of a cycle of empire, reminiscent of Ibn Khaldun but of course of a different sort.

Quality of Workmanship and the Morale of a Culture

Any analogy between the classic cycle of Ibn Khaldun and modern consumerist society must appear far-fetched. There are no longer any despots, and democracy in the social, economic and political spheres still spreads, in practice as well as in principle. Those masses whose lives are still full of want and sorrow may be said to be suffering nearly as much from neglect as from exploitation. And whichever external nations or leaders might claim the status of purifiers of the cultures, they too must establish their plausibility in the forum of international television; and so far none has passed the test. So if we are to establish a fruitful analogy with Ibn Khaldun, we must investigate more deeply than the superficial phenomena of politics.

Let us also leave aside, for the moment, the more obvious worries of the civilization, however much they may seem to contribute to its malaise. I choose to consider quality control, particularly in relation to American technology, in the nuclear, space and military sectors. Here the story is quite amazing, rendered credible only by long familiarity. Perhaps it is best expressed by the condition of American space technology. The Shuttle programme is now (only after the Challenger disaster) revealed to have been incompetent and corrupt;

where each sub-system was deemed safe until proved otherwise; and where finally management simply didn't want to know of any problems. Then, shortly after the Challenger disaster, misfortunes overtook each of the other models of American rockets; so that at the time of writing (late 1986) the United States is incapable of launching a space rocket with any degree of assurance that it will survive.

Here we may speak of a catastrophic collapse of quality control. The implications for the USA as a leading world power, though not discussed much in the English language media, are inescapable. And of course such a case cannot be isolated. American manufacturing industry in steadily losing out to Japan; and American military hardware includes many multibillion dollar boondoggles, with more coming all the time. Star Wars, ostensibly an experiment to test the feasibility of a system already proved impossible, now has its own financial and political momentum; it could well have been a plot hatched by the Russians or (more likely) the Japanese. Business and finance fare no better than manufacturing; we now learn that the Western banking community spent the 1970s in converting other people's money (the petrodollars) into bad debts in the poor countries. Was this neo-imperialism or mega-folly? And if America is in the lead in this doleful respect, its partners (notably Britain) cannot be far behind.

The decline, or collapse, of quality control in these crucial sectors has a significance beyond that of its implications for the strength of the afflicted nation. Quality control is particularly useful in exhibiting the inadequacy of the individualistic–utilitarian ethic for keeping a society together. In any operation, care for quality involves a sacrifice, perhaps small; an expenditure of time and effort which *usually* will have no perceptible effect. If things later go wrong due to inadequate quality now, it will only be sometimes, and anyway it will usually be far from the context of the operation. So it may be argued that the Benthamite 'total net happiness' function may actually be *decreased* by care for quality of workmanship; to make the point plausible, one may imagine cases where quality standards are imposed that are inappropriately severe for the product in question. Certainly, *my* net happiness, in utilitarian terms, is usually quite definitely the better if I cut corners and skimp on quality.

What I have just sketched, with manufacture in mind, holds equally in any sphere of activity: design, administration, research, whatever. And if people doing the work systematically don't care, then no superior can enforce high-quality work on them. In any event, the old Latin motto, 'who guards the guardians?' reminds us that normally slackness goes up and down the line uniformly.

Now, what is the relation between low-quality work and a consumerist culture? Quite simply, consumerism is by its nature hedonistic, Benthamite, however benevolently so in its easygoing way. The legendary American who asked, 'What's posterity done for me?' may have been at variance with the prevailing fashion of sympathy for the natural environment; but his position is essentially that of his culture. And modern orthodox economics reduces to the principle, 'For real love, pay cash.'

At this point my argument is becoming counter-intuitive. For everywhere we see around us evidence of *high* quality—in innovation, design and manufacture, as well as in marketing and advertising. Indeed, the great seductive power of the market economy is that by its 'hidden hand' it shapes its products to fit what consumers want. By contrast, bureaucratic control invariably yields consumer goods of low quality in every respect. But we as consumers only see directly what has been produced for us, on a reasonably competitive world market. Everyone knows that the provision of essential services, such as health and education, cannot be entrusted to such a market. And occasionally, through reports in the media or a live demonstration on TV, we witness those fiascos and disasters involving devices produced under conditions where market quality control is impossible. Such were Three Mile Island and Challenger. While the consumer markets relate to the popular values of a culture, those others (usually involving the State) reflect its real strength as a nation.

Furthermore, a refinement even within the market sector is possible. The Japanese manufacturing miracle, or conquest, can be understood precisely in terms of that particular culture *not* being totally individualistic and consumerist. Very traditional patterns of loyalties and commitments enable them to focus their energies, collectively and individually, and so to excel nearly wherever they choose. By contrast, when there is no such binding force in the productive life of society aside from consumerism, then no one makes a contribution beyond that which pays off directly, and quality inevitably suffers.

Another way of seeing the phenomenon is in the paradox, or joke, about plumbing and rockets. For a long time Western experts and observers were sure that the Soviet Union could never master the sophisticated technology for rocketry or nuclear weapons. The evidence of low-quality consumer goods, including even the plumbing in their best international hotels, seemed conclusive. What such observers missed is the cultural aspect of technology that I have expounded here. It is a commonplace to observe the affinities (political and cultural) between such centralized, totalitarian regimes and the despotisms of old. The core technologies of defence, together with the occasional grand display (such as the legendary Moscow Metro) have had all the available excellence quite deliberately concentrated into them. Housing, plumbing, clothing for the masses could wait, for in such cultures the masses will wait patiently, at least for some decades, provided that they get more security and national pride than hitherto.

Such successors to the charisma-industries of the old cannot survive indefinitely, especially once the Great Leader has departed. In these times, the example of the successful consumerist societies penetrates every curtain. And then, regimes of whatever formal character must come to terms with consumerism, or try with increasing urgency to fabricate a viable alternative in terms of their traditional culture or official ideology. The situation may well become desperate for some governments, for no viable alternative to consumerism has yet been found; and (as some are already aware) the shallowness of the consumerist ethic will eventually become manifest. In the absence of anything to supplement it, a nation, or culture, may well decline or die.

Consumerism and the Survival of Nations

A long time ago the American philosopher William James spoke of the need for a 'moral equivalent of war', and for decades afterwards, liberals condemned him as a militarist. But they missed the point; it is not that war is necessarily good in itself; but that it brings persons and (sometimes) whole sections of a population to a place where the utilitarian ethic cannot apply. Comradeship and sacrifice, whatever their ethical foundation (in religion, patriotism or simple human solidarity) are difficult to justify on utilitarian, hedonistic grounds; witness the contortions of evolutionary biologists in explaining the selective advantage of 'altruism'.

The matter is not merely of theoretical interest; for in this age of democracy or consumerism, it becomes increasingly difficult for governments to persuade peoples to make the sacrifices involved in war or in some other heroic activity. Of course, this is a development that all good liberals applaud; never again could we have a phenomenon like the First World War, men marching off obediently to slaughter and be slaughtered.

But, for better or worse, it does create practical difficulties for statesmen, who occasionally need to display a credible threat of force to establish their policies in a hostile world. This requires that the young men of the nation are generally willing to lay down their lives, in the cause of religion, obedience, or patriotism. Americans, in spite of their rhetoric, are traditionally not eager for such challenges. To gain popular support there, a war must be embraced as a patriotic crusade. In this, Wilson and Roosevelt succeeded, Truman (over Korea) didn't do badly, but poor Lyndon Johnson failed. Then he had to promote and conduct a large military operation as if it were not a patriotic war, but rather a campaign to win 'hearts and minds'. For this the rhetoric of consumerism was the only resource, and so the operation was described, and perhaps eventually conceived, as if it were General Motors marketing cars. The surrogate for sales statistics became body-counts of corpses deemed to be Viet Cong. Computers ruled all, even the selection of targets for remote-control bombing. The results of this vast, bloody pretence were a catastrophe for the USA; it lost geopolitical strength, international credibility, its effectiveness as a military power (outside the fantasy context of nuclear war), and also the willingness of its people to support such adventures again.

It is very easy, and quite justified, to criticize the American governments for the Vietnam War. But they were caught in the historic contradiction of trying to run a great world empire, with all its inevitable material, personal and moral costs, without being able to admit as much to their own individualistic and consumerist population. Usually the dirty work could be done by small specialist forces; but when that failed, the choice naturally seemed between ignominious withdrawal or a larger-scale exercise. When that could not be promoted as a patriotic crusade, the leadership was caught in a cruel contradiction: it had to ask, or try to force, men to go to their deaths in the absence of any symbols or experiences that could produce the commitment which could make such sacrifices meaningful. All this is well known from the analyses of the traumas suffered by the Vietnam veterans, during and after the war. In some ways the moral horrors of Vietnam were worse than those of the trenches of the Great War; in the earlier struggle, it was after all men against men; while here they had to kill, or be killed by, anything that moved. By the end, morale had been corrupted beyond repair; the attempt to run a war without effective meaningful symbols showed itself a disaster.

Thus men would not lay down their lives for General Westmoreland; and without that commitment of soldiers to their group, a war cannot be won. The future of the American empire is thus seriously called into question; if a colonial conflict is not popularly seen as vital to the nation, but only a matter affecting corporations or governments, there will not be a successful war, however much Presidents may scheme, sabotage or engage mercenaries. Nicaragua is a case in point. Good liberals may also applaud such developments, since we all agree that empires based on force are a bad thing. But, we may suppose, suppose it is not armed conflict but some political/economic equivalent of war; such as the sort that in some time of future world crisis to which the Americans may be subjected by the Japanese. Should a people not be able to see beyond their consumerist desires, should 'patriotism' then truly become what Dr Johnson called it two centuries ago, then the prospects for America's survival as a great nation would be dim.

This analysis of America may be justly criticized on the grounds that American individualism pre-dates the consumer society; and so the contradictions which are now becoming manifest may be characteristic of democracy as such, rather than its modern form in consumerism. This may well be; but my analysis is strengthened by consideration of a very different society indeed: modern China. For the first three decades after Liberation, there was certainly no question of consumerism. But Mao wanted to build a great nation from the shattered, impoverished hulk he inherited from centuries of decay. And for him, it had to be a *socialist* nation; otherwise it could too easily slip into colonial dependence on either America or Russia. But how to instil socialist consciousness, getting people to throw off the fendal habits and attitudes of centuries? Mere exhortation, propaganda, laws and Party control did not suffice. So there must be Campaigns, moral equivalents of revolution if you wish; most notoriously, the Great Leap Forward and then the Cultural Revolution. The earlier one was merely a disaster, the later one a catastrophe.

Whether some better design of these campaigns might have been successful is not the issue here. What we know is that the invocation of the symbols of socialism and of the common good failed disastrously. For all his strong similarities to the great unifying emperors of China, Mao did not command the personal charisma necessary for the motivation and control of such a revolution in consciousness.

Now (late 1986) in China there is a near-vacuum in official ideological rhetoric involving socialism or the common good. The message is for each to enrich himself now, so that China will become modern, strong and great. The government will ensure that when that success makes it possible, those now left behind will be enabled to catch up. But such altruism is most definitely relegated to the future; it lives only in this vague promise, as well as in the social welfare programmes whereby the most disadvantaged are protected. And so in this tenth anniversary year of the end of the Cultural Revolution, socialist slogans are nowhere, and militantly socialist themes in the arts are bitterly denounced as dangerous relics of the ten-year catastrophe. By default, consumerism is the word in China. Peasants can get very rich; successful workers can buy their bits of electronic happiness; young people drink coffee, smoke, and take taxis on dates. Just now it seems to be exhilarating, at least for those who are making it.

Of course, there will be a price to pay, there is no doubt that this Chinese government, nearly unique in its public recognition of problems and shortcomings, past, present and future, will do its best to anticipate and alleviate them. Whether it will be able to control the effects of a sudden reversal of the rhetoric of equality, sharing and sacrifice on which a full generation was raised is not at all certain. But it can be argued that, analogously to the Americans trying to conduct a war in Vietnam without invoking the morality of patriotism, the Chinese Communist Party has no alternative but to reconstruct and modernize a society while avoiding the rhetoric of socialism. Those slogans had been completely discredited in the wreckage of the Cultural Revolution and the rule of the Gang of Four. Now they are raising a generation whose consciousness is being formed by the TV commercials, and whose urban working class (blue- and white-collar) will soon experience the vast wage differentials made inevitable by the influx of foreign capital and personnel.

At the moment, such problems are still on the horizon. Although there are still many of the inefficiencies and incompetences that are characteristic of the state of 'underdevelopment', still there is a sense of purpose (in making China great again), as well as a striving for more openness and criticism as well as more efficiency and expertise. There is still much inefficiency and confusion in the running of the Chinese economy, but it perceptibly improves and grows.

One sees the really ugly face of consumerism in those societies where 'developing' is a euphemism; where the traditional values are effectively dead, and 'modern' values sink to their most cheap and meretricious expression. There 'consumerism' can hardly be blamed as a cause; it is but one symptom of a social and spiritual pathology, otherwise manifested in universal corruption and brutality. In such context, it is a bad joke to speak of 'quality' at all, except perhaps in the techniques of oppression and vice. There we see what happens when the ancient symbols have totally lost their effectiveness, and the society cannot make a reality of the new ones, be they democracy or even consumerism. Such societies are rather like cruel, large-scale living laboratories, exhibiting what happens when values collapse. They serve as a reminder that we *cannot* take for granted that civilization as we know it will survive with its elementary decencies intact.

I have used the examples of America and China, because on them I can speak from personal experience. In those cases, appeals to patriotism or to socialism were, each in their own way, futile for the achievement of national goals. Hence a form of consumerism was adopted; in the American case with immediate catastrophic effects, and in the Chinese with profound long-term consequences as yet unpredictable. There may well be other cases, where religion has been invoked, with comparable results; but those I leave to others with more knowledge.

Retrospect

I can now make it clear how this analysis relates to that of Ibn Khaldun. He analysed a repeated cycle of vigour and decay among rulers and consequently their societies. I suppose that this process was superimposed on a stable background of shared religious experience. This enabled the effective deployment of a charisma-industry, which used splendour and beauty as the visible part of the techniques for maintaining social solidarity. Thereby, obedience, loyalty and satisfaction of the masses could be achieved even under conditions which included evils that we can simply not comprehend. We have pale reminders of this in modern times, when even quite sophisticated societies exhibit patriotic fervour or veneration for a truly great leader.

I then suppose that for the past half-millennium at least, that formerly stable background has been universally in decline. The 'developing' societies suffer from more than the pathologies of the inheritance of colonialism; they are caught between the death of an old world, the only one in which their special cultures had any meaning, and the inaccessibility (by a multitude of causes) of the new one. China may escape from this trap, and there may well be some others. The 'developed' societies of the Occident are those which started their careers with an effective denial of that background experience; and so they have flourished as it has dwindled and decayed. But now they exhibit pathologies of their own, and some of them may well be due to the inadequacy of consumerism, a major source of their social solidarity, for the tasks of survival or even of national well-being. Making good plumbing involves different sorts of commitments and endeavours from making good rockets; and General Motors (or its symbolic surrogate) is not a cause for which men will lay down their lives.

When I considered the pathologies of consumerism at the level of commitment and morale, I was drawing on the analysis of John Ruskin in *Unto This Last*. There he defines a profession as an occupation whose members should be prepared to die for its integrity. If someone would not, then he does not have a calling, and his work is utterly without significance. Ruskin's essay was in individualistic, moral terms; I have used his insight not to exhort but to analyse a social phenomenon. This is how I could argue that all my examples are part of the same phenomenon. China after Mao exhibits a recourse to consumerism, unavoidable in spite of all its obvious hazards, after the collapse of socialism as an inspirational ideology. America's failure in Vietnam shows its inadequacy as a substitute for patriotism in a war. And Challenger dramatically illustrates the fate even of industrial quality control in a society where consumerism is fully matured and dominant.

Considered in the light of social theory, this present essay is but another chapter in the long discussion of *Gemeinschaft* and *Gesellschaft*. I raise the question whether *Gesellschaft* can long survive with no moral foundation outside those of rationally calculated individualistic values, now realized on the mass scale as consumerism. It also evokes memories of Habermas's earlier writings, particularly his discussion of the *crisis of legitimacy* of modern governments; these must produce the goods of consumerism, or risk losing the consent of their governed. In the absence of that consent, then corruption and anarchy are the most likely consequences. In those terms, our benevolent, consumerist, democratic societies of the Occident are in a precarious situation indeed; they depend on a maldistribution of the world's wealth that cannot be justified, on an assault on the natural environment that cannot be sustained, and recently on the acquiescence of other nations with no grounds for a permanent loyalty to them.

If this conclusion seems gloomy, the cause lies not in myself but in our situation. I can analyse our predicament with my own experience and reason. To resolve it seems to me to require something more; and that I leave to others.

I am indebted to Isabel Phillips for the discussions in which many of these points were raised and clarified. This is a previously unpublished essay.

Gaia and the Philosophy of Science

This essay is adapted from the transcript of a lecture given in October 1987 at a conference on James Lovelock's Gaia Hypothesis (first propounded in *Gaia: A New Look at Life on Earth*; Oxford University Press, 1979). In editing it, I modified the English style from the spoken to the written. But I felt that to remove the elements of dialogue in the text would deprive the essay of much of its liveliness. Hence readers will find themselves spoken to occasionally; this is not an uncorrected error, but a reminder of the origins of the essay in a very exciting and important encounter.

In thinking of what I could accomplish most usefully here, I decided that instead of giving you my opinions on various philosophical issues, I would try to clarify the issues on which other people can debate. I will therefore try to raise, in a rather condensed form, the different sorts of philosophical issues that have been in play in the discussions of the Gaia hypothesis. The only positive opinions that I shall offer will be not about Gaia but about philosophy.

Philosophy and Gaia

One important thing about philosophy is that down through the ages it is always studying the same problems. Some people consider it inferior to science on that ground, for it never seems to get anywhere. But as humans we do face the same sorts of issues and dilemmas through the centuries; and an analysis given by a Plato or a Descartes can still be illuminating today. Of course, this is a matter of degree; if you are in a traditional Eskimo culture, or even a traditional Chinese culture, the formulation of the problems will be different to a significant degree. In our European culture, since the times of classical Greece, there has been a remarkable continuity of the great themes around which we do philosophy. It is quite reasonable to speak of the Good, the True, the Real, the Just, the Beautiful, and also the Human, while knowing that for each generation these root ideas must be seen somewhat differently and brought to life again.

It is against this background that I find the Gaia hypothesis so exciting. The hypothesis is that the earth is a gigantic homoeostat, and one whose ever-changing equilibrium states are created by life itself; so that our total environment, including the very rocks under our feet, is the product of the endeavour by life to maintain its environment. It seems to me that Gaia may become a very important event in our modern intellectual history. I am generally rather sceptical of new titles or new labels about scientific ideas, because most of them come and go very quickly, more like fashions than like truths. There are some grand organizing ideas that sound very exciting, but then they cannot be made into hypotheses for research science, and so they remain external to science, operating at the level of popularization or propaganda. By contrast, it now seems possible that the Gaia hypothesis will begin to give real coherence to what has hitherto been a rather complex and confused set of ideas about the natural environment. It will thereby become a very powerful organizing principle, analogous to continental drift in geology. It will suggest problems and regulate solutions, over a very wide range of natural phenomena, which had hitherto been considered too vast, and too complex, to be amenable to any approach other than crude and speculative simulations. With that strength, it will affect our perceptions of nature and therefore of ourselves, in a solid and determinate way. Thereby it will change the way in which we approach the perennial questions of philosophy.

In the discussions of Gaia that I have participated in and witnessed, I have sensed a variety of contrasting positions, and also the potential for conflicts among those committed to the Gaia hypothesis. In themselves, these are no bad thing, for they reflect the healthy diversity among our backgrounds and outlooks. But our debates will be more effective and constructive if we are clear about the issues that may divide us, and also understand that in these debates we are doing philosophy and not science.

The Nature of Humanity

This is the first big issue to be raised by Gaia. In its old form, it involved the placing of mankind between the apes and the angels. Now it concerns our relation to non-human nature. Clearly, in some ways we are part of nature, and in some ways not; just as in some ways we depend on nature and in others we change it from outside. The debates can be on the ways in which these relations work out; or there can be a question of whether there is a decisive, essential answer on one side or the other, and if so which. We are interested in ourselves, wanting to know whether there is something very special about us as a species, different in some very important way from amoebas and dragonflies and cats. We *feel* as if we are different, and more important in some scheme of things that is bigger than ourselves; and yet that is a philosophical position that can never be conclusively proved.

Gaia introduces a new element into this picture of ourselves in nature. Within the great dynamic homoeostat of the planetary system, we are a very little thing in physical terms, comparable to a culture in a Petri dish. We may not be very long-lived as a species, and so in another billion years there may be hardly any trace of our temporary presence. But while we are here, we can have quite significant effects on Gaia in her present phase. We may quite possibly be driving Gaia rapidly towards an unstable boundary, to where she must flip to a new phase, with very destructive consequences for ourselves and much else besides. It is even possible that the new phase of Gaia will be one that is at such an extreme of temperature that life as it has built up over the billennia will be extinguished or severely reduced.

Hence we are now forced to look at humankind as not merely inter-dependent with nature, or symbiotic with the rest of Gaia. Rather, in these terms we may be a pathogenic parasite on the whole planetary organism. It had done quite well without us for a long time, going through its cycles smoothly or roughly. Then *Homo 'sapiens'* arrives, and within a twinkling, on the scale of planetary time, he (should I use the masculine here?) does such things as to foul the whole system and destroy his nest and much else. To emphasize the point, let me try another analogy: ourselves (and particularly European man) as a weed. When a previously stable system is disturbed, the weeds invade and choke out everything else. Of course, after a while they create a new stability and are themselves squeezed out by a new flora. Is this the best that can be hoped for ourselves? If so, our pride in our accomplishments becomes rather muted, and we seriously wonder whether we are some sort of mistake.

Now, this pessimistic way of looking at humanity did not start with Gaia; ever since the Bomb and pollution, people, helped by science fiction writers and some scientists, have been aware of such possibilities. What is new with Gaia is that the issue now has a basis in science. The possibility that we are, on balance, a bad thing for our planet can now be stated in a precise, even partly testable form. This can cause a change in our image of ourselves comparable to those wrought by, say, Copernicus, Darwin and Freud. The first of these initiated a change in our picture of heaven and earth so that there is no longer a location for the angels up above, and for the damned souls down below. The second showed that no special creation was required to explain the origin of the many non-human species of living things, and so by analogy none was required for mankind. Finally, with Freud we discovered the unconscious, so that our reason, what really distinguishes us from the animals, turns out to be not so supreme and independent, but is partly governed by causes like the reactions of a goldfish to stimuli. Each of these scientific discoveries was opposed on the grounds that its philosophical interpretation would deny the dignity and uniqueness of mankind; yet humanity has survived them all, and (we think) with greater understanding and perhaps wisdom each time.

The contribution that Gaia makes to this sequence of discoveries is to take the process a step further. We are not merely an integral part of nature, depending on myriads of yet undiscovered natural processes for our very existence. But we are perhaps an unnatural part of nature, unique (to our present knowledge) among all species, in that we threaten to destroy the homoeostatic balance on which our existence depends. Hence the meaning of our existence on this planet is called into question. We can no longer assume that in some way we as a species are 'good' in the sense that each of us strives to be good to those around us. Perhaps collectively we are 'bad'; and if so, what is it all about, if anything? If by our own criteria of richness, diversity and complexity of organization and life, we as a species now threaten to destroy and degrade all of it on this planet, then our own value to — may I call it — the creation is seriously put into doubt.

Suppose that Gaia was doing just fine until we came along and introduced our increasingly unstable perturbations into the system, now possibly culminating in something quite planetismic within our lifetimes. What then of ourselves? Of course I am not predicting this; but since the possibility of such a man-made planetary catastrophe cannot be denied, then the philosophical, or existential, question is a real one. Thus, Gaia raises further disturbing questions about our place in a bigger scheme of things, if there is one; and given the scientific strength of Gaia, the philosophical question, a new form of an old issue, becomes all the more real and urgent.

The Problem of Evil

This more general problem follows on naturally from those discussed just above. It is something that has been with us as a philosophical issue, since Biblical times; we have the book of Job and also the myth of Adam and Eve. Certainly in this century we have seen enough evil, either malevolent as with the Holocaust, or benevolent as with the Bomb. No philosopher or theologian has yet had a permanent success in showing that the apparent evil that pervades, even dominates, so much of human activity and human history is really good in a clever disguise. We have even had people who blame it all on civilization, who imagine what used to be called 'noble savages' as in the eighteenth century, or perhaps 'natural people' now, from Rousseau to Laurens van der Post, contrasting their purity and genuine realization of the values we profess, to our corrupted and sinful state. Others try to find some civilization which seems now, from its records, to have been in an harmonious and stable relation with its environment before some unfortunate accident terminated its life.

Such reflections are the negative reaction to the general optimism that has characterized European civilization for some centuries. We have applied science for the transformation of the means of production, and thereby achieved the solution of the curse of poverty at the material level. It only remains to reorganize our social arrangements, and then there will be enough food and fibre for all, together with an abundance of manufactured goods. And wherever there has been such progress in the material realm, there has been a corresponding improvement in the cultural and spiritual lives of people, with the driving out of the superstition and obscurantism on which thrive a reactionary clergy and their masters.

Here then, are the two contradictory views on the human meaning of industrial society. What contribution can Gaia make to this philosophical issue concerning the good society? In a general way, Gaia tells us that what has been going on over the last few hundred years cannot be extended to all mankind, or even sustained for very long. Regardless of its debatable merits for human advancement, it is only a temporary phenomenon. I like to make the point vividly with a question. Can the biosphere support a billion cars and also a billion air conditioners? This would be the load, if a Western standard of living, with instant transport and domestic climate control, were to be shared equally throughout the world. With the help of Gaia one could calculate the impact of the wastes in materials and energy that would be created by such a multiplication, fivefold or twentyfold, of these processes. Gaia reminds us that the biosphere is governed by interlocking cycles just as much as the biochemistry of a living body; and it can be poisoned in just the same way. But if such burdens on the downstream cycles of Gaia are not sustainable, then the vision of a just society for all mankind being achieved through our present technology is a delusion. We can keep our comforts for some time, and let the world's poor continue to rot; but that would be evil, and would sooner or later become destructive in physical as well as moral terms to us all.

Thus Gaia, as a sharpening of an ecological perspective, provides us with two philosophical issues arising out of the destructiveness of the ordinary operations of our modern industrial technology. In the long run (which may not be very long by planetary standards or even by human ones) the disruptive effects of our material culture will be producing vast and destructive changes; so that our own status as beings endowed with some superior qualities is called into question. Then, even in the short run, the impossibility of extending the current material benefits of our industrial system to all of humanity means that we are the Rich and they are the Poor; and the evil of injustice on a planetary scale is enforced not merely by consciously selfish politics, but by the exigencies of our productive machine.

Knowledge and Ignorance

The last problem involved wastes, and that leads me naturally into my next topic. This is the theory of knowledge, frequently entitled by its Greek name, epistemology. For me the problem needs a new look; for we can no longer maintain the traditional view of science as rolling back the boundary with

215

ignorance, perhaps even approaching truth asymptotically. The lesson of our industrial technology, as sharpened by awareness of Gaia, is that ignorance will always be with us (so long as things persist in their present form); and that indeed a *man-made* ignorance constitutes a great and ever-increasing threat to our survival. This is, I believe, a new move in epistemology.

I can illustrate this philosophical point by continuing my discussion of wastes; this is a paradoxical topic, perhaps even not in the best of taste, but I believe it to be relevant to the sort of philosophy that we need. 'Waste' is an increasingly urgent problem in industrialized societies; and yet we know very little about it. A few years ago I gave a lecture course on waste, and in my preliminary reading I scoured the catalogues of the University of California libraries, to find materials on the problem of waste. There was plenty on particular sorts of waste, but on Waste — nothing. This is probably because the industrial system does not yet recognize that there is a problem of Waste, only of particular wastes. The fact that it is being increasingly threatened with widespread poisoning by toxic wastes, and (in America at least) is becoming choked with nuclear wastes, is not yet seen as a systematic problem.

It can be argued that any culture needs to maintain ignorance, of some sort, about the things that threaten its integrity; we speak of taboos, in both the strict anthropological sense and also in the popular, social sense. Perhaps now, waste, being so nasty, threatening and in the last resort unmanageable by our present approaches, is a taboo of late industrial society. Were we to consider seriously, systematically and publicly what is known of the environmental consequences of its activities, with waste primary among them but including other assaults as well, then so much that we now take for granted as benefits would be revealed as incurring incalculable costs as well. So the system maintains its plausibility by enforcing a sort of 'ignorance of ignorance'. All the concentration is upon our knowledge, of what we understand about nature, and how we can control her. The areas of ignorance, most easily seen in wastes and pollution, are left to the 'garbage sciences', starved of resources, prestige and influence. Mostly this can be accomplished by automatic means, since the whole social structure of science is organized away from effective work on such problems; in that sense we have 'socially constructed ignorance'. But in case that is not enough, many governments now ensure that there will be no trouble, by destroying the meagre research resources still available, on the principle that 'if business won't pay for research it's not worth doing'; here we may speak of 'politically constructed ignorance.'

One result of such tendencies is that we find an increasing number of urgent and intractable problems being thrust upon those with a competence to handle them, ranging from acid to CFCs, ozone and the greenhouse effect. In every case our knowledge, at least at the beginning of their study, is weak and paltry compared with our ignorance. And the policy implications of their uncertain conclusions are even more open-ended. When should we start making the investments for a planned removal of the world's major coastal cities, in anticipation of the rise in mean sea-level consequent on greenhouse heating? Such questions betray our ignorance, which now increasingly swamps our knowledge when we must make long-term decisions.

Of course, science has always had to cope with ignorance; and its progress over recent centuries has seemed so triumphant and inevitable because of the way in which the border with ignorance was rolled back in one field after another. But now we have a new phenomenon, which I call 'man-made ignorance'. This is an absence of necessary knowledge concerning systems and cycles that exist out there in the natural world, but which exist only because of human activities. Were it not for our intervention, those things and events would not exist, and so our lamentable and dangerous ignorance of them is man-made as much as the systems themselves. Most of our wastes are of this character; indeed we may say that the category 'waste' is itself a sign of a bad technology. (Lest I seem to have things too neatly sewn up, I may raise the question whether there is indeed waste in Gaia, such as the vast quantity of nitrogen in the atmosphere.)

Our man-made ignorance can extend quite dramatically to insoluble yet urgent engineering problems, such as the design of a repository for nuclear waste that will be safe for some tens of thousands of years. This is a very good example for illustrating the problem; I use it whenever I lecture on such issues. This impossibly long time-horizon in design is coupled with an urgently brief time-horizon in decision. The American federal authorities are increasingly anxious to 'solve' the problem of the nuclear wastes, at least in principle, lest there be some nasty accident at a temporary storage place when there is no remedy in sight. But, as Barry Commoner said long ago, everything has to go somewhere, and statistically negligible people can have political bite. So in the disposal of nuclear wastes (perhaps appropriately, given the general nature of the technology), we have at Yucca Mountain, Nevada, an exquisite interaction of knowledge, ignorance, Gaia and dirty politics: the classic case. Please excuse my aesthetic appreciation of what is a very nasty problem; I cannot help it.

When we consider the complexity and interrelatedness of the cycles by which Gaia maintains her balances, the massiveness of the disruptions which we now impose on her, the primitive quality of the scientific materials by which we attempt to decipher her clues; then truly we can speak of a man-made ignorance, criminal or pitiful depending on your point of view, in our relations with Gaia. Let me make it clear that I do not think that this ignorance is absolute or static; there is much that is being done by science, both inside and outside the Establishment, on all these problems. One of the enjoyable and exciting things about being at this conference is seeing science of such relevance, originality and excellence being reported and even being in the making. And certainly, more will be done, as the urgency of these problems becomes plain to us all, except perhaps for the most myopic or tyrannical of

217

politicians. But the questions remain, will enough be done to sort out the existing damage to Gaia; and also will the scientists have the appropriate conception of their task?

Methodology

When we reflect on the interaction of knowledge with ignorance in the scientific problems of Gaia, it becomes clear that a very new conception of what scientific work is about will become relevant and indeed necessary. This does *not* mean abandoning rigorous research using any appropriate method, be it quantitative, field research, simulation or what have you. But the relations of the scientists to the materials they explore, and to each other, will have to change. In his classic work on the philosophy of science, Thomas Kuhn described 'normal science' as the 'strenuous and devoted attempt to force nature into the conceptual boxes provided by [one's] professional education'. With such a normality, it is not surprising that attempts to achieve genuine interdisciplinary research always founder. Nor is there any philosophical basis for resisting the inevitable trends for research to become atomized and fragmented, consequently and socially. How can there possibly be an integration of the various sorts of expertise relevant to any real Gaia problem, except when the research is done by those courageous individuals out on the margin, they and their work surviving precariously on the goodwill of supporters in funding agencies?

I believe that the recognition of ignorance can provide some basis for escaping from the atomism of the scientific life as we have experienced it hitherto. I might here paraphrase Winston Churchill's famous remark about greatness, and say that some research problems are invented (as in basic science), some are presented (as in mission-orientated science), and some are *thrust upon us* (as in problems of an assaulted environment). In this last case, scientists do not have the luxury of satisfying professional standards of rigour. Such problems may be described as having uncertain facts, disputed values, high decision stakes and urgent decisions. When we evaluate solutions to such problems, we broaden our perspective from 'correctness' (relative to the state of the art in experiment and theory), to 'quality' in a functional context that is partly technical and partly societal.

This is not the place to enter into a long discussion of the methodology of policy-related research. Let it suffice for now that I can see this as becoming a crucially important area of science, and one in which the assumptions about who is competent to do science and why, become drastically altered. In this, 'housewives' epidemiology' and TV investigative journalism will have their legitimate place, alongside the more conventional research. I could also argue that without the critical presence of such complementary sciences, it will be all the more difficult for the aware minority within the community of established scientists to make any impression on their colleagues and leaders. There is no need for me to labour this point here, since so much of what *The Ecologist* has published and fostered is in just this category of science.

As such science matures, there will be problems aplenty, practical and theoretical. One of the thorniest will be quality control. I wrote on this a long time ago, in my old book; and some of my gloomiest predictions seem to be coming true. We might ask, if the scientists themselves now have difficulty in maintaining good quality in their research, how can there be any chance of this when all problems are confused and conflicted? Well, I think there is an answer to that, not perfect by any means, but at least providing a mechanism. This is, public debate in all forums including those before a mass TV audience. Our system of trial by jury rests on the ability of ordinary people to see through the skills of advocacy, frequently employed on quite abstract and technical arguments. Without proposing any institutional forms at this point (for that would be wandering too far afield), I can imagine how an enrichment of the mechanisms for criticism (which as Karl Popper saw is the life-blood of science) could provide a means of ensuring quality control in this new sort of science, appropriate to the problems of Gaia.

When it is appreciated all around that a Gaia problem, either on a large or a small scale, is simply of a different type from that of atomized traditional science, then appropriate techniques will develop naturally. With them will come appropriate conceptions of the objects of enquiry of the sciences; the ruling assumption that 'anything larger than *E. coli* only serves to confuse the issue' in studying life will join other vulgar prejudices conceived in imitation of a conception of physics that died in 1905. Concepts such as integration and complex functionality will emerge from the backroom where biologists have entertained them somewhat shamefacedly, and be recognized as appropriate for Gaia just as much as consciousness is for humans. Thus, we may have a very exciting time ahead, in our thinking about what science is for, and is.

Ontology

I cannot resist raising this last philosophical issue, even though it might make some people quite uncomfortable. 'Ontology' is the Greek term for the study of Reality; and with this I might seem to be introducing metaphysics or even religion into a scientific gathering. I should say at the outset that no particular conception of reality is entailed by adherence to the Gaia concept. Clearly, an old-fashioned atomist might have a lot of translating to do, back and forth between his concepts and those of Gaia; but for the human mind few such feats are impossible. At the other end, support of Gaia need not take a person further than acceptance of 'systems' and suchlike as real for the purposes of doing the science. And we all know that when Jim Lovelock chose the name 'Gaia' he was most definitely not implying that the earth is a goddess, or alive, or anything of the sort.

And yet, when we look at the earlier history, perhaps the prehistory, of the

219

scientific conception of the earth as a great homoeostat governed by life-processes, we see what must be called metaphysics. There were some quite amazing people around in Paris in the 1920s, and in their dialogues there could not have been any tight, defensive boundaries around their accepted realities. Vernadsky may have seen the whole thing as a vast harmonious hierarchy of systems; but then Bergson had his *élan vital*; and Teilhard de Chardin told explicitly of his experiences of something bigger and more meaningful than any merely perceptual events.

That was all long ago, and now we are all scientists rather than speculators. But, perhaps partly because of the playful name, partly because of the very deep human problems it raises, and also partly because of the approach to science that it fosters, Gaia is likely to make its contribution to the enrichment of realities that we are already experiencing. This is happening mainly on the medical side. When we know that ageing is a disease, and car accidents are an epidemic, heroic bacteriology is no longer the most effective paradigm for health problems. Also, when so many people are helped by acupuncture and allied techniques, it is hard to continue to say that *chi* energy is an Oriental superstition. What is to be done with the mind—body interaction, revealed in many manifestations from placebo effect through psychogenic disease and the practical success of healing therapies, is an exciting topic.

When I think of these enriched, perhaps nesting realities from the crudest atomism out to that of the visionary, I cannot help recalling that marvellous scientific satire of Victorian England, *Flatland*. There the realities were of dimensions; and the protagonist, a Square, was taken on a journey to see the busy Linelander and also the self-satisfied Pointlander. His education was in a third dimension, which (to his cost) he found impossible to communicate to his countrymen; and I must not tell you of the dénouement where awareness was shown to have its limits however high you go. We with Gaia can look down upon the old-fashioned atomist; but who is looking down on us?

I cannot make any prediction as to how Gaia will affect our perceived, accepted and (in a sense) socially constructed scientific realities. But science works in many ways; we know how it was the moon race, that essentially pointless extravaganza, that gave humanity its first effective vision of Gaia, blue, delicate and alone. It also impressed on Jim Lovelock that the earth's atmosphere is an *unstable* system; in this we have the distinction between the living earth and its dead neighbours, and hence the problem whose solution is Gaia. What sorts of perceptions and experiences will come now, is beyond my powers or interest to foresee. But once we have Gaia, it is difficult to keep the lines tightly drawn. I have in mind a metaphor that even Jim Lovelock has used, namely that Gaia can be 'sick'. Now I am sure that such an anthropomorphism can be translated back down into terms of stabilities, responses to shocks, and suchlike. But the term 'sick' is now in play, along with 'Gaia' herself. If we, so long accustomed to thinking of ourselves as the crown of creation, the only reality that really counts, come to see ourselves as guests of Gaia, and moreover bad guests who have been making our hostess sick, well then our reâlity will be that bit different, and the challenge of Gaia will have moved on another step.

This essay is the text, slightly modified, of 'Gaia and the philosophy of science', published in *Gaia, the Thesis, the Mechanisms and the Implications*, (eds P. Bunyard and E. Goldsmith) (Proceedings of the First Annual Camelford Conference); published in 1988 by the Wadebridge Ecological Centre, Worthyvale Manor, Camelford, Cornwall PL32 9TT, UK.

Science, Ignorance and Fantasies

Our modern scientific technological culture is based on two articles of faith. The first, deriving from Bacon, is that knowledge is power, over our material environment. The second, from Descartes and his philosophical colleagues, is that material reality is 'atomic' in structure, consisting of simple elements denuded of interconnection and of causes relating to human perceptions and values. On that basis our civilization has achieved unparalleled success in theoretical knowledge and material power. But we all know that we are dangerously deficient in control. Viewed from *inside*, we may question whether we are only 'sorcerer's apprentices', capable of starting the magic engine but incompetent to control or stop it. Viewed from *outside*, our civilization may appear as a 'weed', dominating and choking out all other cultures in the ground disturbed by its material conquests.

In recent years there has been an increasing tide of criticism of this dominant world-view on all fronts. Following on the explosion of 'consciousness' among the affluent youth in the 1960s, the metaphysics of this civilization has been subjected to critical scrutiny, and many alternatives proposed. Some of these call for a return to world-views and religions which pre-date the rise of the great civilizations. More influential (so far) are those that draw on the cultural resources of the East, particularly the Taoist style of thinking. The presence of 'complementarity' in the structure of the most advanced theories of fundamental physics has been used strongly as evidence for the naturalness and 'scientific' character of this alternative framework of thought. The steady growth of 'alternative' or 'complementary' medicine, in fields where the 'atomistic' style seems ineffectual, counter-productive or positively barbarous, gives this other world-view a firm basis in successful practice and popular experience.

In the area of technology, the focus of Francis Bacon's dream, we have been coming to see more clearly how the solution of a problem at one level, such as in a 'technical fix', can produce more serious, perhaps insoluble, problems at other levels. The various forms of pollution, problems of the disposal of radioactive wastes, and the conversion of the former colonial world into a global slum and sweatshop for the 'advanced' nations are reminders of the inadequacy of a simplistic approach to 'power over Nature'. Here I shall develop some heuristic concepts whereby we may better comprehend such problems. I hope thereby to show how alternative styles of thought are as relevant to the control of material culture as to abstract physics or medicine.

Value-Loading in Science, or the Social Construction of Ignorance

The optimistic philosophy of science of previous generations rested on a simple, linear scheme of the application of science to human benefit. Science produced facts, either in its own pursuits or in response to perceived social problems. In themselves these facts were value-free; the interests or prejudices of the individual investigator did not affect his conclusions, which were tested against the objective world of Nature. But in their totality, they embodied the highest human values. The miseries of mankind were easily seen to result from poverty, ignorance and superstition. The first two of these would be removed directly by the result of scientific enquiry; and the last would be defeated by the exposure of the real causes of human suffering, in material and intellectual culture. Those who espoused this philosophy were well aware that Science would not easily succeed on its own; there had to be a struggle against the institutions that profited from exploitation and oppression; previously, established religion and, more recently, an unjust social system.

The successes of this ideology, at least for the great mass of people in its homelands, must never be overlooked. Even now, when material poverty persists in the most advanced nations, there will be sharp practical contradictions between 'progress' (realized in the relief of drudgery and the production of jobs), and an 'ecological' awareness of the limits of 'growth'.

However, even within those highly developed economies, some systematic complications have been recognized. The theme of 'choice' has been appreciated as vital to the direction of science and technology. The image of the isolated, autonomous 'pure scientist', following his or her own curiosity and accidentally producing results of social benefit, is totally obsolete. Science is now a big business requiring choices for the allocation of limited resources. And technology cannot depend on an automatic mechanism of a market to turn inventions into successful innovations. In each case there must be 'policy', enabling direction to be given, and choices to be made, in accordance with general strategic objectives.

What is the source of such a strategy? It does not come from an immediate contact with Nature that is instantly and rigorously tested by results. Rather, it is found in institutions, which, since they embody power, must necessarily be closely aligned with the general political/economic structures of the society of which they are a part. The ultimate motive of such strategic planning may well

223

be the improvement of the condition of mankind. But this aspiration will inevitably be filtered through the realities of power in any given context. Hence the science that is done (and perhaps more importantly, the science that is *not* done) reflects the values of a society as they are realized in its dominant institutions. In terms of this analysis, such slogans as 'science is not neutral' and 'science for the people' are not merely partisan rhetoric. They represent protests against the particular institutional arrangements for the productions of scientific knowledge, and also against the ideology of 'objectivity' by which it is still reinforced.

It might be thought that in spite of these forces shaping and (by some criteria) distorting the collection of scientific materials available to society, there must still be a hard core of 'facts' independent of these forces. This is a very delicate and sensitive question; for if we abandon all belief in our commitment to 'objectivity' in science, then there is no defence against charlatans or power-politicians deciding public policy on matters scientific and technological. Hence I only argue that 'objectivity' is by no means guaranteed by the materials or the techniques of science, but rather emerges partly from the integrity of individuals and partly from open debate on scientific results.

I can establish this point by an example from a common element of scientific technique: statistical inference. When statisticians test an hypothesis, they cannot possibly decide its truth or falsity; at best they work to within a 'confidence limit', which (roughly speaking) gives the odds (in terms of a mathematical model of the universe to which the given data are assumed to belong) that their conclusion is correct. Different problems conventionally are investigated to different confidence limits, say 95% or 99%. A more rigorous confidence limit requires a more expensive investigation. But a conclusion 'no evidence that . . .' is always relative to the pre-assigned confidence limit. A more searching test might have proved a positive result. Hence the *values* defining the investigation, the costs of 'false negatives' and of 'false positives', as well as the cost of the study itself, can determine the answer. A low-cost investigation can result in an effect remaining concealed. Knowledge is costly; but the price of economy is continued ignorance.

This general point of methodology can become an issue of political struggle in the case of suspected pollutants. When one considers all the methodological problems of field investigations, ranging from the inherent imperfections of data, through the weight to be assigned to indirect evidence (as from animal studies), the assumptions of 'normal' practice, and the implicit burden of proof in any regulatory decision, it is easy to see why at the present time methodology has become overtly political, at least in those countries (such as the USA) where procedures are required to be published and available for criticism. There, the typical situation is for 'the facts' provided by science to be the focus of debate in public forums, regulatory agencies, and the courts as well.

All this occurs only when a scientific issue has become salient, and there are institutions for its public debate. Until then, and generally elsewhere, the public is ignorant of environmental hazards. The ignorance is not due to an essential impenetrability of the phenomena, but to social decisions (taken in leading institutions of state and of science) to neglect certain problems in favour of others. Such problems will usually *not* be those promising prestige and rewards to a scientific élite, but rather those involving diffuse, imperceptible, chronic or delayed effects of the unintended by-products of the industrial system. In that sense, our scientific—technological establishment moulds public awareness, by negative means, as surely as the theological establishment of earlier times did by indoctrination and prohibitions. The 'social construction of ignorance' is a phenomenon of our modern period, all the more important because it happens unnoticed and in contradiction to the received ideology of science as the bearer of Truth.

Technological Blunders

Corresponding to the new uncertainties in science, we have the recent discovery of the possibility of massive blunders in technology. For a long time it had been recognized that the costs and benefits of technological advance are unequal in their incidence. The conquest and destruction of native peoples by those with superior means of production or destruction is no longer easily justified by 'the progress of civilization'. But we must now reckon with a new species of 'bad' arising from the supposed automatic 'good' of technological progress. This will occur most obviously where a technology is strongly innovative and lacking the automatic controls of a competitive market. Then it can happen that ignorance in the design process and incompetence in fabrication and operation can combine to produce a resounding failure. The most notorious present case is the civil nuclear power industry in the USA. There, cost and time overruns have produced crippling burdens of debt on utilities, even when plants are completed. And when they are abandoned after the expenditure of hundreds of millions of dollars, the victims (utilities and their customers) are left with massive debts and the real possibility of bankruptcy. And incompetence in operation, resulting from the power industry's being quite unprepared for the sophistication of the technology with which it was presented by science, produce even more crippling burdens.

Less obvious on the ground, but equally dramatic, are those cases where chemical manufacturers proceed for years to produce substances that are hazardous in all sorts of ways, choosing frequently to remain in wilful ignorance of the dangers to their workforces, consumers and the general public. When this socially constructed ignorance is eventually exploded, it appears that the guilty men were only ordinary people doing their jobs within the constraints of compartmentalized bureaucratic responsibility and generalized cost-cutting.

The question, how could all this happen? is a real one. Engineers and plant managers of all sorts, presumably well trained and competent in their jobs, have as a group allowed major industries to cause great inconvenience and damage, and now to face destructive popular antagonism. A part of the answer may lie in the traditional education and outlook of such persons. It has been overwhelmingly restrictive, and reductionist, preparing for competence in routine operation, but providing no tools, technical or conceptual, for coping with the new problems of modern high technology. These problems include extreme sensitivity of plant to deviations from 'normal', so that simple, unavoidable errors can have costly or catastrophic consequences, most familiar in the case of nuclear power. Further, environmental impacts, no longer the gross, obvious pollutants of nineteenth century factories, lie totally outside the technical competence or experience of those who design and operate installations. Trained to solve simple problems in traditional ways, the engineers are far from being in control of the hyper-sophisticated technologies they have created.

Quality Control—The Moral Element

Such problems in technology may be viewed merely as the growing pains of some industries where progress has been a bit too rapid for comfort for a couple of decades. That may well be; only time will tell. But these phenomena do raise the problem of the maintenance of quality control in these fields. The recent spate of publicized cases of fraud, plagiarism and the claiming of co-authorship on another's work show that the problem is also present in research science.

The maintenance of quality control in industrial production has become relatively straightforward. Once the quality of products is appreciated by consumers, quality control is understood by management to be essential for sales and survival; and techniques for employee participation are easily transplanted between such different cultural milieux as Japan and the United States. But in science it is otherwise; there is no external set of discriminating consumers, no hierarchical management, and no simple tests of quality of unit operations. Hence research science must be self-policing; and the wide variation in quality of work between different fields and different centres shows that the problem has no automatic solution. If we ask what motivates the individual scientist to invest the extra time and trouble to ensure the highest possible quality of his or her research, there can be several answers. The simplest is prudence; poor workmanship will be detected and rejected by colleagues. But this presupposes a collective commitment to high quality, and so, in effect, begs the question. Other reasons lie in the personal integrity, and pride of craftsmanship of the individual scientist, operating either as a researcher or as a quality controller in refereeing or in peer review. However, these are moral attributes; they are not automatic consequences of the research process, nor can they be instilled by simple political or administrative means.

Scientific progress is uniquely sensitive to the maintenance of quality. Innovative work is hard and risky; the minority who dare and succeed can all too easily be smothered by an entrenched mediocrity that wishes to stay comfortable in old routines of problems and techniques. Thus, the maintenance of a generally good quality of research is a necessary background for the emergence of excellence and originality. Governments, even industries, can survive for a long time in a state of complacency and inefficiency, even enduring corruption. When such a situation exists in a field of science, the effects are not visible to the inexpert eye: teaching, research, conferences, grant applications continue smoothly; the one thing lacking is anything worthwhile happening.

Hence the value component of science has another essential element: the commitment by enough scientists, and particularly those in positions of political power in their scientific communities, to the production of good work, really for its own sake. Otherwise all of the world's research science would soon become like that recognizable in various backwater communities: much spurious activity, but no contribution to either knowledge or human welfare.

Similar phenomena can be observed in fields of technology where purchasers can be captured by producers, notably state (particularly military) procurement. It may seem outrageous and incredible that military authorities would endanger the lives of soldiers, and compromise the chances of victory in eventual wars, for the sake of bureaucratic convenience or advantage. But it is so; the examples are best known for the USA, but perhaps mainly because of the greater openness of government there.

Thus, even in the cases of the most 'hard' and 'objective' fields of human endeavour, we can discuss the effects of a 'moral environment'; if not enough people *care* about quality, then it will inevitably be lost. Cyclical theories of civilizations, usually cast in terms of political and military affairs, and standards of private morality, may be seen to apply to science and technology as well.

Fantasy Hardware, the Ultimate Aberration

Before the advent of modern science, there was a well-recognized category of 'secrets too powerful to be revealed'. Whether they were actually so, we will never know. But in any event, the optimistic faith of the seventeenth century prophets of modern science rendered that category void. Although great material powers were promised through the new science, they were understood to be strictly limited. In the materialist world-view, effects were commensurate with causes; enhancements by spiritual or magical means were seemingly absurd.

227

By the later nineteenth century, the technology of war was eroding that basic metaphysical assumption. Inventors were once again producing 'weapons so terrible that they would make war impossible forever'. Thus, nuclear weapons were not a totally new phenomenon; they were in a continuous development ideologically as well as technically. First seen as a cheap but very dramatic extension of means of quickly destroying a city and its inhabitants, they were indeed used, partly for their immediate effect and partly as an extension of diplomacy.

However, the second generation of nuclear weapons, involving enormously enhanced destructive power, effective means of delivery, and a sharing of the technique between the two major antagonists, did introduce a qualitatively new element into warfare. It was universally admitted that it was highly undesirable to use such weapons, even though only a critical minority argued that a nuclear war could not be 'war' in any meaningful sense.

The function of such weapons then shifted drastically: it became 'deterrence'. This concept was twofold: it referred to nuclear war involving an exchange of long-range missiles, but it also extended to the discouragement of a 'conventional' war in Europe. In the 'pure' case of intercontinental ballistic missiles, 'deterrence' introduced a very new sort of problem into military theory. Strategic thinking was concentrated on games of bluff and counter-bluff, with models from 'the theory of games and economic behaviour', and with payoffs in mega-deaths. This was very quickly exposed as an idiotic pseudo-science by an eminent military scientist, Sir Solly Zuckerman. But he was ignored, by politicians, strategists and philosophers of science alike. Hence the gigantic machine of nuclear armament, distorting the economies and the politics of all the world's nations, and presenting an ever-increasing threat to the survival of mankind, had as its rationale a strictly nonsensical theory. What a fate for a civilization that so proudly bases itself on science!

Practical contradictions also afflicted nuclear strategy, though these took a couple of decades to mature. The 'defence' of Europe by the threat of its obliteration through American-controlled weapons led to increasing disquiet there. 'Civil defence' finally revealed its idiocy in American plans for evacuations, requiring (for example) the inhabitants of each of the 'twin cities' Minneapolis—St Paul to seek refuge in the other!

'Independent' deterrents by second-rank powers as Britain and France could be only an expensive means of maintaining fantasies of national glory. And the spread of nuclear weapons to less-responsible ruling élites poses a sinister threat that cannot now be removed.

Such a situation might seem as bizarre as possible, until a new element was revealed in the early 1980s: the weapons themselves are unreliable. American missiles have been tested only on constant-latitude paths. Hence, any talk of 'first-strike', 'counter-force' attack (by missiles travelling over the pole and targeting with great accuracy and precision) is pure fantasy. Further, the coming generation of American missiles seem likely to impose a *de facto* 'freeze'. The MX system is totally devoid of any plausible function, except to keep the Air Force in the nuclear arms business. The Pershing II missile is a design disaster. The Cruise missile can fly sometimes under optimal conditions, but it is so plagued by difficulties that its production run has been seriously curtailed.

All these facts are in the public prints, and yet all sides in the nuclear debate choose to ignore them. Of course, existing weapons are in place, the spread continues, the threat to humanity is as menacing as ever. But it seems to be in no one's interest to make political use of this essential feature of nuclear weapons: as well as being absolutely evil, they are also absolutely insane, even to the point of becoming increasingly a matter of sheer fantasy.

Conclusion

The metaphysics of our civilization is based on an absolute distinction between the 'primary' quality of things, taken from mathematics, and the 'secondary' ones, involving perceptions. 'Tertiary' qualities, involving values, are allowed metaphysical reality only on Sundays. This world-view has been dominant for some three centuries. Now its contradictions have matured. They are most manifest in plans to base a nuclear strategy on a future missile system that will certainly never operate. This complete interpenetration of fantasy and hardware could be seen as a sort of Zen koan; and perhaps some day it will.

This essay was first published as 'Knowledge, ignorance and fantasies in the scientific world view, in Japanese, in *Crises of Today's World and Perspectives for the Future*, Iwanami Shoten, Tokyo, 1984. It was republished under the present title in *The Revenge of Athena: Science, Exploitation and the Third World* (ed. Z. Sardar) Mansell, London and New York, 1988.

References

The general problem of quality control, and tne importance of morale and of moral imperatives, is discussed at length in my book *Scientific Knowledge and Its Social Problems* (London: Oxford University Press, 1971) (also published in Japanese translation).

The phenomenon of the misdirection of science, to the neglect of problems of human and environmental concerns, is discussed in *Quality in Science* (ed. M. Chotkowsky La Follette. Cambridge, Mass.: MIT Press, 1982), particularly in the essay by Harvey Brooks, 'Needs, leads and indicators'.

The most recent study of the provision of low-quality or inappropriate weapons to the American military is *National Defense*, by James Fallows (New York: Random House, 1981). His most striking example is the modification of the M-15 rifle into an ineffective weapon for use in Vietnam, in the interest of the preservation of a bureaucratic monopoly on design and testing.

For the history and institutional/political theory of the development of nuclear weapons and nuclear strategy, an eyewitness account is by Lord Zuckerman; see his *Nuclear Illusion and Reality* (London: Viking, 1982).

4
CONSTRUCTIVE APPROACHES

This section begins with a sample of my recent research, conducted with S.O. Funtowicz, on quality control of scientific information through the management of uncertainties. This is at its core a technical solution, through a notational system; it may not be immediately apparent what relation it has to the vast problems that I have been discussing hitherto. Perhaps the link can be established through the concept of 'ignorance of ignorance' which I have used on occasion in my writings. If we lack means to express the severe uncertainties that affect our information on the major problems, then they will not be expressed; and being unexpressed they will be ignored; and then we will persist in the illusion that we know (because the scientists have provided us with numbers precise to two or three digits) when in fact we have educated guesses at best. I used the term 'we' for the sake of brevity in a general analysis; but when we recall how many debates over environmental threats resolve into disagreements over the quality of official data, then an instrument for quality assessment that is simple enough for use by concerned citizens can make a significant contribution to the quality, and fairness, of such debates.

The interaction of knowledge, ignorance and policy has become an explicit concern among those grappling with the problems on a planetary scale; some years ago I participated in a conference intended to define an international, trans-disciplinary research programme on the biosphere. For this I was encouraged to explore ignorance as it relates to policy; and since I suspected that this would be a new concept for most of the scientists involved, I introduced the topic by easy stages, paralleling the experience of a scientist through his education and career. I was emphatic that this is not a question to be resolved by conceptual analyses; but rather that working scientists would need to revise their management of subject-speciality self-protection. Otherwise such efforts would amount to little more than a pooling of separate

233

uncertainties rather than an integration of common knowledge. It seems to be a general experience that the perils associated with interdisciplinary research are as yet more real to most scientists than the threats to survival that require such work for their control.

If the scientific communities are generally incapable of breaking out of the 'normal science' as defined by Kuhn (puzzle-solving within unquestioned, unquestionable paradigms), what can be done? In the next two essays I review the various alternative approaches that were spawned in the confusion of the 1960s, and which have moved towards stability and maturity ever since. Working first in the political and social dimensions, I review the old 'social contract of science' whereby science enjoyed the immunity of scholars in return for promising the benefits of inventors. That can no longer be sustained, as the old beneficent, omniscient image of science falls apart. A wider involvement of non-experts in 'science', in some sense of the term, is inevitable and appropriate. Here I indicate three sorts, labelled 'alternative', 'activist' and 'practical', very different in their functions and in their supporters; but all of them serving valid purposes. Should such enriched conceptions of science make their way into teaching, then there is a chance that the dusty decline of science education may yet be arrested.

Viewing the same phenomenon historically, in terms of 'orthodoxies, critiques and alternatives', I go back to the prophetic faith of the Scientific Revolution about the Way of Science, and show how its inherent contradictions, latent or manageable then and for centuries afterwards, have matured and become manifest. Most of the twentieth century has been needed for this process to achieve fulfilment; it started first in philosophy, only gradually extended to the social critique of science, and then most recently to a cosmological perspective. The sorts of 'alternative sciences' now flourishing have a variety of purposes, from the more political to the more private. I find 'alternative medicine' or simply 'healing' among the most significant, since it poses the greatest challenge to professional and metaphysical structures, in the most unobtrusive and non-violent way. As such tendencies gain in plausibility and acceptance, the common sense of science, set several centuries ago, must inevitably be modified, in ways that may have surprises for us all.

Finally I reprint (slightly modified) my first attempt at a unified conception of it all, in the discussion of 'critical science' in my previous book. There are many gaps in the vision I had then, which are easily seen by comparison with the recent essays. But in general I feel that it has worn well, and it is useful for showing both the development and the continuity of my thought over the last two decades.

Qualified Quantities:
Towards an Arithmetic of Real Experience

This study has been motivated by two problems at widely separated places in the methodology of the natural sciences. One is the crisis in the philosophy of science, caused by the continuing failure of all programmes to identify a logical structure which could explain the previously successful practice of natural science (Shapere 1986). The other is the failure of the traditional methods of laboratory science to encompass problems of risks and the environment in the policy process. Few people are aware of both problems and their possible connections. Here we will indicate their common root and, while not attempting a 'solution' cast as some formalism, we will exhibit a practical device whereby quantitative statements can be made in a clear and effective way.

The two problems actually come together, implicitly at least, on those issues where in one way or another the traditional methods of science have revealed their inadequacy. In the debates on environmental and occupational hazards, which are bound to increase greatly before they ever abate, popular conceptions of science tend to change drastically from naive trust to embittered cynicism. Having been told in school, in the media, and by all the accredited experts that science (in legitimate hands) can and will solve all our technical problems, citizens may then have a very different sort of experience, frequently involving procrastination, prevarication or even concealment and deception at the hands of the very experts employed to protect them against hazards. All scientific expertise then tends to become used as a debating tool, at the level of courtroom psychiatry. In debates on large-scale problems, such as engineering projects constituting 'major hazards' or major environmental intrusions, or in the speculative technologies of nuclear armaments, the dividing line between science, nonsense and fantasy becomes very difficult to discern. The traditional methodologies of scientific research offer insufficient protection against the corruption of reason that modern conditions encourage, even in our dealings with the world of Nature.

Our contribution is a new notational system (Funtowicz and Ravetz 1986)

235

for the expression of quantitative information, one which provides places for each of the judgements describing the different sorts of uncertainty with every quantitative statement is qualified. We call it NUSAP, an abbreviation for the categories *Numeral, Unit, Spread, Assessment* and *Pedigree*. The last three convey inexactness, unreliability and 'border with ignorance', respectively. Familiar analogues exist for the first two of these, *spread* and *assessment*, in variance or experimental error for the first, and confidence limits or systematic error for the second. The last one, *pedigree*, does not have a precedent in ordinary scientific practice or statistical technique; we define it as an evaluative history of the process whereby the quantity was produced. By means of that history, we characterize the state of the art of the production of the quantity. This exhibits the inherent limitations of the knowledge that can be achieved thereby, and in that sense demarcates the border with ignorance in that case. The first two places, *numeral* and *unit*, are close enough to their traditional analogues to need no explanation as yet. Within each place, or box, appropriate notations, depending on the applications, may be employed.

The usefulness of a tool like NUSAP for application to what we may call 'policy-related research' or 'public-use statistics' is not too difficult to imagine. If highly uncertain quantitative information were required to be written with all its qualifying places explicit, we could more quickly identify pseudo-precise or scientifically meaningless quantitative statements. In this respect the NUSAP notational scheme could function as an instrument of quality control, in an area where it is both urgently necessary and extremely difficult.

On the side of epistemology, the contribution cannot be so direct; but we hope that it will provide a basis for transcending the seventeenth century metaphysics in which geometrical reasoning was to supplant human judgement as the route to real knowledge. Instead of erecting some general, all-encompassing, polar-opposite alternative to our dominant 'reductionist' science, be it in the form of a 'holistic', 'romantic', 'idealist' or 'voluntarist' philosophy, we can in a practical way exhibit the essential *complementarity* of the more quantifying with the more qualifying aspects of any quantitative statement. Human judgements are then seen, not as inhabiting some separate realm from exact mathematical statements, bearing a relation which is either hostile, mysterious, or non-existent; but rather as a natural and essential complement to the more impersonal and abstract assertions embodied in a numerical expression. When this insight, made familiar in everyday experience, is available for philosophical reflection, then we may be in a position to go beyond Galileo's (1632) classic pronouncement that the conclusions of natural science are true and necessary and that '*l'arbitrio humano*' has nothing to do with them. Thus, NUSAP may make a practical contribution to the recently developed tendency in the philosophy of science, which gives some recognition to the informal aspects of scientific argument and rationality (Putnam 1981, Jiang 1985).

The Problem: Uncertain Quantitative Information Represented by a 'Magic Number' Form

The problems associated with the provision and communication of quantitative information for policy-making in economic and social affairs are well known. It might be thought that the difficulties of producing 'usable knowledge' (Lindblom and Cohen 1979) in these fields are caused mainly by the inherent limitations of definition and measurement of their relevant aggregated statistical indicators. But it is increasingly recognized that in policy-making for technology and for the natural environment, similar difficulties arise. Planning for investment in technological and industrial developments is characterized by frequent uncertainty and occasionally by irremediable ignorance (Collingridge 1980).

The matter now takes on some urgency, in view of the growing proportion of scientific effort that is devoted to the understanding and control of the environmental and health consequences of technology and industry. Increasing space, both in the media and in research journals, is occupied by such topics as radioactive pollution, acid rain, agricultural chemicals and pharmaceutical products. A variety of research fields are called on to provide quantitative technical information which, it is hoped, will contribute to the resolution, or at least to the definition, of these practical problems.

Such issues are the subject matter for the policy-related sciences, whose function is to provide this new sort of usable knowledge. Because of the complexity and frequent urgency of some of these issues, the research communities do not always possess the knowledge and skills required for immediate effective solutions. Even experienced advisers may find it difficult to convey to policy-makers an accurate reflection of the scope and limits of the results that can be achieved under these constraints. Solving the problems of representing and evaluating technical information in these contexts, and also of identifying meaningless quantitative expressions, thus becomes of great importance for the proper accomplishment of public policy in these areas.

Policy-analysts have long been aware of this problem, and have searched for means of expressing strongly uncertain information. Thus:

> One of the thorniest problems facing the policy analyst is posed by the situation where, for a significant segment of his study, there is unsatisfactory information. The deficiency can be with respect to data—incomplete or faulty—or more seriously with respect to the model of theory—again either incomplete or insufficiently verified. This situation is probably the norm rather than a rare occurrence. (Dalkey 1969.)

In spite of these manifest inadequacies in the available information, the policy-maker must frequently make some sort of decision without delay. The temptation for her/his advisers is to provide her/him with a single number, perhaps even embellished with precise confidence limits of the classic

237

statistical form. When such numbers are brought into the public arena, debates may combine the ferocity of sectarian politics with the hyper-sophistication of scholastic disputations. The scientific inputs then have the paradoxical property of promising objectivity and certainty by their form, but producing only greater contention by their substance (Nelkin 1979).

Indeed, there is now an increasing tendency for public debate to focus more on the various uncertainties surrounding the numbers than on the policy-relevant quantities themselves. This has happened most notably in the cases of 'the greenhouse effect' and acid rain. Such debates on the uncertainties will always be inherently more difficult to control and comprehend than those at the policy level. They unavoidably involve all aspects of the issue, from policy to methodology and even to state-of-the-art expert practice in the relevant scientific fields.

In all the fields of formalized decision analysis (e.g. Risk Analysis, Multi-Attribute Utility Theory, Operational Research, Decision Research, 'Hard' Systems Theory), practitioners are now searching for means of expressing subjective factors. This endeavour frequently confuses very different aspects of technical information, such as social value-commitments, group interests and personal judgements, as well as qualifying attributes of quantities. Innovations in statistics have not proved adequate to resolve such confusions. Under these circumstances, there is a real possibility that risk-analysis practitioners and those they advise will despair of objectivity, and in the resolution of policy issues will oscillate between emotional interpersonal contacts and ruthless power politics. Some even argue as if 'pollution is in the nose of the beholder', and reduce all environmental debates to a conflict between sensible and sectarian life-styles (Douglas and Wildavsky 1982). We believe that the core of objectivity in policy decisions must be analysed and exhibited afresh, so that consistent and fair procedures in decision-making can be defended and further articulated.

Thus, the traditional assumption of the robustness and certainty of all quantitative information has become unrealistic and counter-productive. The various sorts of uncertainty, including inexactness, unreliability and igno-rance, must be capable of representation. The task was well described by W.D. Ruckelshaus (1984), when Administrator at the US Environmental Protection Agency:

> First, we must insist on risk calculations being expressed as distributions of estimates and not as magic numbers that can be manipulated without regard to what they really mean. We must try to display more realistic estimates of risk to show a range of probabilities. To help to do this we need tools for quantifying and ordering sources of uncertainty and for putting them in perspective.

The above reference to 'magic numbers' is not merely rhetorical. Our culture invests a quality of real truth in numbers, analogous to the way in which other cultures believe in the magical powers of names. The classic statement is by Lord Kelvin:

> I often say that when you can measure what you are speaking about, and express it in numbers, you know something about it; but when you cannot measure it, when you cannot express it in numbers, your knowledge is of a meagre and unsatisfactory kind. (Mackay 1977.)

A quantitative form of assertion is not merely considered necessary for a subject to be scientific; it is also generally believed to be sufficient. Thus, the problems discussed here are not only related to the inherent uncertainties of the subject matter (as for example in risks and environmental pollutants); they originate in an inappropriate conception of the power and meaning of numbers in relation to the natural and social worlds. By their form, numbers convey precision; an 'uncertain quantity' seems as much a contradiction in terms as an 'incorrect fact'. But this image must be corrected and enriched if we are to grow out of the reliance on magic numbers; only in that way can we hope to provide usable knowledge for policy-decisions, including those for science, technology and the environment.

Numerical Language: Pathologies and Pitfalls

The new requirements on quantitative information for policy-making have revealed inadequacies in the traditional numerical means of representation and in the implicit beliefs underlying them. But we should not think that a natural and faultless inherited numerical system is suddenly being stretched beyond its limits of applicability. Reflection on the history and existing uses of numerical systems shows that they contain many pathologies and pitfalls. These derive from the traditional basic conception of numbers as designed for counting collections of discrete objects. For measurement of continuous magnitudes, the traditional tool was geometry, with an 'analogue' rather than 'digital' approach. The combination of counting and measuring in practice involves estimation, for which no notational systems were developed until quite recently. But the uncritical use of numbers, with their connotation of discreteness and hence of absolute precision, still causes blunders and confusions at all levels of practice.

Such imperfections are not advertised by teachers adhering to a 'pure mathematics' pedagogical tradition. The subject of 'estimation' had indeed flourished in nineteenth century 'practical arithmetic'. But the influence of modern academic research in mathematics, culminating in the 'new mathematics', encouraged the teaching of the élite skills of manipulating abstract structures to schoolchildren. These did not complement traditional skills, but effectively alienated even arithmetic from practical experience (Kline 1974). (Such abstraction, perhaps based on disapproval of rote-learned practical craft-skills, had its analogue in the 'global method' for teaching reading while ignoring the alphabet. For several decades children emerged from the best schools unable either to count or to spell!) Such fashions in abstraction enable us to extend the insight of Gödel's famous theorem (1931) to the present context. As Kline (1972) expressed it:

> Gödel showed that the consistency of a system embracing the usual logic and number theory cannot be established if one limits himself to such concepts and methods as can formally be represented in the system of number theory.

Here we are dealing with understanding rather than proof. In the 'new math', a more logical and complicated formalistic language for arithmetic was achieved at the expense of the loss of comprehension of the rich and contradictory world of the practical experience of quantity.

The confusions of arithmetic could be safely ignored so long as tacit craft-skills were adequate for coping with the ordinary problems of application. The task of programming computers for calculations, where nothing can be left tacit, has forced some awareness of the practical problems of managing the uncertainties in all quantitative information. There is already a flourishing literature on 'numerical analysis' at all levels; but as yet no coherent and effective exposition of the management of the different sorts of uncertainty is available. Hence the ordinary practice of calculation is still afflicted with paradoxes and blunders, the sort that 'every schoolboy' should know, but doesn't.

For our first example, we may consider the representations of fractional parts of unity. We may say:

$$1/4 = 0.25 \quad \text{but} \quad 1/4 \text{ inch} \neq 0.25 \text{ inch}$$

In the first case we are dealing with 'pure arithmetic', and the equality results from a simple calculation. But in the second case we are dealing with measurements, in this case inches; our objects are not 'points on the real line' but 'intervals of estimation', characterized by a 'tolerance'. Each representation has its own implied tolerance (or, as we shall call it, *spread*), and so 1/4 inch and 0.25 inch mean quite different things. In the former case, the next lower unit of magnitude (implying the interval of inexactness) is likely to be 1/16 inch, while in the latter it is 0.01 inch, smaller by a factor of 6. Drawings of specifications in the different units have different implied tolerances, and thus mean very different things in practice. Managing such anomalies may be quite trivial to those involved in such work, but this is achieved by the adoption of implicit conventions for interpretation, whose understanding may be restricted to a particular specialist group. (The traditional tables of decimal equivalents of common fractions, with entries such as 1/16 inch = 0.0625 inch, are examples of the deep confusion in this practical matter.)

A mention of tolerance (inexactness, error or *spread*) will usually provoke the response that all that is handled by the 'significant digits' (s.d.) convention.

But to describe exactly what that is, turns out to be far from trivial. Indeed, the rule for preservation of s.d.s in a calculation is not at all straightforward. For example, if we wish to know the circumference of a circle whose radius is 1.2 cm, then we round off π to 3.1; but if the radius is 9.2 cm, then π should be 3.14, since the 'proportional error' in the second radius measure is of the order of 1%, while that in 3.1 is some 3%, inappropriately large. Thus the choice of the number of s.d.s to include in a numerical expression will depend on the calculation at hand, and the rules for choice will not be trivial.

The above examples may seem to relate only to unsophisticated practice. But the following subtle blunder has been observed even in high-level tables of statistics. Suppose (for simplicity and clarity) we have a population of just seven elements divided into three groups of 2, 2 and 3 respectively. A common tabular display would be:

N	%
2	29
2	29
3	42
7	100

There seems nothing wrong here, until we observe that 3/7 is strictly 42.8%; which should be rounded-up to 43%, just as 2/7 or 28.6% was rounded-up to 29%. But then the sum would be 101%; and how often do we see percentages summed to a figure other than 100%? Paradoxically, we may say that a 100% sum is most likely to be the result of fiddling the separate percentages! It reflects an incomprehension of the arithmetic of rounding-off, and is a more amusing example of educated confusion about quantities.

A particular unfortunate consequence of such blunders is that they impart an air of incompetence (however vaguely this may be articulated) to the reports in which they are manifested. Although explicit rules for the criticism of pseudo-precision are not widely diffused, many who use statistics are aware of the principle enunciated by the great mathematician Gauss:

> lack of mathematical culture is revealed nowhere so conspicuously as in meaningless precision in numerical calculation. (Ravetz 1971.)

One simple way to avoid such blunders is to recognize units of aggregation in countings, and the possibility of 'swamping' one quantity by another. Paradoxically this phenomenon is more difficult to recognize because of a fertile ambiguity in the quasi-digit 0. This can function either as a 'counter' or as a 'filler'. Thus when we write '10', we understand 'zero in the unit place' as a digit distinct from the neighbouring digits 9, and 1 in 11, but when we write '1000', this usually refers to a count of 1 on a unit of a 'thousand', analogous to 'dozen' or 'score'.

By these examples we can see that imperfect quantitative information can be managed with greater or lesser skill. Its inherent uncertainties may be hidden, leading to confusion and blunders, and to doubts of the competence of the authors. Or the uncertainties may be clearly exhibited, improving the credit of the authors and providing more useful inputs to decision-making. One can never decrease the inherent uncertainties, or enhance the inherent quality, of any given information by such means; but as we have seen it is possible to transform the information into a more effective tool for decision-making.

Notation, Language and the Concepts of Science

The examples of the previous section show how numbers may sometimes convey confusion rather than clarity; and a diligent search by any reader will reveal many instances where blunders in the manipulation or interpretation of quantities occur in all fields, and at all levels of expert practice. If we accept this phenomenon as real, we should reflect both on how it has come to be, and also why it has not been noted and analysed before now. We believe that such incompetence cannot be ascribed merely to 'bad teaching', when it persists in practice long after the end of formal schooling. Rather, we would say that such defects in practice, particularly because they are unnoticed, are indicators of unresolved contradictions quite deep within the 'paradigm' (Kuhn 1962) that defines that practice.

The paradigm in question is the metaphysical commitment to a certain sort of world of Nature (and by extension, humanity), and to the central role of a certain sort of mathematics in the structure of that world and in our knowing it. This is the world of the seventeenth century scientific revolution, where reality consists of the quantitative 'primary qualities', and where by appropriate methods we are to gain knowledge of those qualities, with no limit in principle to its extent and comprehensiveness.

We should be clear that this world-view, although one that (like any other) imposes a structure on reality as experienced, is far from being 'arbitrary' in the sense that an isolated individual can simply choose whether to adhere to it, or perhaps to switch to some other brand. It permeates not merely our conception of the role of mathematics in knowledge, but also what sort of scientific knowledge can and should be obtained. It was explicitly claimed by such seventeenth century prophets as Galileo and Descartes, and implicitly accepted ever since, that this approach to knowledge is not merely quantitatively exact, but also uniquely assured of truth in its results. Other approaches to knowing, ranging from the humanistic, through the imaginative, to the inner-orientated, have all been rejected with varying degrees of severity at different critical points in the development of the scientific philosophy. Now, some three and a half centuries later, the crisis in the philosophy of science, paralleled by the crisis in the policy sciences, becomes one of

242

confidence. Numerical expressions, representing quantities derived by accredited scientists, cannot be guaranteed to protect us against vague, ambiguous, misleading or even vacuous assertions of a scientific appearance. Where then do we find the rock of certainty on which our scientific knowledge is supposed to be based?

Since that world is our paradigm, by its nature not to be questioned or even noticed in ordinary practice, its flaws will be revealed only occasionally; and they can then be dismissed as anomalies, or as mere anecdotes. Those who would enhance awareness of the problems of the dominant paradigm must then show how a previously unquestioned practice has defects (as we have just done). Or we may show how it reveals other significant features when examined critically. For example, we may consider the language used to describe the results of measurements in the world of experience. These are traditionally said to be afflicted by 'error', implying that a perfect experiment would yield a scientifically true value with absolute mathematical precision (This is reminiscent of the naming as 'irrational' by the Pythagoreans of certain magnitudes that broke their rules, such as $\sqrt{2}$.) Even in sophisticated statistical theory, the crucial terms have a subjective cast, such as in 'confidence' or 'fiducial' (in our work we describe the analogous properties of information as 'reliability', relating to human practice to be sure, but to experience rather than to opinion). And among scientists of many sorts, the old ideal of objective, quantitative certainty has been dominant. Thus, from such dissimilar figures as Einstein and Rutherford, we have the dicta, 'God does not play dice', and 'If your experiment needs statistics you ought to have done a better experiment' (Mackay 1977).

Being a genuine crisis, this one does not manifest itself merely at these two dissimilar areas of experience: abstract philosophical reflection and craft arithmetical practice. The present century has seen the dissolution of many certainties in the mathematical conception of science. The revolutions in physics, particularly quantum mechanics, were explicitly philosophical in part; and similarly was the 'foundations crisis' in mathematics, leading through Gödel's theorems to a radical loss of certainty (Kline 1980).

This erosion of the previously unchallenged epistemological foundations of a scientific world-view has thus proceeded on many fronts. It has been accompanied by an erosion of the moral certainties of science, ever since the industrialization and militarization of scientific research became recognized. As yet there has been no effective presentation of an alternative paradigm, in the Kuhnian sense of a deep scientific revolution. The critical analyses raised in the 1960s (and echoed in Feyerabend's (1975) works) could not have a practical outcome in the absence of a wholesale transformation of society and consciousness. One modest philosophical alternative was suggested in the 1920s by Niels Bohr (Holton 1973), in his famous attempt to resolve the 'dualities' of early quantum physics by means of the essentially Chinese notion of complementarity. This remained a personal, almost idiosyncratic attempt at coherence, for the physicists were able to do quite nicely in making

243

discoveries and inventions of unprecedented power, in spite of totally incoherent basic conceptual structures. Recent attempts to interpret physics in broadly 'oriental' ways have so far remained curiosities of popularized science (Capra 1975, Zukav 1979).

In the NUSAP system we put complementarity to work. Becoming familiar with the notational scheme, through use, entails acceptance of the idea that a bare statement of quantity, in the absence of its qualifying judgements, is scientifically meaningless. To paraphrase the classic formula of the logical positivists of the Vienna Circle (Ayer 1936), the meaning of a quantitative statement is contained in its mode of qualification as much as in its quantifying part. In this respect the NUSAP system makes a contribution towards an alternative approach to the philosophy of Nature.

We may ask, can notations really be so influential as we claim? The history of mathematics shows how they can encapsulate new ideas in such a way as to transform practice. This happened twice in the seventeenth century, first with Descartes' unified conception of algebra, geometry and their relationship, expressed through the symbols $a, b, c \ldots, x, y, z$. Then Leibniz, with dx and $\int$, tamed the infinite in this new 'analysis'. At a less exalted level, the 'arabic numerals' democratized arithmetic in early modern Europe; previously calculation had been the preserve of those who had mastered the abacus, as supplemented by a variety of special tricks. Even when symbols are not designed for calculation, but only for effective representation, they can have a deep influence on a practice and how it is understood; the history of chemical nomenclature and symbolism provides many examples of this (Crosland 1962).

We conceived and developed the NUSAP notational scheme in full awareness of the complex interaction between tools (of which notations are an example), explicit concepts, world-views, and social practice. It is designed as an instrument of analysis and criticism, in an area of practice where such activities have been generally considered to be either unproblematic or even quite unnecessary. To the extent that there has been a mystique of quantities, and that this has been supportive of a mystique of exclusive scientific expertise, the NUSAP system also has functions in the societal aspects of scientific practice. There too, it can enrich the inevitable debates on quantities that enter into policy issues, avoiding the extremes of naivety and cynicism from which participants now have little protection. In that connection too, it can make its contribution to the development of appropriate new conceptions of science.

Principles of the NUSAP Notational Scheme

The NUSAP notational scheme is a system whereby the various sorts of uncertainty contained in all quantitative information may be expressed concisely and also consistently with existing partial notations. It is designed to be applied to any expression given in the form of numbers or more generalized notations. By its means, nuances of meaning in quantitative statements can be conveyed clearly and economically; and various aspects of the quality of the quantitative information may also be expressed. Users need master only the very simplest skills, and the underlying ideas are familiar to all those with experience of successful practice in any quantitative discipline or craft.

Should it come into standard use, there will develop a more competent general level of criticism of quantitative assertions, among both experts and the interested public. Just as quality control is now recognized as an essential component of industrial production, meriting emphasis and appropriate organizational structures, so we can expect that with the adoption of the NUSAP system, quality control of quantitative statements will eventually become standard practice.

NUSAP was designed with several criteria in mind. In addition to the ordinary properties of a good notation (simplicity, naturalness, flexibility, etc.) it enables the distinction between meaningless and meaningful quantitative statements. Further, it protects against the misleading use of quantitative information by preventing the isolation of the 'quantifying' part of an expression from its 'qualifying' part. All this is accomplished because the notational system can distinguish among three sorts of uncertainty which characterize every quantitative expression. These are: inexactness of measurement and of representation; unreliability of methods, models and theories; and the border between knowledge and ignorance revealed in the history of the quantity.

The NUSAP notational scheme is a 'system' because it is not simply a collection of fixed notations. Rather, it is a set of determinate *categories*, each of which can be filled by particular notations appropriate to the occasion. The names of the five categories (or boxes, or places in a string) make up the acronym NUSAP. Considering the expression as proceeding from left to right, we start with those which are more familiar, the quantifying part of the expression; and conclude with those less familiar, forming the qualifying part of the expression. With such complementary aspects of the expression conveyed in a convenient and standard form, some of the classic dilemmas of subjectivity and objectivity in science can be resolved in ordinary practice.

Considered as a formal structure, NUSAP is more than a convenient array of symbols conveying uncertainties in technical information. It is a 'notational scheme' which provides a general framework so that an unlimited variety of particular notations may be employed unambiguously. It is a string of five positions corresponding to the categories of *numeral, unit, spread, assessment* and *pedigree*. By means of this place-value representation, each category can be expressed simply, without need for its explicit identification (this is a 'scheme' of notations at the most abstract level). For each category, there are many possible sets available for conveying particular desired meanings (thus in *unit* we may have Imperial, CGS, MKS or SI units). Any particular array of such sets, we call a 'notation'. Given such a notation, any particular case of representation will be an 'instance' of the notation.

Such distinctions enable great flexibility and power in the expression of quantitative information. In this respect it is analogous to the notational system of 'arabic' numerals, where the meaning of a digit depends on its place, thereby enabling a small set of digits to be used for the representation of any possible integer. By means of this flexibility we can escape from the 'vicious circle' of digital representations, whereby even those notations used to qualify an expression are themselves afflicted by pseudo-precision (as '95% confidence limit').

The first category, in the left-to-right order, is *numeral*. We use this term rather than 'number' as a reminder of the flexibility of the system. The place can be filled by a whole number, a decimal expansion, a fraction, or even a representation of an interval, or a qualitative index. Next is *unit*, which can be a compound entry, consisting of *standard* and *multiplier*. This can be important for the representation of aggregated quantities, such as $k, or perhaps 10^{12}. The middle category is *spread*, generalizing the traditional concept of error. Although this is normally expressed in arithmetical form (perhaps by ± , % or *fn*, for 'to within a factor of *n*') there is a strong qualitative element about it. *Spread* cannot (except perhaps when given by a calculated statistical measure) be given precisely; it is always an estimate, whose own *spread* is not a meaningful or useful concept. There is a way of qualifying the *spread* entry; it can be done by *assessment*, the fourth category in the NUSAP system. This may be seen most familiarly as a generalization of the confidence limits used in statistical practice. Assessment can be relevant in contexts where the problem does not admit of the calculation of confidence limits; and a great variety of notations can be deployed here, ranging from standard percentages, to a simple ordinal scale, such as 'high, medium, low'. The means of arriving at an *assessment* rating are equally various: it may be calculated statistically; it may be obtained by arithmetical operations from a conventional coding of the last category, *pedigree*; or it may be the result of a personal judgement.

Hitherto the categories have analogues in existing practice, ordinary or statistical; and it is natural to consider the NUSAP notational scheme as an extension and ordering of existing notations. But with the *pedigree* category, a novelty is introduced. By *pedigree* we understand an evaluative history of the production of the quantity being conveyed by the notation. Histories do not normally appear as part of notations; and for this category we have developed abbreviated schemes of analysis and representation. So far there are two, one for 'research information' and the other for 'public-use statistics'. In this paper we shall only introduce the *pedigree* for research information.

We said before that the contents of the *numeral* box need not be ordinary numbers. Thus, if a quantity is known only to within an 'order of magnitude', then an appropriate instance of *numeral* would be E6:. We remark that an instance 1:E6 denotes a determinate quantity, a million, very different from the 'order of a million' conveyed by E6:. (Representations in NUSAP have the boxes in the string separated by a colon; in reading them, we express the colon by 'on'. For example, an instance 1:E6 — where E6 is in the *unit* box — reads '1 on E6').

If one quantity is known only as an interval which lacks any preferred point of likelihood or of symmetry, then this should be the entry in the numeral place. Thus we could have (a, b): for an ordinary interval, $(\geqslant a)$: for an open-ended one. In the *numeral* place we may also find expressions of yet more general mathematical structures as numbers of a finite set representing an ordinal scale (as in much of social research), or numbers representing indices with a purely artefactual arithmetic. An extreme example of an ordinal scale with a qualitative notation of *numeral*, which is of direct practical use, is that for Geiger counter readings, such as 'click', 'chatter' and 'buzz'.

By *unit* we understand the base of the physical and mathematical operations represented in the *numeral* position. We distinguish two components of the *unit*. There is the *standard*, the common or generally used unit of the relevant operations; and the *multiplier*, relating to the standard to the particular unit involved in the expression. Thus we frequently see £342M, where the *unit* £M (with £ as *standard* and M as *multiplier*) is the actual basis of the calculations reported, as distinct from the £.p of strict accountancy practice. The meaning of the pair *standard—multiplier* may of course vary with context; thus kg is now a *fundamental* unit in the SI system, in which strictly speaking, 1 g should be written as 1 mkg. These two quantifying categories enable a refined description of topologies and scales of measurement.

Good practice in notation includes the indication of the *spread* of a quantity (which may also be called error or imprecision). For this the significant digits convention is common, as well as such statistical measures as standard deviation. In the case of highly inexact quantities, the *spread* may be conveyed by 'to within a factor of n'.

We can illustrate the application of NUSAP on some simple examples, where existing representations are inadequate. Suppose that we start with 'five million', and we add some smaller quantity. If it is *very* small, such as, say, 180, then the sum is normally understood still to be five million, since the latter quantity is not significant in the context. Writing the sum formally, we have $5\,000\,000 + 180 = 5\,000\,000$. In this sum, the last three zeros are interpreted as fillers rather than true digits; and so we use an artefactual arithmetic, adopting implicit conventions for the neglect of certain digits, just as in rounded-off calculations. But if the second addendum is 180 000 it is not clear from the uninterpreted sum $5\,000\,000 + 180\,000$ just where the counter digits end and the filler digits begin. Only from the context can we know whether to apply a natural or artefactual arithmetic. A notation like 5×10^6 may help, but even that is not conclusive.

Another useful example from ordinary practice is counting in dozens; this shows more clearly the influence of the process of production of the datum, since in this base there is no ambiguity between counter and filler digits. Thus 'eggs' will have, as a typical instance, $4\frac{1}{2}$:doz-eggs: rather than 54:eggs. This example exhibits the phenomenon of pseudo-precision of a *numeral* in digits, when the process has consisted of counts by dozens and half-dozen.

In the NUSAP notational scheme, we can express five million in the alternative forms, $5:10^6$, 5:M or 5:E6. Here it is explicit that the *unit* is millions. Although some ambiguity remains, it can be resolved by the entry in the *spread* position. But it is quite clear that 5:M + 180 = 5:M is the correct sum, unless there is an explicit note to the contrary in the *spread* position. There is no need for an artefactual arithmetic, with all its ambiguities.

NUSAP can also convey some shades of meaning that may be important in particular contexts. Thus five million may be better represented as 50:E5 or $\frac{1}{2}$:E7, denoting different sorts of operations in the different aggregated units. We note that the use of fractions in the *numeral* position enables us to express the meaning of a rough cutting of an aggregated unit; thus a 'third of a million' is represented better as $\frac{1}{3}$:M rather than 0.33×10^6. It can be considered an advantage of a notation that a user can represent, and even calculate with, an instance which expresses a perfectly clear statement of a quantity that previously needed a verbal form.

When representing measurements, we must distinguish between the *multiplier* and the *standard* which make up the *unit*. For an example, 5×10^3: g represents a count of 5000 grams; and this expression implies that the measuring operations were performed in the old CGS system. Turning to $5:10^3$ g, we are still in CGS, now operating in 'kilo' grams, of which there are 5. If we now write 5:kg, this is the expression of a count of 5 in the MKS system, or SI units, where kg is fundamental. Another example of the same sort exhibits a new feature; 5:g is clearly in CGS, while $5:10^{-3}$ kg tells us that we have SI with a scaling in thousandths of a kg. We note that here the *multiplier* represents the scaling of the measuring instrument.

For an example of the *spread* category we return to aggregated counting, with the above-mentioned ambiguous case of 180 000 added to five million. It may be that the larger quantity here has such inexactness that even a tenth of it is insignificant. This could happen if it is part of a sum with much larger quantities, such as 32:E6: and 155:E6:. Then the *spread* would be understood to be as large as E6, the *unit*, and therefore the 180 000 or 0.18:E6 would be meaningless. In this way, the notation represents the practical situation of the swamping of a much smaller quantity in a sum; to be completely explicit we may express this as 5:E6:E6. The *spread* E6 indicates that no interpolation within the scaling has been done; equivalently, every quantity in this sum has an inexactness interval which is E6 in length.

By the use of this notation, the meaninglessness of a quantitative expression can be clearly exhibited. For example, where both *unit* and *spread* are E6, the quantity 180 000 would be expressed as 0.18:E6:E6. The 0.18 would be insignificant and the expression is vacuous. By contrast, if the 180 000 is being added to 'five million', and the *spread* is understood to be 0.1E6, then 0.18:E6:0.1E6 would be naturally rounded up to 0.2:E6:0.1E6; and this is a proper quantitative expression. The sums might read as follows.

248

First, 32:E6:E6 + 155:E6:E6 + 5:E6:E6 + 0.18:E6:E6 = 192:E6:E6 where the 0.18 is suppressed, as being meaningless in this context. If, on the other hand, our summands are, say, 3:E6, 7:E6 and 5:E6, then since these are small integers, it is likely (unless indicated otherwise) that the *spread* is less than E6, perhaps 0.1E6. In this case we may write 3:E6:0.1E6 + 7:E6:0.1E6 + 5:E6:0.1E6 + 0.18:E6:0.1E6 = 15.2:E6:0.1E6, where we have rounded up 0.18 to 0.2.

The notation enables us to identify pseudo-precision in measurements, even when this is forced by an accepted scaling. Thus in the SI, where 'cm' are officially suppressed, measurements which were formerly done in inches, with *spread* of $\pm \frac{1}{2}$ inch, are now frequently expressed in 'mm' to the nearest ten. Thus 'five feet' will be rendered as 1 520 mm. In the NUSAP system, this would be properly represented as 152:10 mm. In this way we retain the *standard* required by the SI system, but modify by the *multiplier* 10, to express the practical scale of operation, equivalent to the illegal 'cm'. A somewhat less rigorous representation makes use of the *spread* category; we can keep the spurious last digit required by the SI, but show that in practice it is not a counter. Thus we would write 1520:mm:10, reminding the user that there is an effective 'spread' in the number as recorded.

Strongly inexact quantities are sometimes expressed 'to within a factor of n', such as '5×10^6 to within a factor of 10'. The convention indicates multiplicative intervals above and below the given quantity; thus the given quantity here may lie between 0.5×10^6 and 50×10^6. In the notation we write 5:E6:f10, meaning 0.5:E6 < 5:E6:f10 < 50:E6. By means of such notations it is possible to convey quantities of the sort characterized by 'the first law of astrophysics': 1 = 10. We can also express inexactness given in proportional terms; for example '5×10^6 with a proportional error of 15%' is represented as 5:E6:15% or as 5:E6:[15 in E2].

In the policy context, fractions less than unity, expressed as percentages, are frequently used to indicate the division of some aggregate. The inexactness of such estimates is extremely difficult to represent in a compact notation, and a misleading impression of precision is all too often conveyed. Thus '40%' may mean 'less than half but more than one-third' or perhaps 'less than half but more than one-quarter'. These inexact estimates may be represented as $\frac{1}{3}$:1:< $\frac{1}{2}$ and $\frac{1}{4}$:1:< $\frac{1}{2}$ respectively. Another way of expressing such estimates involves using the variable x. If there is some *unit U*, we may have x:U:$\frac{1}{3}$< $\frac{1}{2}$ or x:U:$\frac{1}{4}$< $\frac{1}{2}$. By this means, one can express quite fine distinctions among inexact estimates of fractions, avoiding the pseudo-precision of a two-digit percentage. The use of the variable x in the *numeral* place enables us to express clearly that the means for the production of the quantity do not provide us with information for distinguishing among numerical values. The class to which all the relevant values belong is represented in *spread*. We can refer to this as an 'indifference class', in the sense that no one numerical value can legitimately be taken as a representative of the class in preference to any other. In symbols, we write the general case as x:U:S.

The *assessment* category expresses the reliability of the information, generalizing not only the confidence limits of classic statistics, but also those of Bayesian statistics, interpreted as 'degree of belief' (Keynes 1921) or 'betting odds' (Savage 1954). Such formally defined measures are properly applicable only in special cases, and are not free of conceptual problems of their own. The *assessment* category is not to be formalized in the logical sense, but is designed to convey judgements of reliability in a convenient form. Where statistical notations are familiar and appropriate, they may be freely used. Otherwise, a more qualitative notation, such as, for example, an ordinal scale, should be adopted. Thus, we may have the set (*Total, High, Medium, Low, None*), perhaps codified as (4, 3, 2, 1, 0) to convey this kind of judgement. As in the cases of *numeral*, *unit* and *spread*, a great variety of notations are available for *assessment*.

A familiar case from scientific research is that of a number which historically belongs to a sequence of experimentally derived results describing the 'same' physical quantity. It is well known that elements of such a sequence may well jump about by amounts far exceeding the *spread* of any of them; this is described as systematic error as distinct from random error. A reader of technical literature may estimate a numerical entry for the *assessment* place, by an examination of the published versions of such a variable 'physical constant'. With *spread* representing average, a sample case might read $4.32{:}\mu U{:} \pm 0.17{:} \pm 0.3{:}$.

In traditional statistical practice, the *assessment* (or confidence limits) is closely associated with the *spread* (or variance). Unfortunately, this association tends to conceal the radical difference between the two categories, and to inhibit the understanding of either. When we generalize *assessment* from the simplest notion of reliability, the independence of the two categories becomes apparent. For example, consider a statistical distribution where we are interested in estimating the 95th upper percentile, or the top 5%. The entry of the *numeral* place is then qualified by the expression '%95' in the *assessment* place, the order being inverted deliberately to distinguish this from the more traditional '95%' confidence limit. In such a case, the *spread* will depend on the number of trials or of simulations of the same process. So, if we are comparing the results of two different experiments involving different numbers of trials or simulations (as for instance obtaining the top 5% of a distribution of experimental coin-toss results), we can have *spreads* varying with the size of the sample while the *assessment* entry is always '%95'.

Another illustrative example is of a case where the *spread* box is empty, but where a definite (though qualitative) *assessment* is appropriate. This can happen in a 'back-of-envelope' calculation, where the basic *unit* is expressed through a *numeral* entry of a small integer number. In such cases, *spread* is meaningless; but the calculation can be qualified by, say, '*Upper Limit*' (or *U*) in the *assessment* box. This is not an ordinary sort of reliability as calculated in traditional statistical practice; but it provides the user of the information with an appropriate interpretation for reliable use in practice.

250

The flexibility of the system is further enhanced by the use of combinations of entries in boxes to convey nuances of meaning. A particularly direct case of this is in a trade-off between 'strengths' of entries in the *spread* and *assessment* places. This also generalizes statistical practice; so that we may describe a distribution more tightly by its range over the $25\% - 75\%$ percentiles or more broadly over the $10\% - 90\%$ percentiles. This translates directly into a lower *spread* with lower *assessment*, or higher in both categories. In NUSAP, this can be expressed by μ (the mean in the N place), S_Q and S_D (the interquartile and interdecile ranges in S). The notations would read $\mu:U:S_Q:50\%:$ and $\mu:U:S_D:80\%:$. For an example, we imagine a distribution with a mean of 46, $S_Q = 12$, and $S_D = 20$. Alternative representations would be $46::12:50\%$ and $46::20:80\%$; the percentages in the *assessment* box relate to the amount of the total distribution represented in the *spread* place.

When uncertain quantities are directly involved in a policy process, the flexibility of the system can be very useful indeed. An illuminating example is cited by Mosteller (1977): estimation of the number of American men who emigrated during the Vietnam War. These ranged from 2.5k through 30k to 70k or even 100k, though the higher figures were less reliable. If the absolute number is not critical for policy purposes, then a convenient NUSAP expression would be $\geqslant 3:E4::Good:$. With a one-sided interval in *numeral*, it is appropriate to leave *spread* empty. If the lower bound on the estimate is very sensitive for policy, the *numeral* entry could be reduced; and the expression reads $\geqslant 2\frac{1}{2}:E4: + 20\%:High:$. In this way, a policy-maker is told that she/he is unlikely to go wrong in acting on the basis of an estimate in the range $2\frac{1}{2}$ to 3 on a *unit* E4.

These examples show how the system can be used to provide alternative communications, each valid in its own right, for a single statistical result. Each version focuses attention on a different aspect of the distribution, corresponding to different needs of users.

Pedigree for Research Information

In the NUSAP notational scheme, the most qualifying category, located in the far right position, is *pedigree*. This expresses the most extreme of the various sorts of uncertainty conveyed by the notation: its border with ignorance. The previously discussed categories can be seen as a preparation for the introduction of this one. Thus, *spread*, expressing the inexactness of quantities, served as a reminder that a quantitative expression is not 'clear and distinct'. Even if there is some realm of ideal mathematical entities (such as lines without breadth), represented in necessarily true mathematical statements (such as $\exp(\pi i) + 1 = 0$), the world of empirical objects and their measurements always involves 'more or less', or 'tolerances', about quantities possessing a fringe of vagueness. In that sense, the specification of an object in respect of its

251

quantitative attributes implicates the rest of the world, things other than our particular object of attention, as it shades into them.

This can be seen clearly by reflection on the normal practice of indicating *spread* or the misnamed 'error'. When we write 4.32 ± 0.05, that extra term must surely be other than perfectly precise. How is its imprecision to be conveyed? Is 0.05 drastically different from 0.04 or from 0.06? In normal practice, we simply record an *assessment* of confidence, which is a very different kind of judgement. We do not ordinarily attempt a 'spread of the spread', for many practical reasons; and also because if we were to iterate once, then why not twice or more? Hence we satisfy ourselves with an informal, tacit convention on the formal, misleadingly precise representation. Once aware of this we see how the simplest and most common of conventions for expression of the lack of perfect exactness in quantities leads us into paradoxes of infinite-regress. The border between the measured thing and its environment, or between our knowledge and our ignorance, can never be specified precisely.

Thus, our quantitative knowledge can never be fully exact or perfect, even in itself. When considered in the context of its usefulness, further qualification is necessary. Even a simple assertion carries an implicit claim to be true; and therefore also to be completely reliable in use under appropriate conditions. But every statement of fact needs some sort of *assessment*, since it is impossible to achieve perfect reliability any more than perfect truth. As we have seen, technical statements involving probability and statistics include notations for the expression of their confidence limits, which can be interpreted as the odds against a 'failure in use' of the information. (This interpretation is closer to practice, and also less paradoxical, than that of 'confidence in its truth'.)

Of the three sorts of uncertainty expressed in NUSAP, ignorance is the most novel and complex, and also the most difficult to convey explicitly. In ordinary scientific practice, ignorance of a special sort is vital to the enterprise: the interesting problems which can be stated, but whose solubility is not assured. In this sense, science deals with controllable ignorance; successful science involves, in the classic formula, 'the art of the soluble'. Not all ignorance comes in such convenient packages; in contemporary science/technology policy, the most important problems are frequently those of 'trans-science' (Weinberg 1972): problems which can be stated, whose solution can be conceived, but which are unfeasible in practice because of scale or costs. Such trans-science problems may involve ignorance that is quite important in the policy realm, such as when decisions must be taken before there is any prospect of the relevant information being produced.

In the *pedigree* category, we do not characterize information (or ignorance) in technical detail. Rather we exhibit the mode of production of the quantitative information being represented, through an evaluative history. This defines the border with ignorance, through a display of what more powerful means were *not* deployed in the production of the information. Thus, if we report a 'computation model' as the theoretical structure for the information, that implies that there was no 'theoretically based model' available, and still less 'tested theories', involved in the work. Thus, in each phase we are comparing existing results with conceivable alternatives of greater strength. As research fields develop through practice, early pioneering efforts may be superseded by stronger work in such a fashion as this. Hence we may imagine the choice of modes in a *pedigree* matrix as indicating the border between what is currently feasible and accepted as known, and that which is unfeasible and unknown.

In this respect a *pedigree* code is analogous to the statement of a proved theorem in mathematics. Such a statement includes more than the result; equally important are the conditions under which it holds. As to other possible conditions, there is ignorance; and the statement of a theorem constitutes an implicit challenge to explore that ignorance. Although quantitative information is not 'true' in the same sense as a mathematical result, there is this analogous border between knowledge and ignorance in the specification of its production.

We may describe the three qualifying categories of NUSAP in terms of the various contexts to which they apply. In practice, they operate in interaction, so that no one is truly prior. By abstracting somewhat we may speak of contexts of production of information, of its communication and of its use. These correspond to the categories of *pedigree*, *spread* and *assessment* respectively. In production, the border with ignorance is shown by the limitations of each chosen mode in the *pedigree* matrix. In communication, the 'unknown' is that into which the stated quantity blends by means of the (non-iterated) *spread* term. In use, the implied testing by future experience, revealing possible ignorance, is conveyed by the reliability rating of *assessment*. The order in which we have discussed these categories is not the same as that in NUSAP; in the scheme we adhere more closely to existing usages, where a notation starts with the quantifying part and proceeds towards the more qualifying.

For the evaluative history of the quantity as recorded in the *pedigree* matrix, we analyse the process into four phases. These indicate, by their various modes, the strength of the different constituents of quantitative information resulting from a research process. We have theoretical, empirical and social phases, the last being split into two in order to encompass all the sorts of evaluation that we may want to provide. In order, the phases are: *Theoretical Structures*, *Data Input*, *Peer Acceptance* and *Colleague Consensus*. The *pedigree* matrix is displayed as follows (with corresponding numerical codes and abbreviations):

Discussing the separate phases in order, we have first *Theoretical Structures*. Following the traditional scientific methodology, we accept that the strongest mode here is *Established Theory*. The general term 'established' includes such modalities as: tested and corroborated; or theoretically articulated and coherent with other accepted theories. Thus Einstein's General Theory of Relativity was in this sense already 'established' when it was tested by the famous astronomical experiment of 1919. When the theoretical

	Theoretical Structures	Data Input	Peer Acceptance	Colleague Consensus
4	Established Theory (TH)	Experimental Data (Exp)	Total (Tot)	All but cranks (All)
3	Theoretically based Model (Th.bM)	Historic/ Field Data (H/F)	High (Hi)	All but rebels (All-)
2	Computation Model (Mod)	Calculated Data (Calc)	Medium (Med)	Competing Schools (Sch)
1	Statistical Processing (St)	Educated Guesses (Ed.G)	Low (Lo)	Embryonic Field (Emb)
0	Definitions (Def)	Uneducated Guesses (Gues)	None (Non)	No Opinion (No-O)

component lacks such strength, and is perhaps rudimentary or speculative, then its constructs must be considered as in a 'model', but one which is theoretically based; we have then the mode *Theoretically Based Models*. Although still involved in explanation, such a model makes no effective claim to verisimilitude with respect to reality. In this latter respect it is similar to a *Computation Model* which is some sort of representation of the elements of a mathematical system by which outputs are calculated from inputs. In such a case, there is no serious theoretical articulation of its constructs; the function is purely that of prediction. Such a mode is particularly common in the mathematical behavioural sciences; a well-known example is IQ. This mode, *Computation Model*, characterizes the use of high-speed computers for simulations where real experiments are difficult or expensive.

Important research can exist where neither articulated constructs nor elaborated calculations are present; this is the case in classic inductive science. Then, with techniques varying from simple comparisons (formalizing J.S. Mill's Canons of Induction) through to very sophisticated statistical transformations, we have *Statistical Processing*. Such forms of *Theoretical Structure* can provide no explanation and only limited prediction; but used in exploratory phases of research, they can yield interesting hypotheses for study. Epidemiological work of all sorts, leading to identification of likely causes of known ill-effects, is a good example of this mode. Finally, we have those situations where data which are gathered and analysed are structured only by working *Definitions* that are operationalized through standard routines. This will be the case with field data, frequently destined for public-use statistics. A *pedigree* for public-use statistics has been developed by the authors but it is not discussed in this paper.

The normative ordering among these modes is clear; the higher generally includes the lower as part of their contents. But this does not imply judgements on craftsmanship, effectiveness, or on the quality of the investigators or of a field. We do not share in the traditional judgement that all science should be like physics. However, if (in its present state of development) a field can produce only relatively weak results (as gauged by the modes of this scale), that should be an occasion neither for shame nor for concealment.

The other phase deriving from traditional scientific methodology is called *Data Input*. We use this name rather than 'empirical', to include certain inputs (quite common in policy-related research), whose relation to controlled experience may be tenuous or even non-existent. Starting again with the classical and strongest mode, we have *Experimental Data*. Not so strong, our next entry is *Historic/Field Data*; data of this sort are 'accidental' in the sense of being taken as they occur, and lacking tight controls in production and/or strict reproducibility. *Historic Data* are those that were accumulated in the past, out of the control of the present study; *Field Data* are produced by large-scale procedures of collection and analysis.

Historic/Field Data have at least the strength of a relatively straightforward structure, so that its possible errors and deficiencies can be identified. But sometimes *Data Inputs* are derived from a great variety of empirical sources, and are processed and synthetized by different means, not all standardized or reproducible. The numbers are then themselves 'hypothetical', depending on untested assumptions and procedures. Even to estimate the *spread* and *assessment* in such cases may be quite difficult. Hence we assign *Calculated Data* to a weaker point in the scale even than the *Historic/Field Data* mode.

Traditionally, the last mode discussed would have been considered the weakest in a scientific study. But with the emergence of policy problems calling for data inputs regardless of their empirical strength, formalized techniques were created whereby opinion could be disciplined so as to provide a reasonable facsimile of facts. Such were subjective probabilities, Bayesian statistics, and other ways of eliciting quantitative estimates from experts. These we call *Educated Guesses*. Sometimes even such a mode is absent; *guesses* can be simply uneducated, and yet accepted as data, hypotheses or even facts, whichever seems plausible. In this respect, *Data Inputs* in modern times have come a long way from the relative certainties of the classical methodological framework for science.

The social aspects of the *pedigree* are here given in two phases: *Peer Acceptance* relates to the particular information under evaluation; and *Colleague Consensus* describes that aspect of the field in relation to the particular problem area. These are the phases to which users (and those who advise them) could turn first, for preliminary evaluations of possible effectiveness of the technical information. Thus, if there is weak *Colleague Consensus* and a research field is seriously divided (with *Competing Schools* or perhaps only *Embryonic*) then there will be no security in any piece of quantitative information (Funtowicz and Ravetz 1984). Even the sampling of expert opinions, to obtain *Educated Guesses*, can lead to a bimodal distribution or worse; from this the policy-maker learns the important lesson that scientific ignorance still dominates the problem. Stronger *Colleague Consensus*, as with *All but rebels* or *All but cranks*, may well be time-bound. Since, as T.H. Huxley said: 'It is the customary fate of new theories to begin as heresies and to end as superstitions' (Mackay 1977), who is a 'rebel' or even a 'crank' depends on circumstances. There is a real distinction between the two cases; rebels have some standing among their colleagues, whereas cranks have none.

At the other extreme from scientific orthodoxy, we have the mode *No Opinion*, where there is simply no cognitive framework or social network in which the proffered information can make any sense when it appears. This may be from its apparent lack of substance or of interest, or both.

Once we have an appreciation of the context in which peers can receive and evaluate a piece of information, it is useful to characterize that process. The modes of *Peer Acceptance* range in linear order from *Total* to *None*. It is important to realize that the significance of any given degree of *Peer Acceptance* depends critically on the state of *Colleague Consensus*. Thus, if there is a strong general *consensus* and weak *acceptance*, the information must be judged as of low quality of craftmanship (given trust in the general competence of the field). But if *consensus* is as weak as *acceptance*, even such an adverse judgement is not proper; and ignorance rules again. The degree to which consensus can be weak, even in 'matured' scientific fields, is generally underestimated quite seriously by outsiders. Hence low acceptance is liable to be interpreted in a misleading fashion, as a well-founded adverse judgement on the technical information and by extension on its author as well. We have split the 'social' phase into these two parts, partly to avoid such errors as this.

We now discuss various instances of quantitative information that were important in the development of science, and which illustrate significant features of our *pedigree* category.

Not all quantitative information is appreciated on its first publication; the classic example is Mendel's simple arithmetic ratios between frequencies of different sorts of hybrid peas. For the first thirty years after its publication, the *pedigree* was, as seen retrospectively by historians: (Th. bM, H/F, Non, No-O) or (3, 3, 0, 0). Of course, any contemporary who might have scanned Mendel's paper would not have been so complimentary on the cognitive side. A (reconstructed) *pedigree* code for that period would be (St, Calc, Non, No-O) or (1, 2, 0, 0). The *Calculated* mode conveys the suspicion that the simple ratios were the result of a coincidence or of 'massaged' data. In the earlier twentieth century, the rediscovery of Mendel changed the *pedigree* to (Th. bM, H/F, Tot, All) or (3, 3, 4, 4). With the further development of genetics, the ratios themselves are strengthened to have a *pedigree* (Th, Exp, Tot, All) or (4, 4, 4, 4). But greater sophistication in statistics and its application to experimental design led to a scrutiny of the aggregated numbers by R.A. Fisher, who found them 'too good to be true'; and so the modern historians' judgement of Mendel's own work in his own time now has *pedigree* (Th. bM, Calc, Non, No-O) or (3, 2, 0, 0) (Olby 1966).

A sort of inverse example was provided by T.S. Kuhn (1961) in his seminal essay on measurement in science. This was an experimental value for a constant of crucial importance in the caloric theory of gases: the ratio of the two sorts of specific heat. The setting for the production of this number was quite dramatic: the Laplacian Theory of Gases could explain the experimentally known velocity of sound in air, if (and only if) the constant in question had a certain predicted value. The *Academie des Sciences* devoted its annual essay award competition to this topic in 1819; and the desired value was duly obtained by Delaroche and Berard, whose work won the prize. All was perfect; and here we have a *pedigree* (Th, Exp, Tot, All-) or (4, 4, 4, 3), the only reservation being among the nascent scientific/political opposition to the Laplace school. Unfortunately, the result was simply incorrect; and its background theory became discredited for many reasons. A retrospective *pedigree* for the result, a decade on, could be (Th. bM, Calc, Non, All-) or (3, 2, 0, 3); here the *Colleague Consensus* embraces the victorious anti-Laplacian party, comprising nearly all save the lonely disciple Poisson (Fox 1974).

There two examples of the rise and fall of *pedigree* ratings for quantitative information provide a warning that the evaluation of scientific results is a matter of judgement, which can change drastically. What is effectively scientific knowledge at any one time is very much liable to subsequent revision by the wisdom of hindsight. The reliability of quantitative information in practice does not require it to be continuously confirmed and corroborated. In this respect it can be like theories which, in spite of being superseded or perhaps refuted are still reliable in particular contexts of use ('caloric' being one good example; Newtonian mechanics is another). The *pedigree* coding, by analysing the different phases of the history of the production of the relevant quantity, can assist in the description of such changes, and perhaps thereby also contribute to the resolution of the philosophical problems of such 'fallible knowledge'.

Use of the *pedigree* code will also help to clarify relations between providers and users of technical information. Frequently there is a clash of interests and perceptions. Users want unambiguous and certain facts (of the sort science traditionally promises) as inputs to their decisions. This would relieve them of the burdens of evaluations of inputs and of responsibility for decisions that turn out to be 'wrong'. Typically, the world still expects science to define a 'safe limit' for toxicants of all sorts. The scientists, however, are keenly aware of the imperfections of their offerings in such contexts (unless they are partisan experts in a dispute). Their interest is to hedge their statements with disclaimers and alternatives. With the *pedigree* evaluation, there is a means whereby the most radical uncertainties can be clearly expressed, and then form part of a reasoned discussion of the reliability of the available quantitative information.

Conclusion

We have indicated how NUSAP can contribute to the resolution of the two urgent problems in the methodology of natural science. In epistemology the problem is effectively transformed away from the need for a logical structure, independent of human judgement, whereby uncertainty and ignorance can be conquered. With the notational scheme, these complementary aspects of our knowledge are exhibited in a coherent form. Thus, the experience of successful practice in the quantitative sciences is codified; and the management of the uncertainties becomes a definable task.

In those areas of policy-related research where severe uncertainty prevails, NUSAP provides a standardized means for communications. Debates on the necessarily imperfect and contentious quantities that are invoked will then have a structure and a discipline. The acceptance of NUSAP will also enhance clarity of understanding among those who provide quantitative information and contribute to the improvement of quality control. In such ways, it will increase familiarity with 'uncertain quantities' among all who use them; and in that way enable a shift in 'scientific common sense', so that a more mature understanding of the scope and limits of science may be achieved.

Written jointly with S.O. Funtowicz, this essay was first published in *Measurement, Realism and Objectivity*, ed. J. Forge (Reidel, 1987), pp. 59–88. Our book, *Uncertainty and Quality in Science for Policy*, is to be published by Kluwer in 1990.

References

Ayer, A.J. 1936, *Language, Truth and Logic*, Gollancz, London.

Capra, F. 1975, *The Tao of Physics*, Wildwood House, London.

Collingridge, D. 1980, *The Social Control of Technology*, Frances Pinter, London.

Crosland, M.P. 1962, *Historical Studies in the Language of Chemistry*, Heinemann, London.

Dalkey, N. 1969, 'An experimental study of group opinion. The Delphi method', *Futures* 1 (5), 408–26.

Douglas, M. and D. Wildavsky 1982, *Risk and Culture*, University of California.

Feyerabend, P.K. 1975, *Against Method*, New Left Books, London.

Fox, R. 1974, 'The rise and fall of Laplacian physics', *Historical Studies in the Physical Sciences* 4, 89–136.

Funtowicz, S.O. and J.R. Ravetz 1984, 'Uncertainties and ignorance in policy analysis', *Risk Analysis* 4 (3) 219–20.

Funtowicz, S.O. and J.R. Ravetz 1986, 'Policy related research: A notational scheme for the expression of quantitative technical Information', *J. Opt. Res. Soc.*, **37** (3), 1–5.

Galileo, G. 1632, *Dialogue Concerning the Two Chief World Systems*, University of California (1953), 53.

Gödel, K. 1931, *On Formally Undecidable Propositions*, Basic Books (1962), New York.

Holton, G. 1973, *Thematic Origins of Scientific Thought, Kepler to Einstein*, Harvard University Press, 115–61.

Jiang, J. 1985, 'Scientific rationality, formal or informal', *Brit. J. Phil. Sci.* **36** (4), 409–23.

Keynes, J.M. 1921, *A Treatise on Probability*, St. Martin's Press (1952), New York.

Kline, M. 1972, *Mathematical Thought from Ancient to Modern Times*, Oxford, University Press, New York, 1206.

Kline, M. 1974, *Why Johnny Can't Add: The Failure of the New Math* . . ., Vintage Books, New York.

Kline, M. 1980, *Mathematics: The Loss of Certainty*, Oxford University Press, New York.

Kuhn, T.S. 1961, 'The function of measurement in modern physical science', *Isis* **LII**, 161–93.

Kuhn, T.S. 1962, *The Structure of Scientific Revolutions*, University of Chicago.

Lindblom, C.E. and D.K. Cohen 1979, *Usable Knowledge: Social Science and Social Problem Solving*, Yale University Press, New Haven.

Mackay, A.L. 1977, *The Harvest of a Quiet Eye*, The Institute of Physics, Bristol and London.

Mosteller, F. 1977, 'Assessing unknown numbers: order of magnitude estimation'. In *Statistics and Public Policy*, Fairley, W.B. and F. Mosteller (eds), Addison-Wesley, 163–84.

Nelkin, D. (ed.) 1979, *Controversy: Politics of Technical Decisions*, Sage Publications, London.

Olby, R.C. 1966, *Origins of Mendelism*, Constable, London, 116/182–5.

Putnam, H. 1981, 'The impact of science on modern conceptions of rationality', *Synthese* **46**, 359–82.

Ravetz, J.R. 1971, *Scientific Knowledge and Its Social Problems*, Oxford University Press, 158. See also Chapter 10 for 'Quality control in science'.

Ruckelshaus, W.D. 1984, 'Risk in a free society', *Risk Analysis* **4**, 157–62.

Savage, L.J. 1954, *The Foundations of Statistics*, J. Wiley, New York.

Shapere, D. 1986, 'External and internal factors in the development of science', *Science and Technology Studies* **4** (1), 1–9.

Weinberg, A.M. 1972, 'Science and trans-science', *Minerva* **10**, 209–22.

Zukav, G. 1979, *Dancing Wu Li Masters: An Overview of the New Physics*, Morrow, New York.

Usable Knowledge, Usable Ignorance:
Incomplete Science with Policy Implications

For centuries the dominant theme of our science has been taken from Francis Bacon's aphorism 'Knowledge and power meet in one'. I need not relate here the transformation of humanity's material culture that science has brought about, nor the enhancement of human life, social, moral, and spiritual, that this has enabled through the conquest of the traditional curse of poverty (in at least the more fortunate parts of the world). But now we face a new, unprecedented problem. Along with its great promises, science (mainly through high technology) now presents grave threats. We all know about nuclear (and also chemical and biological) weapons, and about the menaces of acid rain, toxic wastes, the greenhouse effect, and perhaps also the re-emergence of hostile species, artificially selected for virulence by our imprudent use of drugs and pesticides. It would be comforting to believe that each problem could be solved by a combination of more scientific research of the appropriate sort, together with more goodwill and determination in the political and technological spheres. Doubtless, these are necessary, but the question remains: Are they sufficient? The record of the first round of an engagement with these biospheric threats is not encouraging. For example, we do not yet know when, how, or even whether global temperatures will be influenced by the new substances being added to the atmosphere. This is why, we believe, a novel approach is called for if our science-based civilization is to solve these problems that are so largely of our own making.

Indeed, we may see the issue not merely in terms of science, but of our industrialized civilization as a whole, since it has science as the basis of its definition, the science defined by the motto of Francis Bacon. And the problem that faces us is that the sum of knowledge and power is now revealed to be insufficient for the preservation of civilization. We need something else as well, perhaps best called 'control'. This is more than a mere union of the first two elements, for it involves goals, and hence values, and also a historical dimension, including both the remembered past and the unknowable future.

Can our civilization enrich its traditional knowledge and power with this new element of control? If not, the outlook is grim. There are always sufficient pressures that favour short-term expedients to solve this or that problem in technology or welfare, so that the evaluative concerns and long-range perspectives necessary for control will, on their own, lose every time. That is what has been happening, almost uniformly, in our civilization until quite recently. Only in the last few decades have scientists become aware that control does not occur as an automatic by-product of knowledge and power. Our awareness has increased rapidly, but so have the problems. And we are still in the early stages of defining the sort of science that is appropriate to this new function.

We might for a moment step back and look at this industrialized civilization of ours. It is now about half a millennium since the start of the Renaissance and the expansion of Europe. That is roughly the standard period of flourishing for previous civilizations; will ours prove more resilient to its own characteristic environmental problems? It seems likely that some of the ancient 'fertile crescent' cultures declined because of excessive irrigation, and in various ways the Romans consumed great quantities of lead. What would our be our auto-intoxicant of choice?

In some ways our material culture is really rather brittle; our high technology and sophisticated economies depend quite crucially on extraordinary levels of quality control in technology and on highly stable social institutions. Whether these could absorb a really massive environmental shock is open to question. The real resilience of our civilization may lie not so much in its developed hardware and institutions, as in its capacity for rapid adaptation and change. It has, after all, continued to grow and flourish through several unprecedented revolutions: one in common-sense understanding of Nature in the seventeenth century, another in the material basis of production in the eighteenth and nineteenth centuries, and yet another in the organization of society over much of the world in the twentieth century. Perhaps it could be that the latest challenge to this civilization, resulting from the environmental consequences of our science-based technology, will be met by the creation of a new, appropriate sort of science. We can only hope so, and do our best to make it happen.

What could such a new, appropriate sort of science be? Isn't science just science? In some ways, yes, but in others it is already differentiated. We are all familiar with the differences between pure or basic research on the one hand, and applied or R & D on the other. In spite of the many points of contact and overlap, they do have distinct functions, criteria of quality, social institutions, and etiquette and ethics. To try to run an industrial laboratory as if it were within the teaching and scholarship context of a university would be to invite a fiasco; and equally so in reverse. Now we face the task of creating a style of science appropriate to this novel and urgent task of coping with biospheric problems. Of course, there are many different institutions doing research with just this end in view. Sometimes they are successful, but success is more common when they have a problem where the conditions for success can be defined and met, and where the input from research is straightforward. To the extent that the problem becomes diffuse in its boundaries (geographically, or across effects and causes), entrained in cross-currents of politics and special interests, and/or scientifically refractory, then traditional styles of research, either academic or industrial or any mix of the two, reveal their inadequacy.

This is the lesson of the great biosphere problems of the last decade. Faced with problems not of its choosing (though indirectly of its making), science, which is the driving force and ornament of our civilization, could not deliver the solutions. When asked by policy-makers, 'What will happen, and when?' the scientists must, in all honesty, reply in most cases, 'We *don't* know, and we *won't* know, certainly not in time for your next decisions'.

If this is the best that science can do, and it seems likely to be so for an increasing number of important issues, then the outlooks for effective policy-making and for the credibility of science as a cornerstone of our civilization are not good. Yet, I believe, so long as scientists try to respond as if they face simple policy questions determined by simple factual inputs, the situation cannot improve.

But what else can scientists do except provide facts for policy? I hope that we can define the task in new terms, more appropriate to our situation, and *that* is an important component of the goal of this project.

My work on this project has already involved me in an intellectual adventure; recasting my earlier ideas about science had led me into paradox and apparent contradiction. Rather than leading colleagues into them by gentle and easy stages, I have chosen to exhibit them boldly in the title. We all know what is 'usable knowledge', although it turns out to be far from straight-forward in practice (Lindblom and Cohen 1979). But 'usable ignorance?' Is this some sort of Zen riddle? I hope not. But if we are to cope successfully with the enormous problems that now confront us, some of our ideas about science and its applications will have to change. The most basic of these is the assumption that science can indeed be useful for policy, but if and only if it is natural and effective, and can provide 'the facts' unequivocally. So long as it seemed that those facts would be always forthcoming on demand, this assumption was harmless. But now we must cope with the imperfections of science, with radical uncertainty, and even with ignorance, in forming policy decision for the biosphere. Do we merely turn away from such problems as beneath the dignity of scientists, or do we learn somehow to make even our own ignorance usable in these new conditions? In this exploratory essay, I hope to show how even this paradox might be resolved, and in a way that is fruitful for us all.

Images of Science, Old and New

If I am correct in believing that our inherited conception of science is inappropriate for the new tasks of control of these apparently intractable biospheric problems, then we shall all have to go through a learning experience, myself included. Scientists, scholars and policy-makers will need to open up and share their genuine but limited insights of science, so that a common understanding, enriched and enhanced by dialogue, can emerge. My present task is to call attention to the problem, and to indicate my personal, rough, provisional guidelines toward a method.

Insoluble Problems

I may well seem to be speaking in paradoxes, so I will suggest a question that may illuminate the problem. For background, let us start with the historical datum that in the year 1984 we cannot predict when, or even whether, the Earth's mean temperature will rise by 2°C due to an increasing CO_2 content in the atmosphere. Yet this prediction can be cast as a scientific problem, for which there are both empirical data and theoretical models. *Why* these are inadequate is a question I must defer; but we can (I hope) all agree that here is a scientific problem that cannot be solved, either now or in any planned future. And this is only an example of a class that is growing rapidly in number and in urgency.

I believe that such problems are still very unfamiliar things, for our personal training in science progressed from certainties to uncertainties without any explicit, officially recognized markers along the path. Almost all the facts learned as students were uncontested and incontestable; only during research did we discover that scientific results can vary in quality; later we may have come across scientific problems that could not be solved; and only through participation in the governing of science do we learn of choices and their criteria.

Now I can put the question, for each of us to answer for himself or herself: When, at what stage of my career, did I become aware of the existence of scientific problems that could not be solved? *My* personal answer is not too difficult. As a philosophically minded mathematician, early in my postgraduate studies, I learned of classic mathematical problems and conjectures that have defied solution for decades or even centuries. I have reason to believe that my experience was exceptional for a scientist. Certainly, I have never seen an examination in a science subject that assumed other than that every problem has one and only one correct solution. Some such problems may well exist, but they will be a tiny minority. Similarly, research students may learn of the tentativeness of solutions, the plasticity of concepts, and the unreliability of facts in the literature. But this is a form of insiders' knowledge, not purveyed to a lay public, nor even much discussed in scholarly analyses of science.

Indeed, it is scarcely a decade since insoluble scientific problems have become 'news that's fit to print'. Alvin Weinberg (1972) brought them into recognition with the term 'trans-science'. Were these a new phenomenon of the troubled 1960s? — that period when environmentalists began to raise the impossible demand that science prove the impossibility of harm from any and all industrial processes and effluents. No, ever since the onset of the scientific revolution, science had been promising far more than it could deliver. Galileo's case for the Copernican Theory rested on his theory of the tides, where he contemptuously rejected the moon's influence and instead developed a mechanical model that was far beyond his powers to articulate or demonstrate. Descartes' laws of impact, fundamental for his system, were all wrong except in the trivial cases. The transformation of the techniques of manufacture, promised by every propagandist of the century, took many generations to materialize. In the applications of science, progress toward the solution of outstanding, pressing problems was leisurely; for example, the break-even point for medicine, when there came to be less risk in consultation of a physician than in avoidance, seems to have occurred early in the present century.

None of this is to denigrate science; however slow it was to fulfil the hopes of its early prophets, it has now done so magnificently, nearly miraculously. My aim here is to focus our attention on a certain image of science, dominant until so very recently, where the implicit rule was 'all scientific problems can be discussed with students and the public, provided that they're either already solved or now being solved'. Each of us (including myself) has this one-sided experience of science as 'the facts' embedded deeply in our image of science. That is why I think it is a useful exercise for each of us to recall *when* we first discovered the existence of insoluble scientific problems.

'Atomic' Science

If I am still struggling to find a new synthesis out of earlier ideals and recent disappointments, in spite of having earned my living on just that task for 25 years, I cannot really expect colleagues or members of the general public to provide immediate insights that will neatly solve my problems. All I can do is to offer some preliminary ideas, to share with colleagues from various fields of practice, and to hope that out of the resulting dialogue we may achieve a better understanding of the practice and accomplishments of science, as a mixture of success and failure, and of our achieved knowledge and continuing ignorance.

It appears to me that we must now begin to transcend an image of science that may be called 'atomic', for 'atoms' are central to it in several ways. The conception of matter itself, the style of framing problems, and the organization of knowledge as a social possession — all may be considered atomic. I believe that such an image inhibits our grasping the new aspects of science, such as quality control, unsolvable problems and policy choices, that are essential for an effective science of the biosphere.

The idea of atomic was at the heart of the new metaphysics of Nature conceived in the seventeenth century, the basis of the achievements of Galileo, Descartes and Newton. The particular properties of the atoms were always contested, and are not crucial. What counts is the commitment to Nature being composed of isolated bits of reality, possessing only mathematical properties, and devoid of sensuous qualities, to say nothing of higher faculties of cognition or feeling. Such a basis for experimental natural science was quite unique in the history of human civilizations, and on that metaphysical foundation has been built our practice and our understanding of science.

That practice is best described as analytical or reductionist. It is really impossible to imagine laboratory work being done on any other basis. But we can now begin to see its inadequacy for some fields of practice that are largely based on science, such as medicine. To the extent that illness is caused by social or psychological factors, or indeed by mere ageing, the atomic style of therapy through microbe hunting is becoming recognized as inadequate or even misdirected.

With the atomism of the physical reality goes an atomism of our knowledge of it. Thus, it has been highly effective to teach science as a collection of simple hard facts. Any given fact will be related to prior ones whose mastery is necessary for the understanding of it; but to relate forwards and outwards, to the meaning and functioning of a fact in its context, be it technical, environmental or philosophical, is normally considered a luxury, regularly crowded out of the syllabus by the demands of more important material. This is not just yet another deficiency to be blamed on teachers. In his important analysis of 'normal science', T.S. Kuhn (1962) imagines an essentially myopic and anti-critical activity, 'a strenuous and devoted attempt to force nature into the conceptual boxes provided by professional education'.

Our conception of the power based on scientific knowledge is similarly atomic. Engineers are trained to solve problems within what we can now see to be exceedingly narrow constraints: operational feasibility within commercially viable costings. The environment hit engineering practice with a sudden impact in the 1970s because of protective legislation, generally first in the United States and then elsewhere. It is understandable that engineers should find it inappropriate for the fate of important dams to depend on the breeding habits of a local fish; but it does reflect on their training and outlook when they repeatedly plan for nuclear power stations in the state of California without first checking for local earthquake faults. To be sure, the calculation of all environmental variables, including the cultural and psychological health of affected local residents, does seem to take engineering far from its original and primary concerns; but the demand for such extreme measures arises from a public reaction to a perceived gross insensitivity by engineers and their employing organizations to anything other than the simplest aspects of the power over Nature that they wield.

Now we have learned that power, even based on knowledge, is not a simple thing. It is relatively easy to build a dam to hold back river water; there is power. But to predict and eventually manage the manifold environmental changes *initiated* by that intrusion is another matter. The flows and cycles of energy and materials that are disrupted by the dam will, all unknown to us, take new patterns and then eventually present us with new, unexpected problems. The dam, strong, silent, and simple, engineering at its most classic, may disrupt agriculture downstream (Aswan, the Nile), create hydrological imbalances (Volga), or even be interpreted as imperialism (Wales)! Hence the constant need for continuous, iterative *control*, lest an atomized knowledge, applied through myopic power, sets off reactions that bring harm to us all.

We may say that a sort of atomism persists in the social practice of science, where the unit of production is the paper, embodying the intellectual property of a new result. This extends to the social organization of science in the erection of specialties and subspecialties, each striving for independence and autonomy. The obstacles to genuinely interdisciplinary research in the academic context, hitherto wellnigh insuperable, point up the disadvantages of this style for the sorts of problems we now confront. It is significant that when scientists are operating in a command economy, being employees on mission-orientated research or R & D, and not in a position to seek individual advancement as subject specialists, an effective exchange of skills *is* possible. Thus, the atomic ideal of knowledge is not an absolute constraint; it can be suspended in the pursuit of knowledge as power; our present task is to see whether it can be transcended in the attempt to apply knowledge, produced by independent scientists and scholars, to the new tasks of control.

Quality Control in Science

We may now begin to move outward from this previous atomism, to enrich our understanding of the scientific process. Here I am trying only to make explicit what every good scientist has known all along. I may put another question concerning the personal development of each of us: when did I become aware of degrees of quality in scientific materials presented ostensibly as complete, uncontestable facts? I know that for some, either exceptionally independent, or having a gifted teacher, the awareness came very early, even at school. For me, the moment was in my final year at college, when I studied a table of basic physical constants. There I saw alternative values for a single constant that lay outside each other's confidence limits. I realized then that the value of a physical constant could be quite other than an atomic fact. Among the discordant set not all could be right. Was there necessarily one correct value there; or was it a matter of judgement which cited value was the best?

The issue of quality is at the heart of the special methodological problems of biospheric science. Hard facts are few and far between; in many areas (such as rate constants for atmospheric chemical reactions), today's educated guesses are likely to appear tomorrow as ignorant speculations. The problem of achieving quality control in this field is too complex to be resolved by goodwill and redoubled efforts. Later I build on Bill Clark's ideas on making a first analysis of the task.

The problem of quality control in traditional science has quite recently achieved prominence, but still mainly in connection with the extreme and unrepresentative cases of outright fraud. The enormous quantity of patient, unrewarded work of peer review and refereeing, where (in my opinion) the moral commitment of scientists is more crucial, and more openly tested, than in research itself, has received scant attention from the scholars who analyse science. Yet quality control is not merely essential to the vitality and health of normal science. It becomes a task requiring a clear and principled understanding, if the new sciences of the biosphere are to have any hope of success. The inherited, unreflected folkways and craft skills of compartmentalized academic research are inadequate here; and here we lack the ultimate quality test of practice, realized mainly through the marketplace of industrial research and R & D.

I envisage a major effort in our project being devoted to the creation of appropriate methods and styles of quality control. I hope that this will emerge naturally from reflection on their own experience by scientists who have already been engaged in such work; but it cannot be expected to form itself automatically, without explicit attention and investment of the resources of all of us. I return to this theme in the final section.

Choice in Science

My next theme is that of 'choice': here too it was Alvin Weinberg (1963, 1964) who first raised the issue, early in the 1960s. Previous to that, the ruling assumption, one might almost say ideology, had been that real science required an autonomy that included choice of problems and the setting of criteria for that choice. But with the advent of 'big science', the public that supported the effort through a significant burden on state expenditure was inevitably going to demand some voice in the disposition of its largesse. This is not the place to discuss the detailed arrangements, or the deeper problems, of that new 'social contract of science'. Anyone involved with this biosphere project is fully aware that biosphere problems are not to be solved without massive investment of funds, in which public and private corporate agencies are inevitably, and quite legitimately, involved.

All this may seem so natural that we must remind ourselves how new it is, and also how little impact it has made on the philosophical accounts of science to which we all go for enlightenment and guidance. There is a real gap between conceptions here: if science consists of true atomic facts, whose value lies in themselves, then what possible genuine criterion of choice can there be for research? Of course, the experience of research science is that not all facts are of equal value; they vary in their interest and fruitfulness, as well as in their internal strength and robustness. Hence policy decisions on research are possible, however difficult it is to quantify or even to justify them with conclusive arguments.

When we consider the criteria for choice governing mission-orientated projects, we find some components that are more or less internal to the process

267

and others that are not. In the former category are feasibility and cost (this latter being measured against the demands of competing projects within some pre-assigned limited budget). For this we must take into account the aims or objectives of the project, which are necessarily exterior to it and different from the research itself, for they employ values.

In considering these external values, I make a distinction between functions and purposes: The former refers to the sort of job done by a particular device, and the latter to the interests or purposes served, or the values realized, by the job being done. Functions are still in the technical realm, while purposes belong to people and to politics. It is at the intersection of these two sorts of effects that policy-making for sciences and technology is done.

The question of feasibility, while mainly technical, is not entirely straight-forward. The assessment of feasibility depends on a prediction of the behaviour of a device or system when it is eventually created and in operation. To the extent that the proposal involves significant novelty or complexity, that prediction of the future will inevitably be less than certain. Indeed, it is now clear in retrospect that the great technological developments of recent decades were made under conditions of severe ignorance concerning not merely their social and environmental effects, but even their costs of construction, maintenance and operation. There is an old and well-justified joke that if a cost–benefit analysis had been made at the crucial time, then sail would never have given way to steam. But many American utility companies might now reply that a proper analysis, made on their behalf, of nuclear power might have protected them from the financial disasters that now threaten to engulf them.

This point is not made by way of apportioning blame for the troubles of that once supremely optimistic industry. It can be argued that, say, 15 years ago, it was impossible to predict which of the possible mishaps would afflict the industry, and how serious they would be. But in that event, we should recognize the ineradicable component of ignorance, not merely uncertainty, in forecasting the prospects for any radically new technology.

Ignorance

The pervasiveness of ignorance concerning the interactions of our technology with its environment, natural and social, is a very new theme. 'Scientific ignorance' is paradoxical in itself and directly contradictory to the image and sensibility of our inherited style of science and its associated technology. Coping with ignorance in the formation of policy for science, technology and environment is an art that we have barely begun to recognize, let alone master. Yet ignorance dominates the sciences of the biosphere, the focus of our project.

The problems of applying science to policy purposes in general have been given a handy title, 'usable knowledge'. For those problems of the imminent future, we would do well to remind ourselves of their nature by using a title like

268

'usable ignorance'. Its paradoxical quality points up the distance we must travel from our inherited image of science as atomic facts, if we are to grapple successfully with these new problems. How we might begin to do so is the theme of my discussion here.

Elements of a New Understanding

To some extent, the preceding conceptual analysis follows the path of the maturing understanding of many scientists of the present generation. First, as students, we mastered our standard facts; then, in research, we became aware of quality; as we became involved in the government of science, we recognized the necessity for choice; involvement in environmental problems brought us up against functions of devices and of systems, and the frequently confused and conflicting purposes expressed through politics. Still, we could imagine that there was a hard core to the whole affair, in the sort of basic, incontestable facts that every schoolboy knows. Hence the intrusion of ignorance into our problem-situation did not immediately raise the spectre of the severe incompetence of science in the face of the challenges—or threats—produced by the environmental consequences of the science-based technology on which our civilization rests.

Science in the Policy Process

This rather comfortable picture is analogous to the traditional model of science in the policy process. We may imagine this as a meeting of two sides. The public, through some political machinery, expresses a concern that some particular purposes are being frustrated or endangered, say through the lack of clean water. Administrators then devise or promote devices and systems, physical technology, or administrative agencies to perform particular functions whereby those purposes may once again be protected. For this they need information about the natural process involved in the problem, for which they turn to the scientists. The scientists provide the necessary facts (either from the literature, or produced by research to order) that either determine the appropriate solution, or at least set boundaries within which the normal processes of political bargaining can take place. In that way, the problem is solved or, at least, effectively resolved in political terms.

However well such a model has fitted practice in the past, it no longer captures the complexity and inconclusiveness of the process of policy-related science in the case of biospheric problems (Otway and Ravetz 1984). Indeed, we may define this new sort of policy-related science as one in which facts are uncertain, values in dispute, stakes high, decisions urgent, and where no single one of these dimensions can be managed in isolation from the rest. Acid rain may serve as the present paradigm example of such science. This model may

269

seem to transform the image of science from that of a stately edifice to that of a can of worms. Whether this be so, the unaesthetic quality is there in the real world we confront and with which we must learn to cope somehow.

It may help if we employ another model: how problems come to be chosen for investigation. In the world of pure or academic science, problems are *selected* by the research community. If a particular area is not yet ripe for study, available techniques being insufficiently powerful, it is simply left to wait, with no particular loss. (The adventurous or foolhardy may, of course, try their luck there.) In the case of mission-orientated work, they are *presented* by managerial superiors, though these are expected to have some competence in assessing feasibility and costs of the research in relation to the goals of the enterprise. But in policy-related science, the problems are *thrust upon* the relevant researchers by political forces that take scant heed of the feasibility of the solutions they demand. Indeed, it will be common for such problems not to be feasible in the ordinary sense. Drawing on low-prestige and immature fields, requiring databases that simply do not exist, being required to produce answers in a hurry, they are not the sort of inquiry where success of any sort can be reasonably expected.

It may be that our traditional lack of awareness of the interaction of ignorance with scientific knowledge has been maintained because science could proclaim its genuine successes and remain at a safe distance from its likely failures. Through all the centuries when progress became an increasingly strong theme of educated common sense, science could be seen as steadily advancing the boundaries of knowledge. There seemed no limit in principle to the extent of this conquest, and so the areas of ignorance remaining at any time were not held against science—they too would fall under the sway of human knowledge at the appropriate time.

Now we face the paradox that while our knowledge continues to increase exponentially, our relevant ignorance does so even more rapidly. And this is ignorance generated by science! An example will explain this paradox. The Victorians were totally ignorant of the problem of disposal of long-lived radioactive wastes. They had no such things, nor could they imagine their existence. But now we have made them, by science, and the problem of guaranteeing a secure storage for some quarter of a million years is one where ignorance, rather than mere uncertainty, is the state of affairs. Thus, we have conquered a former ignorance, in our knowledge of radioactivity, but in the process created a new ignorance, of how to manage it in all its dangerous manifestations.

Interpenetrating Opposites in Science

Science in the policy process is thus a very different thing from the serene accumulation of positive and ultimately useful factual knowledge, as portrayed in our inherited image. Indeed, given the intrusion of subjective elements of judgements and choice into a sphere of practice traditionally *defined* by its objectivity, we may wonder whether there can be any endeavour describable as science in such circumstances. To this problem I can only begin to sketch a solution, by giving two analyses, one static and the other dynamic. The former elucidates the paradoxical, or contradictory, nature of our situation, and the latter indicates paths to resolution of the paradox.

To begin with it is necessary for us to transcend the simplistic picture of science that has been dominant for so very long. For generations we have been taught of a difference in kind between facts and values. The latter were seen to be subjective, uncertain, perhaps even basically irrational in origin. Fortunately, science supplied facts, objective and independent of value judgements, whereby we could attain genuine knowledge and also order our affairs in a proper manner. Those who protested that such a sharp dichotomy was destructive of human concerns were usually on the romantic or mystical fringe, and could be ignored in the framing of curricula and in the propaganda for science.

Similarly, the opposition between knowledge and ignorance was absolute. A scientific fact could be known, simply and finally. It could, of course, be improved upon by the further growth of science; but *error* in science was nearly a contradiction in terms. The boundary between knowledge and ignorance was not permeable; it simply advanced with each increment of science, bringing light to where darkness had hitherto reigned. Of course, there have been many disclaimers and qualifications tacked on to this simple model; we all know that science is tentative, corrigible, open-ended, and all the rest. But the idea that a fact could be understood imperfectly or confusedly, or that a great scientific discovery could be mixed with error, has been brought into play only very recently by historians of science.

Hence we are really unprepared by our culture to cope with the new phenomenon of the interpenetration of these contradictory opposites. The impossibility of separating facts from values in such a critical area as the toxicity of environmental pollutants is a discovery of recent years (Whittemore 1983). And the creation of relevant ignorance by the inadequately controlled progress of technology is still in the process of being articulated by philosophers (Collingridge 1982).

An immediate reaction to these disturbing phenomena can be despair or cynicism. Some scholars have elaborated on the theme that pollution is in the nose of the beholder, and reduce *all* environmental concern to the social–psychological drives of extremist sects (Douglas and Wildavsky 1982). Politicians and administrators can take the easy way out and treat scientists as so many hired guns, engaging those who are certain to employ technical rhetoric on behalf of their particular faction. Such solutions as these, if considered as cures, are really far worse than the disease. If dialogue on these urgent scientific issues of the biosphere is degraded to thinly veiled power politics, then only a congenital optimist can continue to hope for their genuine resolution.

Viewed socially, these oppositions or contradictions show no way through. But the situation is not desperate once we appreciate that decision-making is not at all a unique event requiring perfect inputs if it is to be rational. Rather it is a complex process, interactive and iterative; the logical model for it is perhaps less demonstration than dialogue. Seeing decision-making (or policy-formation; I use the two terms interchangeably) as a sort of dialectical process, we may imagine those central contradictions of usable knowledge and usable ignorance being transcended, or synthesized, through the working of the dialectical process.

Varieties of Policy-Related Research

First, I show how these problems of policy-related research may be differentiated, and in such a way that the natural tendency of their dynamics is toward a resolution. Drawing on recent work by myself and my colleague, S.O. Funtowicz (Funtowicz and Ravetz 1985), I distinguish two dimensions of such problems: systems uncertainties and decision stakes. The former refers to the complex system under consideration, including aspects that are technical, scientific, administrative and managerial; the uncertainties are the ranges of possible outcomes, corresponding to each set of plausible inputs and decisions. The decision stakes are the costs and benefits to all concerned parties, including regulators (both field employees and administrators) and representatives of various interests, that correspond to each decision. In each case, we have complex sets of ill-defined variables for aggregation into a single index, hence each of the dimensions is only very loosely quantitative. We distinguish only the values low, medium and high (Figure 1). When both dimensions (systems uncertainties and decision stakes) are low, we have what we may call applied science; straightforward research will produce a practical band of values of critical variables within which the ordinary political processes can operate to produce a consensus.

When either dimension alone becomes large, a new situation emerges; we call it technical consultancy. This is easiest to see in the case of system uncertainty; the consultant is employed precisely because his or her unspecifiable skills, and his or her professional integrity and judgement, are required for the provision of usable knowledge for the policy process. It is less obvious that, even if uncertainties are low, large decision stakes take the problems out of the realm of the routine. But on reflection, this is the way things happen in practice. If some institution sees its interests seriously threatened by an issue, then no matter how nearly conclusive the science, it will fight back with every means at its disposal, until such time as further resistance would cause a serious loss of credibility in itself as a competent institution, and a damaging loss of power as a result. The public sees such struggles most clearly in notorious cases of pollution, when a beleaguered institution persists in harmful policies (such as poisoning its work-force or the local environment) to the point of being

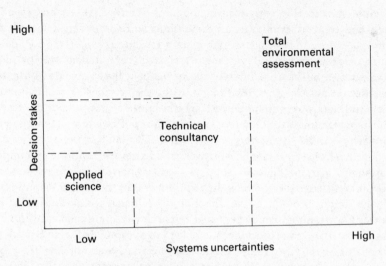

Figure 1 *Interaction of decision stakes and systems uncertainties*

irresponsible, immoral, or perhaps even culpable (industrial asbestosis is a notorious recent case in point). The outrage in such cases is fully justified, of course; but it is an error to believe either that those particular firms are uniquely malevolent, or that all firms casually and habitually behave in such a way. No, it is just when caught in such a trap, however much of their own making, that institutions, like people, will fight for survival.

Such cases are fortunately the exception. It is more common for both systems uncertainties and decision stakes to be moderate. Funtowicz and I have been able to articulate a model of consultancy practice, wherein the traditional scientist's ideal of consensual knowledge is sacrificed on behalf of a more robust sort of knowledge appropriate to the problem. We call it clinical, from the field of practice in which such a style has been developed successfully. In it we eliminate safety as an attribute (the term now has a largely rhetorical meaning anyway) and substitute good performance (which may include the possibility of failures and accidents). In the same vein, we generalize probability (with its mathematical connotations) to propensity, and measure to gauge; and for prediction we substitute prognosis. In this way, we hope to express the degree to which non-quantifiable and even non-specifiable expert judgements enter into an assessment. The outcome of the process (which is conceived as continuously iterating) is not a general theory to be tested against particular facts, but rather a provisional assessment of the health of a particular system together with the relevant aspects of its environment. I hope that this model will be useful in the biosphere project as it develops.

Passing to the more intractable case, where either dimension is very large, we have what we call a total environmental assessment. For here, nothing is certain, there are no boundaries or accepted methods for solving problems;

273

the problem is total in extent, involving facts, interests, values and even life-styles, and total in its mixture of dimensions and components. Even here a review of history shows that in such cases a resolution can emerge. A debate ensues, once an issue is salient; and while at first the debate may be totally polarized and adversarial in style, it may evolve fairly quickly. Both sides are attempting to gain legitimacy with the various foci of opinion, which ultimately represent power: special-interest groups, administrators, politicians, the media, respondents in opinion polls, voters. They therefore necessarily invoke the symbols of universality and rationality whereby uncommitted observers can be won over; and in however oblique and implicit a fashion, a genuine dialogue emerges. Most important in this process, new relevant knowledge is created by the requirements of the various disputants, so that the issue is brought in the direction of technical consultancy, if not yet science. For example, issue-generated research can eventually transform the terms of a debate, such as in the case of lead in automobile fuel in Britain and Europe during the early 1980s. Events that previously had not been significant news suddenly became so: thus the various nuclear accidents of the 1950s and 1960s were of no great moment for policy purposes, while Three Mile Island was a mortal blow to the American nuclear power construction industry. Hence a problem does evolve; a dominant consensus can emerge; and then the losing side is forced into a retreat, saying what it can while the facts as they emerge tip the balance ever more decisively against it.

There is, of course, no guarantee that any particular total environmental assessment will move down scale in this way, or will do so quickly enough for its resolution to prevent irreparable harm. But at least we have here a model of a process whereby a solution can happen, analogously to the way in which great political and social issues can be (but, of course, need not be) resolved peacefully and transformed.

Debates on such issues are usually very different from those within a scientific community. They cannot presuppose a shared underlying commitment to the advance of knowledge nor presuppose bounds to the tactics employed by the antagonists. In form they are largely political, while in substance ostensibly technical or scientific. Confusion and rancour of all sorts abound. Yet, I argue, such apparently unedifying features are as consistent with effective policies for science and technology as they are for political affairs in general. And they *must* be, for the great issues of the biosphere will necessarily be aired in just such forums; there are no other forums to render them unnecessary.

The Policy Process and Usable Knowledge

Now I discuss the policy process itself, in relation to these phenomena of the interpenetration of facts and values and of knowledge and ignorance. This is not the place to develop schematic models of that process, so I will content myself with a few observations. The first is that no decision is atomic. Even if an issue is novel, even if its sponsoring agency is freshly created, there will always exist a background, in explicit law, codes of practice, folkways and expectations, in which it necessarily operates even while reacting on the background. And once an issue exists, it is rare indeed for it to fade away. It may become less salient for policy and be relegated to a routine monitoring activity; but it can erupt at any time should something extraordinary occur.

Indeed, when we look at the duration and complexity of those dialectical processes whereby a total environmental assessment problem (its common initial form) is gradually tamed, we see the necessity for a differentiation among the functions performed by the facts — or better, the inputs of technical information. Here I can do no better than to use materials recently developed by Bill Clark (personal communication). He starts with authoritative knowledge — the traditional ideal of science, still applicable in the case of applied science issues. This is supplemented by reporting — not in newspapers, but in the accumulation of relatively reliable, uncontroversial information on a variety of phenomena of no immediate salience, but crucial when a crisis emerges. This is the descendant of natural history, popular in past epochs when clergymen and other gentlemen of leisure could gain satisfaction and prestige through their mastery of some great mass of material, perhaps of a locality, perhaps of a special branch of nature. The decline of this style of science, under the pressure of changing institutions and the dominant criteria of quality, is a clear example of what I have called the social construction of ignorance. Harvey Brooks (1982) has recently shown what a price we now pay for our ignorance, in the impotence of what I call the clean-up or garbage sciences in the face of our various pollution problems.

When science is involved in the policy process, particularly in the technical consultancy mode, then impersonal demonstrations give way to committed dialogue, and no facts are hard, massy and impenetrable. They are used as evidence in arguments, necessarily inconclusive and debatable. In this case we invoke metaphors to describe their nature and functions; Steven Toulmin (1972) has suggested the term 'maps' (not pictures, or we might say dogmas, but rather guides to action). I have developed the idea of a tool, something that derives its objectivity not so much through its correspondence with external reality as through its effectiveness in operating on reality in a variety of functions and contexts (Ravetz 1984).

Passing to the more contested issues, we mention enlightenment, which might involve enhancing awareness or changing common sense. Perhaps the most notable example of this sort of product in recent times is *Silent Spring* by Rachel Carson (1962). Through it, the environment and its problems suddenly came into existence for the public in the United States and elsewhere. We note that this function is performed partly through the mass media; the role of investigative journalism in the press, and especially television, in enhancing the awareness of the non-scientific public (and perhaps of scientists, too) should be more appreciated.

275

Once an issue has been made salient for the political process, then science can be a complement to interaction—that is, not being decisive in itself in any unreflective way, but correcting common-sense views, and providing crucial inputs when a debate is sharpened. To take an example from another field, the regulation of planned interference with the life-cycle of embryo and fetus will not be reduced to the scientific determination of the onset of life and individuality. But, just as technical progress creates new problems of decision and regulation, scientific information can provide channels and critical points for the ethical and ideological debates on such issues.

Finally, Bill Clark mentions ritual and process: since science is the central symbolic structure of modern industrialized society, the invocation of science to solve a problem has a political power of its own. But such an action, if abused or even abortive, may lead to a wider disillusionment with the secularly sacred symbols themselves, with consequent harm to the social fabric. W. D. Ruckelshaus (1984), sometime Administrator of the Environmental Protection Agency, has identified this danger clearly, in his warning of chaos if his agency is perceived as not doing its job. Analogously, we may say that the best thing to happen to the American nuclear power industry was the outstandingly independent and critical Kemeny report (1979) on Three Mile Island. If such a report had been widely and effectively denounced as a whitewash operation, the loss of credibility of the industry and of its governmental regulatory agencies could have been catastrophic.

With this spectrum of different sorts of usable knowledge, and their corresponding variety of institutions and publics, we begin to see a practical resolution of the abstract dichotomies of fact and value, knowledge and ignorance. Of course, the system as a whole is complicated, underdetermined and inconclusive. But that means it's like social life itself, where we have many failures but also many successes. The only thing lost, through this analysis, is the illusion that the scientist is a sort of privileged being who can dispense nuggets of truth to a needy populace. Seeing the scientist as a participant, certainly of a special sort, in this complex process of achieving usable knowledge provides us with some insights on how to make his or her contribution most effective.

Towards a Practical Approach

Here I hope to be constructive, and I can start my argument with a topic mentioned early in my analysis of the enriched understanding of science that every researcher develops: the assessment of quality. This is frequently the first exposure of a scientist to the essential incompleteness of any scientific knowledge—not merely that there are things left to be discovered, but that the border between our knowledge and our ignorance is not perfectly defined. Even when scientific statements turn out to mean not quite what they say, they are not necessarily the product of incompetence or malevolence; rather, they reflect the essential incompleteness of the evidence and the argument supporting any scientific result. In a matured field, the assessment of quality is a craft skill that may be so well established as to be nearly tacit and unself-conscious: we *know* that a piece of work is really good (or not), without being easily able to specify fully why. By contrast, one sign of the immaturity of a field is the lack of consensus on quality, so that every ambitious researcher must become an amateur methodologist in order to defend his or her results against critics.

Scientific Quality—A Many-Splendoured Thing

When we come to policy-related science, that simple dichotomy of the presence or the absence of maturity is totally inadequate to convey the richness of criteria of quality, with their associated complexity and opportunity for confusion. Here I can only refer to the deep and fruitful insights of Bill Clark, in his taxonomy of criteria of quality among the various legitimate actors in a policy process involving science. In his table of critical criteria, he lists the following actors: scientist, peer group, programme manager or sponsor, policy-maker, and public interest group. For each of these, there are three critical modes: input, output and process. Mastery of that table, reproduced here (Table 1), would, I think, make an excellent introduction to the methodological problems of policy-related science.

It may well be that, as this project develops, we will need to go through that exercise, if only to the extent of appreciating that the research scientist's criteria of quality are not the only legitimate ones in the process.

However different or conflicting may be the other criteria of quality, they must be taken into account, not only in the reporting of research but even in its planning and execution. Now, any one of the actors in such a process must, if she or he is to be really effective in a co-operative endeavour, undertake a task that is not traditionally associated with science: to appreciate another person's point of view. This need not extend to abandoning conflicting interpretation of facts (for a fruitful debate is a genuine one), nor to empathy for another's life-style or world-view. But for strictly practical purposes each participant must appreciate what it is that another is invoking, explicity or implicitly, when making points about the quality of contested materials.

This new and important skill has been called (by Bill Clark) 'a critical connoisseurship of quality in science'. One does not merely apply one's own specialist criteria blindly or unselfconsciously, however excellent or valid they may be for one's own scientific expertise or role. One must be able to assess productions from several points of view in succession, by means of an imaginative sympathy that involves seeing one's own role, one's own self, from a slight distance. It may be that I am here calling for the cultivation of attitudes proper to literary criticism, a prospect that to some may be even more alien than Zen riddles. But given the complexity of policy-related science, in

277

Table 1 Critical Criteria

	Critical Mode		
Critical Role	Input	Output	Process
Scientist	Resource and time constraints; available theory; institutional support; assumptions; quality of available data; state of the art	Validation; sensitivity analyses; technical sophistication; degree of acceptance of conclusions; impact on policy debate; imitation; professional recognition	Choice of methodology (e.g. estimation procedures); communication; implementation; promotion; degree of formalization of analytic activities within the organization
Peer group	Quality of data; model and/or theory used; adequacy of tools; problem formulation; input variables well chosen? Measure of success specified in advance?	Purpose of the study; conclusions supported by evidence? Does model offend common sense? robustness of conclusions; adequate coverage of issues	Standards of scientific and professional practice; documentation; review of validation techniques; style; interdisciplinarity
Programme manager or sponsor	Cost; institutional support within user organization; quality of analytic team; type of financing (e.g. grant versus contract)	Rate of use; type of use (general education, programme evaluation, decision-making, etc.); contribution to methodology and state of the art; prestige; can results be generalized, applied elsewhere?	Dissemination; collaboration with users; has study been reviewed?
Policy-maker	Quality of analysts; cost of study; technical tools used (hardware and software); does problem formulation make sense?	Is output familiar and intelligible? Did study generate new ideas? Are policy indications conclusive? Are they consistent with accepted ethical standards?	Ease of use; documentation; are analysts helping with implementation? Did they interact with agency personnel? With interest groups?
Public-interest groups	Competence and intellectual integrity of analysts; are value systems compatible? Problem formulation acceptable? Normative implications of technical choices (e.g. choices of data)	Nature of conclusions; equity; analysis used as rationalization or to postphone decisions? All viewpoints taken into consideration? Value issues	Participation; communication of data and other information; adherence to strict rules of procedure

response to the complexity of biospheric problems, I can envisage no easier alternative.

Usable Ignorance

The preceding analysis has, I hope, made us familiar with the richness of the concept of usable knowledge in the context of incomplete science with policy implications. Now I can attempt to make sense of that paradoxical category, usable ignorance; for in many respects this defines our present task as one that is qualitatively different from the sorts of science with which we have hitherto been familiar.

First, I have indicated one approach to taming ignorance, by focusing on its border with knowledge. This should be easily grasped with an experience of research. Indeed, the art of choosing research problems can be described as sensing where that border can be penetrated and to what depth. Similarly, the art of monitoring for possible accidents or realized hazards, be they in industrial plant or environmental disruption, consists in having a border with ignorance that is permeable to signals coming from the other side, signs of incipient harmful processes or events that should be identified and controlled. Thus, the technical consultancy problem is one where ignorance is managed, through expert skill, in just this way.

Where ignorance is really severe, as in total environmental assessment, then it is involved in the problem in ways that are both more intimate and more complex. For if ignorance is recognized to be severe, than no amount of sophisticated calculation with uncertainties in a decision algorithm can be adequate for a decision. Non-quantifiable, perhaps non-specifiable, considerations of prudence must be included in any argument. Further, the nature and distribution of a wider range of possible benefits and costs, even including hypothetical items, must be made explicit. Since there can be no conclusive or universally acceptable weighting of these, the values implicit in any such weighting must be made explicit. In terms of a dialogue between opposed interests, this effectively takes the form of a burden of proof: in the absence of strong evidence on either side do we deem a system safe or do we deem it dangerous?

By such means we do not conquer ignorance directly, for that can be done only by replacing it with knowledge. But we cope with it and we ensure that by being aware of our ignorance we do not encounter disastrous pitfalls in our supposedly secure knowledge or supposedly effective technique.

The preceding account is prescriptive for future practice rather than descriptive of the past. Had ignorance been recognized as a factor in technology policy, then, for example, the nuclear power industry would today be in a far healthier state. The easy assumption that all technical problems could be solved when the time came has left that industry, and the rest of us on this planet, with such problems as the disposal of long-lived radioactive wastes. In this case we must somehow manage our ignorance of the state of human society some tens of thousands of years into the future. How many professional engineers have been prepared by their professional training for such a problem?

Coping with ignorance demands a more articulated policy process and a greater awareness of how that process operates. Great leaps forward in technology require continuous monitoring to pick up the signals of trouble as they begin to arrive, and both physical symptoms and their institutions should be designed with the ignorance factor in mind, so that they can respond and adapt in good time. (This point has been amply developed by Collingridge (1982).)

Recognition of the need for monitoring entails that the decision process be iterative, responding in a feedback loop to signals from the total environment of the operating system. Also, the inclusion of ignorance in decision-making via the explicit assignment of burden of proof involves a self-conscious operation of dialogue at several levels, the methodological and regulative simultaneously with the substantive. All this is very complicated, of course, and the transaction costs of running such a system might appear to be very high, not least in the absorption of time and energy of highly qualified people. But if those costs become a recognized element of the feasibility of a project, let it be so; better to anticipate that aspect of coping with ignorance than either to become bogged down in endless regulator games, or to regress to a simplistic fantasy of heroic-scale technological innovation, thereby inviting a debacle sooner or later.

Coming now to an idea about the biosphere project itself, I find the category of usable ignorance influencing it in several ways. First, it should condition the way we go about our work, for we will be aware that just another programme of research and recommendations is not adequate to the solution of biospheric problems. Also, the concept of usable ignorance may provide topics for a special research effort within the project. What I have described above is only a rudimentary sketch of some of the elements of a large, important and inherently complex phenomenon. With colleagues at Leeds University, I have begun to articulate themes for a co-ordinated research effort involving the logic of ignorance, studies of how some institutions cope with the ignorance that affects their practice, as it reveals itself in error and failure, and more studies of how institutions cope with the threats posed by their ignorance when their monopoly of practice, or their legitimacy, is threatened.

More directly relevant to the immediate concerns of colleagues on the biosphere project is the way in which we will need to make our own ignorance usable. We are, after all, inventing a new scientific style to respond to the new scientific problems of the biosphere, simultaneously with the special researches that are at its basis. We have various precedents to remind us what is *not* likely to work. The simplest is a scattered set of groups of experts, each doing their own thing and meeting occasionally to exhibit their wares. Synthesis of the efforts is then left to the organizers of the meeting and the editors of their proceedings. At a higher level, we have the experience of multi-disciplinary teams, where each member must protect his or her own private professional future by extracting and cultivating research problems that will bring rewards by the special criteria of quality of his or her subject subspecialty. Here, too, the whole of the nominally collaborative effort is only rarely greater than the sum of its parts. Nor can we turn with much hope to the task-force model, which does bring results in technology, for that depends critically on the simplicity of the defining problem, and on an authoritarian structure of decision and control. Our problems are multidimensionally complex by their very nature, and trans-national co-operation is achieved more by cajoling than by command. Hence, none of the existing styles of making knowledge usable is appropriate for ignorance.

Conditions for Success

It appears, then, that we need some sort of dialectical resolution of the contra-diction between the auto-archy of academic-style research and the dictatorship of industrial-style development. There seem to be two elements necessary to make such a new venture a success. One is motivation. Enough of us on the biosphere project must see it as a professional job, developing a new sort of scientific expertise in which we can continue to do satisfying work after the completion of the project. I have no doubt that if this project succeeds, it will become a model for many others, enough to keep all of us busy for a long time. The other element is technique: devising means whereby the genuine mutual enhancement of ideas and perspectives can be accomplished. I indicated some of these at the very beginning of this chapter, in describing some ways in which the biosphere project will be novel.

We may well find ourselves experimenting with techniques of personal inter-action that have been developed for policy formation, but that have hitherto been considered as irrelevant to the austere task of producing new knowledge. But since we, even in our science, are trying to make ignorance usable, we should not be too proud to learn about learning, even in the research process.

The crucial element here may lie in quality assessment and the mutual criticism that makes it possible. Can we learn, sufficiently well for the task, to have imaginative sympathy with the roles and associated criteria of quality of others in different corners of this complex edifice? We will need to compre-hend variety in scientific expertise, in methodological reflection, in organi-zational tasks, and in policy formation. If so, then we can hope to have what Bill Clark has called a 'fair dialogue', in which we are each an amateur, in the best sense of the term, with regard to most of the problems on which we are engaged.

I believe that such a process is possible and that it is certainly worth a try. The environmental problems that confront us, as residents of this planet, are now global and total. We in this group cannot hope to legislate for all of humanity over all the salient issues. But we can at least indicate a way forward, showing that our civilization is genuinely resilient in meeting this supreme challenge.

Conclusion and Perspective

As an historian, I like to find support and understanding in the pattern of the past as it may be extended into the future. In this connection, I can do no better than to quote from an early prophetic writing of Karl Marx. In the Preface to his *Critique of Political Economy* (1869), he gave an intensely concentrated summary of past human history as he understood it, in terms of class structures and class struggles. His concluding motto was, 'Mankind only sets those problems that it can solve'. We must try to justify his optimism in the case of this present challenge. We may understand it as our civilization's characteristic contradiction: the intensified exploitation of nature through the application of knowledge to power, which threatens to become self-destructive unless brought under control.

For my historical perspective on this, I would like to review the evolution of science as a social practice, as it has developed to create new powers and respond to new challenges. In the seventeenth century, the scientific revolution had two related elements: the disenchantment of nature, and the articulation of the ideal of a cumulative, co-operative public endeavour for the advancement of knowledge. With the decay of the ancient belief in secrets too powerful to be revealed came a commitment to a new style of social relations in the production of knowledge. This was promoted as both practically necessary and morally superior. From this came the first scientific societies, and their journals provided a new means of achieving novelty while protecting intellectual property.

As this system matured in the nineteenth century, with the creation of complex social structures for the organization and support of research and researchers, the early dream of power through secular, disenchanted knowledge took on reality. For this there were developed the industrial laboratories and applied research institutes, first in Germany, but eventually elsewhere. From these came the high technology of the present century, on which the prosperity and even survival of our civilization now depends.

The idea of using such applicable science as a significant contribution to the planned development of the means of production was first articulated in the socialist nations, and popularized everywhere by the prophetic writings of J.D. Bernal. It lost its ideological overtones during the Second World War; and now that planning is an essential tool even in the market-economy nations, science as 'the second derivative of production' (in Bernal's phrase) is a commonplace (Ravetz 1974). Even academic research is now strongly guided by priorities, set in the political process, and related to the requirements of the development of the means of production and of destruction. Boris Hessen's classic thesis on *The Social and Economic Roots of Newton's 'Principia'* may have been crude and over-simple for the seventeenth century, but for the twentieth it is a truism. There still remains a difference in slogans—in the socialist countries it is 'the scientific—technological revolution', in the others it is 'don't come last in the microelectronics race'—and only time will tell how these will work out in practice.

Our present concerns are centred on the new problems of the biosphere, involving an ecological vision that runs counter to that of Bernal, and the tradition to which he was heir. The 'domination of nature', the driving vision of our science-based civilization, may turn out in retrospect to have been just a disenchanted variety of magic (Leiss 1972). The recently discovered fact that we cannot dominate, though we can destroy, may be the decisive challenge to our civilization. The solution of the problem of world-wide poverty through the development of material production in imitation of the West, even if possible in the social sphere, could become ecologically devastating. Can the biosphere provide the sources and sinks for a world-wide population of a billion private automobiles? Hence, I believe the new task for science is a total one, requiring new concepts of its goals in human welfare as well as new methods of achieving knowledge and wielding power over Nature under appropriate control.

This essay was first published in *Sustainable Development of the Biosphere* (eds W. Clark and R. Munn), Cambridge University Press, 1986. It was republished in *Knowledge* 9 (1987), 87−116.

References

Brooks, H. (1982) 'Science indicators and science priorities', pp. 1−32 in M.C. La Follerte (ed.), *Quality in Science*. Cambridge, MA: MIT Press.

Carson, R. (1962) *Silent Spring*. Boston: Houghton Mifflin.

Clark, W.C. 'Conflict and ignorance in scientific inquiries with policy implications', personal communication.

Collingridge, D. (1982) *Critical Decision Making*. London: Frances Pinter.

Douglas, M. and A. Wildavsky (1982) *Risk and Culture*. Berkeley, CA: University of California Press.

Funtowicz, S.O. and J.R. Ravetz (1985) 'Three types of risk assessment: a methodological analysis', *Risk Analysis in the Private Sector*. New York: Plenum.

Kemeny, J.G. (1979) *Report of the Presidents Commission on the Accident at Three Mile Island: The Need for Change, The Legacy of TMI*. New York: Pergamon.

Kuhn, T.S. (1962) *The Structure of Scientific Revolutions* (p. 5). Chicago: Chicago University Press.

Leiss, W. (1972) *The Domination of Nature*. New York: Braziler.

Lindblom, C.E. and D.K. Cohen (1979) *Usable Knowledge: Social Science and Social Problem Solving*. New Haven, CT: Yale University Press.

Marx, K. (1971) *A Contribution to the Critique of Political Economy* (p. 21). London: Lawrence & Wishart. (Original published in 1869)

Otway, H. and J.R. Ravetz (1984) 'On the regulation of technology, 3: Examining the linear model', *Futures* 16: 217−32.

Ravetz, J.R. (1974) 'Science, history of', pp. 366−75 in *Encyclopedia Britannica* 16.

Ravetz, J.R. (1984) 'Uncertainty, ignorance, and policy'. Presented at the International forum for Science and Public Policy at the International Institute for Applied Systems Analysis, Laxenburg, Austria; an abridged version appears as 'Scientific uncertainty', in the US German Marshall Fund, *Transatlantic Perspectives, II* (April 1974): 10−12.

Ruckelshaus, W.D. (1984) 'Risk in a free society', *Risk Analysis* 4: 157−62.

Toulmin, S. (1972) *Human Understanding: The Collective Use and Evolution of Concepts*. Princeton, NJ: Princeton University Press.

Weinberg, A.M. (1963) 'Criteria for scientific choice', *Minerva* 1: 159−71.

Weinberg, A.M. (1964) 'Criteria for scientific choice, II: The two cultures', *Minerva* 3: 3−14.

Weinberg, A.M. (1972) 'Science and trans-science', *Minerva* 10: 209−22.

Whetstone, G.S. (1984) 'Scientific information and government policies: A history of the acid rain issue', presented at the IIASA International Forum on Science for Public Policy (unpublished).

Whittemore, A.S. (1983):'Facts and values in risk analysis for environmental pollutants', *Risk Analysis* 3: 23−33.

A New Social Contract for Science

In this essay I am viewing science in the perspective of several hundred years of continuous internal growth and external support. During this period the 'material' side of science had been doubling every fifteen years, with remarkable constancy; and science enjoyed general prestige and the confidence of a variety of publics. For some, science (in its discoveries and methods) promised a Truth that was genuine and reliable, unlike opinions derived from arguments about words or from obedience to authority. For others, science promised the means to the conquest of Nature for the achievement of general welfare as well as private profit. For many, there was the sheer delight and fascination in sharing the discovery of the structure and workings of the natural world. Whatever its function, science gave satisfaction. Although there were always some who opposed it, in part or in whole, they were a steadily decreasing band. All the different aspects and images of science, appealing to its different publics, were in harmony.

This picture, holding roughly for all the eighteenth and nineteenth centuries and a bit beyond, now seems a bit too good to be true. Yet the historical record shows that science *was* nearly universally accepted as the embodiment of progress, itself the symbol of our secular civilization. Also, the steady growth of 'pure science' in size and effectiveness is evidence of a sort of 'social contract' mentioned in the title. Science enjoyed ever-increasing support, complete freedom in choosing its problems, and considerable autonomy in setting its criteria of quality. In return, it was not constrained to provide direct benefits for any particular client. It was sufficient for science to promise indirect benefits in ideology (its particular form of truth), in industry and in education. In the later part of that period, a particular aspect of science became accepted as representing its essence, that of 'discovery' rather than, say, 'invention' or learning. In our times, that has become modified to 'research'; so that for these closely associated with a university, and hence near the centre of the endeavour of science, research is what it is all about.

In retrospect all that seems a golden age. From the very opening of the

284

twentieth century, complications set in. Philosophers of science know of the unsettlement caused by Einstein's work. The image of science as the cumulation of Truths never recovered from those intellectual revolutions. The Great War, its aftermath, then the Second World War culminating in the Bomb, brought evil into the life of science. Since then, problems and complications have increased, so that 'science' is blamed for our afflictions, as indiscriminately as it was formerly praised for our blessings.

All that is quite familiar, yet there is a new and very troubling element that has recently become noticeable. It is not merely that science must now endure many critics. Worse, science now seems to have no effective champions, who can speak from inner conviction, to bring a doubting public back to their traditional confidence in science. As a result, science is increasingly vulnerable to any and all criticism and attack, whether from anti-Establishment intellectuals, or from an anti-intellectual Establishment. This is just now worse and more obvious in Britain than elsewhere; but it is not at all unique to that country. Certainly there is plenty of money for science in the USA. But this is increasingly in the form of contracts for specified research, from the federal government or from private industry, so that it is more in the nature of long-term R & D than the scholarly pursuit of knowledge.

This is the symptom which I shall use to introduce my study of science in its social setting: the old social contract of science seems to be weakened, indeed discredited; and there is as yet nothing to take its place. I will *not* here offer a clean and tidy solution to this problem; for I do not know of any. Rather, I will offer some examples and ideas, as an invitation to a discussion; only that, and no more. It may be that such a style, rather than theories and blueprints, might even be appropriate for an eventual 'New Social Contract for Science'.

Why Science Has No Champion

There is no need for me to run through the doleful tale of attacks on scientific research, both within and outside the universities, that are the hallmark of the present (Thatcher) UK government. Nor need I remind you of the silence of the other major parties on this issue. In the next government, there might well be more money for science and education, but at a political price, in reorganization or redirection to someone else's priorities. The old British social contract, so well epitomized in the hallowed principle of the old Medical Research Council to 'back chaps' (selecting for self-defined excellence), is no more.

Elsewhere the hostility and contempt are not so obvious, but the end of an era is unmistakable. In America, biology has for some years been increasingly under the sway of the commercial interests that are developing nascent technologies. And the physical sciences there have needed to sup at the table of the promoters of Star Wars, in spite of the obvious mendacity and corruption of that programme.

285

In these English-speaking countries, the struggle to maintain the health of the scientific enterprise is especially sharp, at times nearly desperate. It is not made any easier by those critics, generally from within the educated sector of society, who attack science for its alleged lapses from morality or integrity. This goes beyond the common practice of blaming an undifferentiated 'science' for all the threats to humanity, from nuclear weapons to environmental pollution. The scientific experts employed by state agencies and private corporations are routinely treated as hirelings, paid to reassure the public that their organizations can and would do no wrong. Worse, the conduct of research, even within universities, is condemned on ethical grounds as lacking in any humane sensitivity to the interests of its sentient subjects, mainly but not exclusively non-human.

Now, I am sure that every one of these criticisms can be countered as being misguided, inaccurate or unfair. But at this point in history we seem to lack of conviction that they are all beside the point. We cannot simply dismiss them as impertinent, resting on our assurance that science does not need to justify the details of its conduct or of its consequences to unsympathetic sectarian critics. Under the old social contract, such would have been the defence, all the more effective for being implicit. Now such a point cannot even be stated publicly. What has happened?

Clearly, the image of science, before its various publics, has changed drastically over the last generation. This change can be ascribed to the growth of science, and the problems raised by the applications of its results. For myself, I have been able to understand it through the idea of 'industrialization'. This has several aspects. Most obvious is the union of science with technology, and the great increase in the aggregate size of the scientific enterprise. With these developments, science has become more like industry, and has necessarily and inevitably lost some of its independence and innocence. But the process of industrialization also penetrates into the life of science itself. Formerly scientists were independent craftsmen, whose equipment costs were of an order of magnitude commensurate with their means, or at least with those of a patron. In this respect, their situation approximated to the ideal of 'intermediate technology' as first defined by E.F. Schumacher. Their standing as members of a community then depended on what they did with that equipment, as seen by the quality of their accomplished work. Now, the assessment by 'output' has been seriously modified, for research *cannot begin* until some funding agency has decided to invest in it. Scientific research is now a capital-intensive enterprise, rather than a craftsmen's community, in this important respect.

Once that science, or even an individual scientist, needs to justify a claim on someone else's resources, then that someone else's values inevitably enter the endeavour. With industrialization has thus come a decisive shift in the balance between knowledge and power in the goals of scientific effort. Formerly, 'science' was devoted to the pursuit of knowledge; it was thereby 'pure' in several senses. The application of that knowledge to power was the task of others; science derived credit for making the means available, and escaped blame when something went wrong. That happy state of affairs is with us no longer. Science, as a socially organized activity, is no longer insulated from the consequences of its applications. The supposed 'neutrality' of scientific knowledge, whose good or evil consequences are the responsibility of the user, has lost plausibility. Now the 'industrialized' scientist usually gets some agency to invest in his research only by promising that its applications will help their missions, commercial or military. Hence the disinterested scientific seeker after truth, ignorant — and hence innocent! — in relation to the morality of the applications of his work, is no longer credible.

Hence, the traditional sorts of power achieved indirectly through science, in the industrial and military fields, reflect their moral ambivalence back on to scientists and science. Worse, some new sorts of power, indeed those that promise to realize some of the greatest humanitarian aspirations of science, show themselves to be even more ambivalent. Here I refer to 'biomedical engineering', achieving ever deeper intervention in human reproduction, disease and life and death. This whole field is characterized by the paradox that each innovation increases the happiness of *some* client group, and so can be justified in terms of medical ethics. Yet as a whole these developments raise many troubling problems. In the public discussion of these, we now witness an amazing inversion of roles from those in a traditional debate. For, from the time of Galileo through that of Darwin and beyond, 'science' has been displacing 'theology' and 'philosophy' as genuine human knowledge. But now that scientific power has invaded the areas of the private and the sacred, science alone cannot prescribe bounds to what is proper; and moral philosophy and even theology win places at the conference table on ethical issues in biomedicine.

Thus, the powers achieved by science have become compromised in the moral sphere. And still worse, they have produced a new sort of ignorance, something we might even call science-based ignorance, which threatens our very survival as well as our faith in science. For examples, I may remind us of some questions and problems concerning the environment. 'Will there be a "greenhouse effect"?' 'can forest death from acid rain be reversed?'; 'what will happen when the tropical rainforests are destroyed?'; and in the engineering field, 'how can we design a repository for nuclear wastes that will be safe for 10 000 years?'

Such grand insoluble questions are paralleled by quite mundane problems that can be classed under industrial reliability and quality control. Thus we may ask how to prevent a repetition of Challenger, Chernobyl, Bhopal, the poisoning of the Rhine, and so on. In *each* case there were identifiable failures in the management of the system; but can all possible failures be prevented in advance by scientific management skills? We do know 'good' management tends to produce a reliable, safe operation; but achieving 'good' management is a problem more in the political and moral sphere than in the scientific or technological.

This state of science-based ignorance is revealed to the general public not only in the great disasters, but also in the daily debates over local hazards. Local militancy of the sort more familiar in America or on the Continent has been successful here in England in forcing a complete re-planning of radioactive waste disposal. The official experts, like those monitoring radioactivity from the British Nuclear Fuels Ltd plant, and those monitoring fall out from Chernobyl, were revealed as only partially in command of real scientific knowledge. To us in the universities, the unfortunate technical experts who are interrogated by journalists on TV may not count as real scientists; but to the viewing public they are the scientists who matter. The loss of the aura of objectivity and certainty from such experts then reacts back on 'science' in general.

Returning now to science as we understand it, I must also mention those academic scholars who analyse science, philosophically, sociologically, or whatever. Their consensus filters out to schoolteachers and the public within a couple of decades; and their images then come to dominate public discourse. What do we find there? It is just one generation since Kuhn published his classic *Structure of Scientific Revolutions*; and since then, for the defenders of science, it has been downhill nearly all the way. Increasingly, scholars become more sceptical, more relativist, and more disenchanted with the received verities of science. These are people who, in general, do not support any particular external or social criticism of science; they are content merely to corrode its heart, from within.

In such a context, the writings of eminent scientists about the pleasures of research, or the promise of science for human welfare, can seem like the ramblings of old men about their bygone happy youth. At this time, to study science as a scholar is to criticize, indeed to attack and deny, its past pretensions to merit. Should such developments continue, and there is no sign of their abating, it will become increasingly difficult to find anyone who can make an effective case *for* science to an increasingly disenchanted public. As science needs a champion ever more, he will be ever less likely to appear.

What Sort of New Image?

I am arguing that the *malaise* of science, its inability to dismiss its enemies and detractors, reflects the obsolescence of the old social contract of science. And with this comes the irrelevance of the old dominant image of science, as the provider, directly, of the True and, indirectly, of the Good. The improvement of the state of science, in its self-confidence, morale and integrity, will require a creative response to its new circumstances. What options are available?

The easiest course to follow is to try more of the old mixture, perhaps modernized by some market research into what the public particularly wants. Of course there will be an admission that science does not have all the answers; and that values necessarily enter into policy decisions on technological and industrial questions. But the message will be, that 'science', meaning the activity of the leaders of the research community, is still at the centre of things. Trust them to continue managing, pressure the government to provide them once again with the prestige and perquisites they so sadly miss, and all will be well. To accomplish the enlightenment of the public to appreciate so obvious a message, it only needs more and better-trained schoolteachers, and more and better-disposed journalists (and fewer of those nasty TV investigators). With a complacency befitting just such a cause, this case is advanced by our surviving scientific élite.

The other approach is that of tough realism. There was a famous advertisement in the 1960s, by one of the leading aerospace contractors for the Vietnam War. This displayed the proud motto, 'North American Rockwell, where science gets down to business' — an exquisitely designed ambiguity, so expressive of the current social contract of science. We could say that since the seduction of industrialized science by its external clients, in business and the state, is historically inevitable, why not lie back and enjoy it? Already, the 'pure' research sector has been renamed 'basic', and anyway occupies a shrinking portion of the total effort. How much funding of research is now devoted to sheer scientific curiosity? And certainly, the rate of innovation in key sectors of technology and medicine is evidence that enthusiasm and creativity still flourish.

In this proposed social contract, science becomes the servant of society. Its work can be planned, at least in outline; by negotiation there could be derived the proportions of total societal support to be spent on, say, civil technology, defence, medicine, environment, 'basic', and odds and ends. As such a situation stabilized, new foci of power and prestige would emerge. The old 'pure science' image, corresponding to the old social contract, could be allowed to wither away. Indeed, in the heavily bureaucratized societies, with a scientific tradition deriving from the Académie des Sciences of Paris rather than from the Royal Society of London, such a social contract has been a strong, sometimes dominant pattern. So what would be wrong with it here? One thing wrong is that it is not in our traditions; it presupposes a strong, centralized state which confidently intervenes and directs in many other sectors of civil society. To try to accomplish a complete, self-conscious 'incorporation' of science (I owe this felicitous term to Hilary Rose) in the context of a weaker, self-limiting central state apparatus as in the Anglo-American tradition could produce the sorts of problems of interfering yet ineffective control that plagued the nationalized industries in Britain. Also, it is important in our political and social traditions to have universities, not technical training schools, as the foci of excellence in education and learning; for these to be kept healthy under modern conditions requires that they do their teaching in the atmosphere of research. Furthermore, the experience of the centralized administrations of science, even in the market-economy countries such as France, does not suggest that this 'incorporated' social contract provides all the answers.

More to my present point, which is about the social problems of science, even such an absorption of science into the state would not resolve any of the problems of criticisms and morale. Science could become seen as even more to blame for environmental problems, as it became yet more monolithic in its support, active or passive, of policies of the governments in power.

Let us look forward. Suppose that schoolchildren get a constant diet of criticisms of science—where it is blamed for all our ills—for decades to come. Then a steadily *de*creasing number will experience that excitement and fascination which is essential if they are to make the choices, and possess the commitments, to enter creative careers as scientists. I have known personally, and I have stated as the cornerstone of my philosophical analysis of science, that that excitement and fascination is both a highly rewarding individual experience and also an element in the social life of science that is necessary for maintaining its health and integrity. Should disillusion and discouragement set in, now in science teaching and then in research, then there could develop a vicious cycle of decay in morale which would be very difficult indeed to break.

Hence, I shall argue that neither a cheap nostalgia, nor an easy acquiescence of present pressures and tendencies, will suffice. What will? I confess that, in detail, I do not know; I cannot provide you with a 'blueprint for survival' for science. But I can offer an analysis of the problem in terms of the social and institutional history of science. On that basis, I can offer some ideas, by way of an invitation to a discussion of possible solutions.

The Social Constitution of Science

So far I have argued that science, in its present partly industrialized and incorporated state, will not be able to maintain its integrity and its cultural meaning until it achieves a new understanding of itself that coheres with its real situation. This is not merely a matter of passive reflection, for a scientific enterprise that is *merely* the servant of industrial firms and state agencies will *not* command the popular respect and enthusiasm that science needs if it is to remain healthy and vital. Hence, our attempts to achieve an understanding of the present state of science must be guided by our commitment to help the forward evolution of science, through the present into the future, beyond simple industrialization.

It is in this sense that I speak of a new 'social contract': some new appropriate understanding of what science *is* and how it relates to its context in society. Before this can be accomplished, we must be clear about the present state of science in this respect. As a contribution to such a clarification, I want to suggest certain ideas that may strike you as paradoxical as well as unsettling. I shall argue the following thesis: although the connections between 'science' and 'democracy' are manifold and deep, in some important respects Science retains traces of the time of its origins, and has important features of hierarchy and of absolutism resembling those of the type of Church and of State to which it has always been considered antithetical.

Let me first remind you why this thesis is paradoxical. A democracy of culture was an integral part of the programmes of the prophets who created our modern European science. Indeed, nearly the only positive feature common to Descartes, Galileo and Bacon was an appreciation of the practical knowledge of craftsmen, and a commitment to the unity of that practice with philosophical theory. They were quite explicit on this in their writings. For their lay audience, already using the vernacular for their intellectual work, this may not have been shocking. But for *our* institutional ancestry, the scholars and learned professionals of the universities, it must have seemed to be a degradation of learning, a dilution of culture, with dangerous consequences for knowledge and society.

Then as science began to fulfil its promise of material power over nature, another important connection appeared. It was the *applications* of science that transformed material culture, and then social and political life, so that 'democracy', in our sense, became possible. Norbert Wiener's phrase, 'The human use of human beings', reminds us that, so long as the productive process, on farms or in factories, is such as to make the life of ordinary people 'nasty, brutish and short', there could be no real democracy in society. There may be some *forms* of democracy, and perhaps too some protections of personal liberty; but genuine democracy, where ordinary people have a real share in the power of shaping their lives, is absent or illusory, Hence, as one sees in any developing country, there is a great respect for science as *applied*, for the improvement of the material conditions of life and thereby the eventual achievement of democracy.

There is also a great tradition of popularization of science, frequently led by leading scientists who wanted to share their exciting discoveries, or to enlist a broader public on their side in struggles against the enemies of science. Those were broadly labelled as the promoters of 'dogma, metaphysics and superstition', or theologians, philosophers and priests respectively. They were seen as fostering ignorance and illusion, in the service of outworn institutions. Thus, science had a real relation, however complex, partial and ambivalent, with movements towards greater democracy in society. Popularization enabled people of quite humble origins to feel that they were participating in a great adventure, and indeed sometimes to do so actively as amateurs. Furthermore, science found a large proportion of its most distinguished recruits outside the privileged classes, and so too close an identification with the élite would have been damaging to its own activity. So well diffused was the positive image of science that movements of reform or even of revolution would make their social analyses in the name of 'science' and derive assurance thereby.

Democracy is also inherent in the processes of research science. Research results are (in principle) evaluated without any regard for the personal characteristics or social location of the author. Entry into science, and rewards for excellence, are based on merit, not on personal connections.

Power in the scientific community is diffused among members (through peer-review of proposals and refereeing for journals); and positions of professional leadership are awarded for excellence and wisdom, rather than for political connections. All this is of course more strongly characteristic of pre-industrialized science; and it has provided inspiration for scientists as widely different in their political outlook as Michael Polanyi and J. Desmond Bernal.

In view of all this, it may well seem paradoxical, as well as unsettling, if I say that in some important respects modern science bears strong traces of the times of its origins, when hierarchy in society and absolutism in religion and knowledge were still dominant.

Absolutism and hierarchy—these may seem very inappropriate as descriptions of science. But the points are not new with me. As to absolutism, we find in Kuhn's classic work *Structure of Scientific Revolutions* a vivid description of an absolutist regime in scientific knowledge. The 'paradigm' is the unquestioned, indeed *unquestionable*, framework of current research. To secure its permanence, students are indoctrinated, history is distorted, and difficulties in research practice are, as he says, 'suppressed or evaded'. The world of open criticism and free debate, so prized by Popper in his account of science, is emphatically conspicuous by its absence in Kuhn's picture of 'normal science'. Small wonder that Popper described it as a 'danger to science, and to our civilization', though tending reluctantly to agree with it as a description of science education.

Kuhn's account of the research process has been widely criticized; but no one, to my knowledge, has argued that science education is Popperian, critical and democratic, rather than Kuhnian, dogmatic and absolutist. There *are* some final Honours examinations that include questions with the instruction: 'critically evaluate' a theory; but they are only a minority. In our science teaching, we have a formal curriculum that generally purveys hard incontestable facts; and a hidden curriculum that moulds students' thinking into the ruling assumptions on what sorts of problems, solutions and even ways of analysing problems are 'truly scientific'. This seems to be as absolutist as any doctrines imposed by ecclesiastical or political authorities in the past.

Well, you may say, there *are* some problems in realizing the critical spirit in science teaching. But this teaching, as well as research practice, is uniform and open to all; how could one possibly conceive it as hierarchical? Of course, the form and content of natural science is abstracted from all social considerations. But the practice of science as a social institution cannot be so abstracted. There are enough well-documented accounts of the history of sexism and of racism in research communities that I need not labour the point here. Such unfair practices are indeed regrettable, but is this 'hierarchy'? No; these examples were introduced merely to establish the point that even 'pure' science does not necessarily have a 'pure' social practice.

Hierarchy comes in more subtly, in the dominant assumptions of what is 'real' science, in what institutions and by what people it is done, and also how it relates to the 'less real'. This point does not require political radicals for its expression; for many years we have heard complaints that 'applied science' and 'engineering' enjoy significantly less prestige than 'pure science' in our country. The effects of such differences in status operate in many ways; the less favoured activities tend to accept their inferiority and try to ape their betters. In America, 'physics-envy' is a well-known neurotic disorder of the behavioural sciences.

The perspective here, particularly as seen from the educationalist's viewpoint, is of a pyramid of prestige, with the Royal Society and its special style at the top, and 'technology' somewhere near but not at it. Teaching is orientated towards getting the pupils as high up that pyramid as their effort and talent will take them. The skills of comprehending and controlling one's own personal environment are *generally* (though with an increasing number of important exceptions) relegated to sub-academic courses in schools, and to independent self-help organizations for adults (tending to reach those whose need is in some ways least severe). Some of us know of the uniformly negative response to requests for funding for development of 'adult science literacy'. This does not mean that there is a conspiracy to keep most adults scientifically illiterate. For none is needed; by the hierarchical assumptions on 'real' science and its social location, there is simply no interesting problem to which 'adult scientific literacy' provides a solution. Science, in the sense of the institution enjoying official prestige and support, is the property of our power and social élite, no less effectively so because the status is implicit and unofficial.

I am far from being the first to recognize this situation. Whenever, in modern times, there has been conflict and instability in relations between the different orders of society, science has been brought into the arena. The rather abstract intellectual democracy proclaimed by the founders of modern science was quite quickly given its limits in the world of real politics. The most famous instance of open conflict occurred here in England in the 1650s, when some of the radical 'Puritans' demanded a democratic education in practical, Paracelsian, Christian natural philosophy for students at Oxford University. In their reply, the future founders of the Royal Society made it very plain that their job was to provide a finishing-school for the sons of the élite; and thus the social location of the new science was explicitly and firmly settled. There were similar exchanges during the French Revolution; and the Lysenko episode in the Soviet Union can be understood, partly at least, in the same light.

All these earlier attempts at 'science for the people' were bound to fail, because there were simply so very few people with sufficient literacy to comprehend, let alone apply, science. These early failures were analogous to those of the campaigns in the political and social spheres, like free elections, abolition of slavery, trades unions, generalized civil liberties and equal civil rights, which were quite Utopian when first proposed, but are now commonplace. Perhaps now, with the widespread diffusion of education and of political activity, the extension of science outside élite culture could in its

293

turn cease to be Utopian. I shall now discuss some examples that indicate that this may be starting to happen.

I must make it clear that any significant change in the social character of science will depend on prior changes in many aspects of our social and cultural lives. It is quite beyond my topic here to discuss how such changes could ever come about; hence when I offer these examples, it is only as illustrations of what might take root in the event of some general change in the social relations of knowledge. But it is worthy of reflection that our society is one of those now considered as 'developed', a static condition of perfection to which the rest of humanity aspires, even though roughly a mere quarter of our adolescent population finds it rewarding to remain studying beyond the date of formal release. This is not to propose an even longer incarceration on the American model; but to remind us how the skills of literacy and numeracy are still effectively the possession of a privileged minority.

Science as Experienced from Outside

As I have said before, the problems of maintaining and enhancing the health and vitality of science cannot be resolved until science as *experienced* by its many publics is in harmony with science as proclaimed by its official leaders and propagandists. Science is still portrayed as essentially 'pure' knowledge when it is now predominantly 'applied' power; and science is still portrayed as thoroughly democratic when it has such strong traces of absolutism and hierarchy. So long as such anomalies persist, science will not again enjoy full public prestige, and the necessary protection that it brings. It will remain vulnerable to sectarian attacks and to criticism and contempt, from *every* quarter in society that has grounds for hostility to some aspect of it.

How can this change? Only by education; but this is to be understood in the widest sense. Obviously those now outside science will need help in developing the skills and the clear understanding necessary for self-confidence, if science is to develop as an integral part of a democratic society. And we on the inside can also benefit from education, perhaps getting some help in seeing ourselves as others see us.

Perhaps the beginning of such a re-education will have to be conducted mainly outside the classrooms. At the start there must be groups of people, acting on their own initiative, independent of, or perhaps even in opposition to, established authorities; forging their own conceptions of science as knowledge and power. Then these can eventually be synthesized, and expressed in a form suitable for teaching. As a contribution towards the enhancement of our perspective on science, I would like to offer three examples. These might be labelled 'alternative', 'activist' and 'practical' science, respectively.

For the first, let me remind you about the state and significance of 'alternative medicine'. If you say, 'but that's not science', you are revealing your preconceptions of what is really science. Modern 'mainstream' medicine claims, with considerable justification, to be based on science; and traditionally it had adopted just the absolutist, hierarchical style that I have identified for science in general. While not always claiming infallibility for itself in its cures, it has certainly demanded the exclusive power to *decide* what is real and legitimate in the healing arts, and what is not. In all this, its professed basis is science: scientific knowledge as the foundation, and scientific method as the warrant for its claims.

Hence, when a steadily increasing number of people defy the bans and proscriptions on 'alternative' medicine, they are implicitly rejecting the exclusive claims of mainstream medicine in some respect or other: for them either it is not truly scientific, or its idea of science is itself defective. To some extent the latter must be the case, especially when the patient invests her or his practical trust and tentative belief in a treatment whose theoretical basis is utterly at variance with science as we know it, such as acupuncture or homeopathy.

Alternative medicine is a useful example for us in forming a perspective on the evolution of science, for it forces us to think again about what we mean by 'science', in relation to the lives of people and also to its own essential character. For brevity I want to consider another example at the opposite extreme: campaigning by local groups on environmental issues that involves an intimate mixture of science and politics. This is what I mean by 'activist' science. In this case, the character of science is not challenged; but its public manifestation as official expertise is held up to sharp, critical scrutiny.

Such groups, sometimes called NIMBY (Not In My Back Yard), are found world-wide; as yet they have no formal unifying organization or ideology. But their campaigns, assisted by special-interest pressure groups, have already caused important changes in the thinking of industry and government about 'the environment' and its proper care. In this country the movement started with the anti-motorway action groups of the 1960s and 1970s; and it is now most visible with those opposing the storage of dangerous wastes in their neighbourhoods. Up to now, the leadership has come from the USA, where traditions of strong local politics, of citizens' initiatives, and of a helpful judicial system have combined to enable the growth of movements of considerable strength and sophistication.

Through their struggles they have come to their own awareness of what science is, in the context of its employment in the control of technology. The picture is not flattering, but it is important for us to comprehend it, as a symptom of the present difficulties of science, and of the way to their resolution. I shall summarize an article in the journal *Everyone's Back Yard*, published by the Citizens' Clearinghouse for Hazardous Waste Inc., in the issue of Winter 1986. It's called 'Lessons we've learned'; and there are four. The first is that 'science and technical information *alone* will not solve problems', mainly because government agencies would rather *not* know about problems lest they be required to find the money to do something about them.

Then that 'There are only a *few* answers to the *many* scientific questions raised by dump sites', because science out in the raw, confronting disturbed and degraded natural systems, is a totally different thing from science in the teaching or research laboratory. Third that 'often scientists don't admit that they don't know', lest they lose credibility; instead they argue for the 'acceptability' of supposedly 'small' risks. Finally, it was a particularly hard lesson for the author to learn that 'scientists are not objective', but have their biases like anyone else. Perhaps in the old-fashioned lab, where scientists enjoy control over their experiments and are insulated from the economic and political consequences of their work, 'objectivity' is possible. But out in the world of policy, where scientists encounter great uncertainties in their research results *and* experience direct pressures from their employers, they require exceptional strength to withstand the interests that are concerned with power rather than either truth or welfare.

We should notice that this account, unlike some from the extreme 'green' fringe, appreciates that scientists may mean well and do their best. But the new problems of science in the environment, or policy-related research, strip scientists and science of those protections which had previously enabled the endeavour to seem 'pure' in so many ways. Now the innocence is lost, as that of a vanished childhood; the question is whether, or rather how, science can attain a mature understanding of itself in its complex and contradictory social setting. It seems to me that to approach the members of the Citizens' Clearinghouse for Hazardous Waste, or even the clients of alternative medicine, with the standard proposals for more and better schoolteachers and journalists would be somehow missing the point.

Perhaps the most important lesson of the preceding examples was one nearly implicit aspect of them both. This is, that 'science' in each case means something quite different from the activity centred on original research, which we in the universities generally take for granted as defining real science. Alternative medicine is, nearly by definition, not science; some would even call it anti-science. Similarly, debates between hired or partisan experts on the hazards of a rubbish dump may seem best kept *quite* distinct from what goes on in the university lab. Yet such are examples of people's direct, personal experience of science. Other direct experiences might be in their jobs, where 'science' can make their tasks better, or worse, or perhaps even non-existent; alternatively, in their homes, where it appears as nutrition, gardening, do-it-yourself, hobbies, first aid, advice on illness, counselling on medical problems, child psychology, marriage guidance, and so on. Of course hardly any of this 'practical science' is 'science' as understood in the context of British university Honours degree courses. However, some courses at polytechnics include such practical matters; and at American universities all sorts of 'science' can be found. Perhaps we in the universities have in some ways been living in an ivory tower, not being reminded of the differences between our rather precious, esoteric conception of science, and that of the broad public on whose goodwill our survival ultimately depends.

Perhaps in this discovery of the varieties of scientific experience, we can find some clues to the eventual recasting of the social contract of science. The first is that such 'practical science' (as distinct from the 'popular science' purveyed from on high) is neither hierarchical nor absolute. It is mainly a handbook literature, commercially successful where it is felt to be useful, and embodying much disagreement between sources. This 'science' generally lacks institutions for direction, quality control and adjudication of debates. Yet it survives and flourishes, as the background to the more self-conscious, intellectually demanding activities like alternative medicine or environmental campaigning.

Second, there is an increasing continuity of content between such 'practical' materials and syllabuses everywhere outside universities. This is the result of many pressures, not least the need to make science more attractive somehow, so as to keep up the numbers of students. At the same time, the media provide many discussions, at a good intellectual level, of the open-ended problems raised by science, ranging from medical ethics to environmental protection. These are used to good effect, again outside universities, to enliven science teaching and ameliorate its Kuhnian dogmatism. Hence the separation between science as taught more generally, and science as experienced by the public, is far less extreme than the traditional university syllabuses would lead us to believe.

Third, in all this endeavour we witness creativity, and personal growth, in spite of the absence of 'discovery' as defined in establishment science. It is all too easy for scientific discovery itself to become routine, and devoid of, or even inimical to, creativity; such is a very common situation in 'industrialized' scientific research contexts. In this 'practical' science, just as in orthodox science studied as hobby or avocation, lies a resource of creativity and enjoyment which could provide that élan, enthusiasm and commitment without which science of any sort cannot long survive. Finally, all of this 'practical' science has a very important function, only imperfectly realized in institutionalized education, that of enabling people to control their own personal environments and hence their own lives. In this sense it is profoundly democratic.

This large body of literature and practical skills, generally ignored in polite discussions of 'science', offers some important lessons for us. It is not hierarchical, nor absolute, and it is genuinely 'enabling', to use that term in its new sense. Perhaps it is all the more interesting in that it was not designed that way, but just happened. These three sorts of science, the 'alternative', 'activist' and 'practical', are only roughly sketched examples. In one obvious sense they are not 'science'. But why not? They all involve investigations of Nature, for human understanding and control; and that is as good a definition as any. Of course, they are not disciplined research, and so they do not yield the sort of knowledge as a social possession, that we ordinarily consider to be science. I would only say this: perhaps our definitions are in need of revision, so that we could overcome the barriers, social, cultural and intellectual, between our mainstream science, with its tendencies to hierarchy and absolutism, and these other sorts of endeavour.

Conclusion and Perspective

Through all this I have preferred to cite examples rather than to articulate theories. This has had a double use; it has (I hope) made the matter more comprehensible and interesting; and it has also enabled the argument to proceed in spite of the rudimentary state of development of my theoretical ideas. As I have said, this is only an invitation to explore a problem.

Hence, here I can be quite modest in my claims for these other forms of experience of science, including 'alternative', 'activist' and 'practical' science. I need not claim that these are a panacea for our problems of education and of science. I doubt that they are. But they can serve as suggestive examples of resources, and of activities, whose significance has hitherto been insufficiently appreciated.

The main function of my examples is to remind us of the possible usefulness of *diversity* in any new social contract for science. Rather than a pyramid of prestige, explicitly defining what is real and valid, and implicitly defining what is not, we could enjoy a diversity of activities and experiences. Each would have its appropriate institutions and images of science, and its appropriate publics. Some would be very similar to those we have now, serving 'basic' or 'industrial' research; others (as we have seen) could relate to education, leisure, health or politics. In society at large, both religion and politics survived the transition from hierarchy and absolutism to diversified, more democratic forms. Perhaps, some centuries later, science will soon manage it too. Such could be the basic idea of a 'new social contract for science'.

Let me now recapitulate briefly. Over the previous centuries, science enjoyed a 'social contract' whereby it obtained societal support and protection. Until recently, its patrons were largely *within* the élite section of society, though the image of science always and necessarily had a broader appeal. In these modern times, with its industrialization, science has been transformed both as a social activity and in its social contract. This new state is not stable, nor is it one in which science can easily flourish. The next change in the social contract *may* involve only some shuffling among the various state and corporate patrons and paymasters, accompanied by some putting out of more flags for science. Or we could engage on a really new look at science in society, the sort of self-scrutiny that becomes possible when, and only when, complacency is shaken and the scientific community's leaders do not know who are their friends, if any.

In this unsettled and therefore potentially creative situation, we can look again at science, and think again about its future. I hope that the perspectives I have offered, on the industrialized state of science, the present remnants of hierarchy and absolutism in science, and the diversity of perspectives and activities in science, can provide materials for a discussion of the shape of a new social contract for science.

Finally, let me briefly defend my style of argument, of offering examples rather than advancing a theory and a plan. For some, this may well be disappointing, as if I am shirking my duty to argue in a systematic, scientific way about this important problem. As I have already indicated, this approach seems to me to be coherent with my conception of any new social contract for science, and of its means of achievement. For this I have an example from recent personal experience, in the way that in the People's Republic of China the government and Party organize their discussions and activities towards the creation of a new society. For them it is an accepted and public fact that they are as yet ignorant of the character of their desired state, and of the means for achieving it. They *expect* to make mistakes, and to need to retrace their steps along the path. Such honesty, and the philosophical perspective underlying it, can provide us with the occasion for useful reflection on the knowledge achieved by science, now and in its possible new social contracts.

The Chinese also have a valuable perspective on themselves: they know that their nation is poor, and that their culture has many deficiencies. I almost said 'underdeveloped', in contrast to our supposedly 'developed' state. Certainly the rest of the world sees us as 'developed', essentially as having arrived and with nowhere to go. Perhaps that illusion of perfection is at the root of some of our present ills.

Suppose that we accept that our society is still very 'underdeveloped' culturally; and that the continued absolutist and hierarchical character of science is one manifestation of our backward state. It is difficult to imagine 'science of the people' as things are now; any detailed scheme is necessarily Utopian, and any practical initiative must be small scale and tentative. But with such a realistic humility about ourselves, analogous to that of the Chinese, we at least have a hope of proceeding forward with facts rather than fantasies.

This Chinese attitude is not a perennial, unchanging Oriental wisdom. Only a few decades ago the leaders of China were sure that they had a science of society which provided all the correct answers to their problems; and then they lurched from crises to catastrophes. Their version of Marxism was, like so many others of its time, both absolute and hierarchical, just like the image of natural science on which it was modelled. Now, through all their very real, passionate debates on extremely difficult problems, they know that free discussion and diversified experimentation are their only security against another disaster.

In the same spirit, I could remind us that the absolute, hierarchical character of science under its old social contract has given us a very one-sided sort of progress; and that the myopic, hubristic attitudes it has fostered among scientists and experts have brought us to the very brink of ecological disaster. If we are to think about a new conception of science appropriate to the future,

299

then I would rather start with an awareness of our ignorance, mine as much as anyone else's. Otherwise, the sins of scientific pride may be our final undoing, both as members of a scientific community in a social context, and as members of a total civilization, which will live or die with its science.

Based on an invited public lecture at the University of Leeds, March 1987; an edited version of that text was published in the *Bulletin of Science, Technology and Society* 8, 1988, 20–30.

Note Added in Proof

My comments about China were based on my experiences there through the first student demonstrations in 1986. This essay had gone to press when the tragedies of June 1989 occurred. I have decided to leave the text unchanged, partly as a reminder of my own fallibility, and partly as a gesture of goodwill to the Chinese people, hoping that even now progress must continue.

Science:
Orthodoxies, Critiques and Alternatives

The concept of 'alternative science' has been current for a very brief period, about two decades at most; hence an historical survey of the movement lacks the normal preconditions in prior scholarly productions and separation in time. But, however recent, it is of great importance for any projection of the shape of science in the future; and the period in which the idea was born, the 1960s, is definitely in the past. Also, a genuine history, rather than a mere chronicle, is made possible by the essential feature of this movement: its roots lie in the establishment of our sort of science in the seventeenth century. Its ideology was then given a very clear expression, partly in programmatic terms and partly in contrast to other conceptions of natural knowledge then prevalent. The contradictions within that ideology, some latent and others then capable of resolution, could subsequently, with the advance of science, be suppressed or ignored. With the recent full maturing of science in its organization, effectiveness and power, these contradictions have become manifest. This explains the apparent paradox that in a period of the greatest triumphs of science, its opponents became most strident and effective. Out of the movement of criticism on all issues, new foci of practice and reflection have come to exist and to find stable niches in society. These are what we call 'alternatives'.

Early Contradictions and Their Resolution

The early vision of modern science was explicitly millenarian in Bacon; and implicitly so (within the limits of their respective styles) in Galileo and Descartes. From their writings, we may distil the prophetic message: that through the study of an abstract aspect of nature, with a style of enquiry that was alienated from its object but open to all persons, error would be banished, ignorance abolished, and truths easily achieved that would be powerful, beneficial and safe. Thus a straight and narrow path of enquiry into Nature was to be the gateway to the material and moral redemption of mankind.

For analysing the contradictions in that programme, we may rephrase it in terms of certain themes. That is, this style of science promised the *security* of gaining truth (and avoiding error) through *discovery* within a particular *reality*; its social practice was one of *openness* (to all participants and also in its results); to its external patrons it promised ideological *innocence* in its teachings and the practical *beneficence* of its powers in application. All this is an ideology; and it was an essential part of the endeavour, in the Scientific Revolution and for some three centuries afterwards. The aspect of the ideology of science that was later to become its greatest strength, security, was the weakest point in the early programme. Galileo's attempt at a scientific proof of the Copernican system failed disastrously; Descartes' general physics was obviously speculative; and Bacon successfully induced very little indeed. Nor did the initial protestations of innocence carry sufficient weight, particularly with those Roman Catholic authorities who had cause for concern. The claims of openness were more successful, although (perhaps because of) being restricted to the more polite orders of society.

The problems of reality also solved themselves; although some of the great earlier discoveries of modern science (such as those of Kepler, Gilbert and Harvey) were made within the framework of 'animated' world-views, the accelerating secular change in common-sense consciousness soon made such 'alternative' world-pictures implausible and obsolete. The progress of discovery within the new paradigm, in the seventeenth century and beyond, seemed to guarantee beyond doubt that this is the one and only secure way to the True. Although the practical beneficence of the new science took a long time to materialize, it seems that its public were generally prepared to take that on trust. Jonathan Swift's portrait of addled natural philosophers and corrupt 'projectors' of Laputa (in *Gulliver's Travels*) was only part of his general denunciation of secularized eighteenth century high society. The powers of the new science also had a quality of innocence: with the decline of the magical arts, there were no longer secrets too powerful to be revealed. All effects were proportionable to their natural causes, and so the idea of science producing real evil was nearly a logical impossibility, until our own times.

Early Challenges, Resolved and Unresolved

Thus did the ideology of modern science gain its form, and increase steadily in strength through the eighteenth and nineteenth centuries. One of the greatest strengths of that ideology was that it saw science as simple and absolute, the antithesis to mere belief or to 'ideology' itself. The earliest conflicts involving science were easy victories. The perennial struggle about openness surfaced in the French Revolution, with vain complaints that Lavoisier's chemical nomenclature made a barrier against all those artisans who lacked the erudition to master his classicisms. The issue of reality erupted with *Naturphilosophie*; and with its downfall, the hardest of world-views generally ruled supreme. The triumph of Darwinism was due only in part to the overwhelming weight of his separately inconclusive arguments; equally it was the conviction of his audience that no other sort of explanation could be 'scientific'.

By the sort of double-think that is possible only within a well-established ideology, science's propagandists could continue to proclaim its innocence (as the vehicle of simple truth) while vigorously attacking what for the unlettered majority of people was the foundation of their personal morality: religion revealed through sacred texts. The beneficence of science was equally secure; while the propagandists of industrialization lauded science as their own, those who spoke for the suffering masses were equally determined to enlist it; thus Marx called his the 'scientific' socialism, which would replace the futile 'Utopian' varieties.

The security of scientific knowledge grew to the point of becoming a new dogma. Those who debated such questions as the nature of 'force' in the eighteenth century, or of infinity in projective geometry, or atomism in chemistry in the nineteenth century never doubted that there was a unique true solution. Outsiders who criticized the foundations of a science, such as Bishop Berkeley on the calculus, were dismissed as not possibly being really serious. Even the great 'critical' philosopher Kant took Newton's mechanics, along with Euclid's geometry, as the necessary framework for our experience of the world.

By the later nineteenth century some independent spirits were beginning to uncover obscurities and contradictions at its base. Their intent was not at all destructive; they wished only to strengthen science against certain weaknesses that had developed through its years of easy triumphs. But directly and indirectly they prepared the groundwork for the revolutions, philosophical and scientific, of the next century. Ernst Mach's critical history of mechanics (1883) showed that Newton's idea of 'force' was confused and anthropo-morphic, his 'mass' was incomprehensible, and 'absolute space' non-scientific. Thus, for nearly two hundred years scientists had been living in an illusion of security; their paradigm science could then be seen to be resting on very shaky conceptual foundations. Similar developments afflicted mathematics. Non-Euclidean geometries created a schism between 'intuition' and mathematical truth; while a series of interrelated developments in theories of sets, of infinite numbers and aggregates, and of logic, led to a full-blown 'foundations crisis' at the century's end.

Within the space of a very few years, Albert Einstein made discoveries which would soon revolutionize the foundations of the world-picture of physics, and also of scientific truth; hence this greatest triumph of discovery would fatally weaken the traditional security of science. The combination of his theoretical work with that of the revolutionary 'atomic physics' eventually led to the atomic bomb, which shattered the beneficence of science as well.

The first philosopher to appreciate the full significance of Einstein was Popper; with his 'falsificationism' he jettisoned the True of science to save the

Good, as realized through the intellectual integrity of the (legendary) Einstein who in 1919 dared the world to prove him wrong (Popper 1963). Popper was far ahead of his time; through three decades of his career he witnessed the dominance of the last 'triumphalist' philosophy of science. This was logical positivism, born in anti-clerical struggles in Vienna, and transplanted by refugees in ideologically neutralized form to the English-speaking world. By the time Popper came into prominence, his message for science was obsolescent. The revolution within philosophy of physics of the earlier twentieth century had given way to a revolution of consciousness and experiences, in which the old ideology of science was a principal object of rejection and contempt.

The Radical Critique of the 1960s

Although the millenarian aspirations of the 1960s, in politics and in experience, are now reduced to an object of historical study, the permanent changes achieved then should not be underestimated. The concept 'alternative', including science, is a mark of these. The conditions for that revolution in consciousness were multiple. First, there was a new class, of 'affluent' youth, enjoying incomes to spend and markets organized around their desires. They were also free of the bondages of parental control, of fear of poverty, and of ambition for advancement. They could cultivate new experiences ranging over idealistic politics, communal life-styles, intense aesthetic experience, and altered states of consciousness. In relation to science, this 'counter-culture' was full of contradictions. Its devotees would cheerfully utilize all its benefits, including the standard equipment of post-war consumerism, high-technology music and synthetic mind-expanding drugs. Yet on the ideological plane science was a prime focus for their attack. All the contradictions in the ideology of science that had been latent through the centuries of triumph now became manifest.

Developments in philosophy of science were at first unrelated to the 'counter-culture', but they soon interacted. Motivated by his disillusion with the standard 'accumulationist' vision of science, T.S. Kuhn produced his epochal *Structure of Scientific Revolutions* (1962). This was so influential perhaps because of its confusions, ambiguities and ironies. Its effective message was of a science whose content is strongly 'arbitrary', where 'progress' consists of an alternation between anti-critical puzzle-solving within paradigms, and anti-rational combats between paradigms. In vain did Popper protest that Kuhn's 'normal [*sic*] science' is a menace to civilization; equally vainly did Lakatos try to blend Popperian idealism with Kuhnian realism in his 'methodology of scientific research programmes' (Lakatos and Musgrave, 1970). The security of science was lost, irretrievably, for some generations to come.

The executioner of scientism was Paul Feyerabend, who in *Against Method*

(1975) showed that for every principle of method or even of intellectual integrity, there was a violation committed by some great scientist, usually Galileo. Although his professed message was 'playful anarchism' he formed the link between epistemology and radical activism. He had been in Berkeley in the late 1960s, experienced cultural imperialism in the classrooms and also benefited from 'alternative medicine'. Thenceforth, for him science was a white, male, middle-class racket, protecting itself by a dogmatic orthodoxy as intolerant as any other in history.

Although Feyerabend was in a small minority among philosophers of science, his message of denial of the beneficence of science had already been expounded on many fronts. Ecological consciousness among the reading public was created suddenly with Rachel Carson's *Silent Spring* (1963); and within a remarkably few years, the American government had environmental legislation drafted and enacted. More radical ecological messages came from Paul Ehrlich, with his *Population Bomb* (1968), and Barry Commoner, with *Science and Survival* (1966), who blamed post-war high-technology consumerism rather than just people. Most radical of all was the communalist—Christian Ivan Illich, in his broadside attacks on all the institutions of Western science-based intellectual culture; these included *De-Schooling Society* (1971), *Energy and Equity* (1974) and *Medical Nemesis* (1975). In a more practical vein, E.F. Schumacher showed that 'aid' to the poor nations was counter-productive, materially as well as ethically. His vision was of 'intermediate' (later 'appropriate') technology, described as *Small Is Beautiful* (1973) but founded on his 'Buddhist economics' conception of the meaning of work and ultimately on his own private religious experience.

With the beneficence of science falling into disrepute, its innocence could not be far behind. It was in the public record that with the A-bomb, science had tasted sin, and that with the H-bomb it had found it sweet. The evil and insanity of nuclear 'deterrence' were appreciated by only an eccentric few until the Cuba crisis of 1963; thenceforth this greatest production of the scholars brought back visions of the sorcerer's apprentice, and worse. The complicity of American science in some of the most reprehensible dirty tricks of the dirty Vietnam War was signalled by dissident students and researchers, culminating in a one-day research strike at MIT itself. And even within the world of 'pure science', the image of the slightly eccentric other-worldly searcher of old-fashioned academic science gave way, in the age of industrialized science, to 'Professor Grant Swinger' (immortalized by Dan Greenberg in *Science* magazine) (1969), and the real-life swashbuckling opportunist Jim Watson. Some fifteen years after the great event, Watson cheerfully revealed the squalid side of his Nobel prize-winning achievement (1968). Further, problems of quality control, with the implication that many scientists will not or cannot do work of adequate quality, have intruded into the governing of science in an age of restricted support; and there has been no shortage of cases of flagrant, even flamboyant, fraud and plagiarism in prestigious fields and institutions.

This loss of innocence also affected scholarly reflection on science as a human activity. Up to the 1960s, historians of science, as led by such as Sarton, and sociologists of science, as led by such as Merton, were at one with the great popularizers and propagandists in presenting a picture of science, and of scientists as well, in which anything but the Good and the True, in consequences and in behaviour, was nearly inconceivable. But, after the messages of Kuhn and Feyerabend had been assimilated, historians eagerly lifted the lid off questionable scientific practices among the great, so that the situation was eventually summed up in a classic paper, 'Should history of science be X-rated?' by Steven Brush (1974). I attempted to comprehend the positive and negative aspects of science as a social activity, combining a Polanyi-ite theory of craft knowledge of research with a Marxist conception of 'industrialized science', and concluding with a call for a 'critical science' (Ravetz 1971).

A new generation of epistemologically radical social scientists soon found their target in the old faith that science proceeds by *discovery* of something objective out there. Scientific knowledge was shown to be the product of social construction, of negotiation among interests, or to be merely 'relative' to a professional consensus, or capable of being illuminated by the approach of cultural anthropology (the seminal work in 'the scientist as aboriginal' being *Laboratory Life* by Latour and Woolgar (1977)). The collapse of the old positivistic faith among philosophers of science was complete by the end of the 1970s: though of course there would always be those in the mathematical–behavioural sciences who had not heard of Kuhn any more than they had of Heisenberg.

The inherited ideas on discovery in science were further eroded by the movements of environmental activism that got under way in the later 1960s. Hitherto, no one had seriously considered the prospect of the impotence of science as worthy of serious reflection. To be sure, in previous generations the limits of our knowledge, as of disease, had been painfully obvious; but there was the sense that the progress of knowledge would eventually eliminate all such ignorance. But with the environmental crises of modern times, a new category appeared, which we may call science-based ignorance. The new technologies, particularly nuclear power, created problems of risks and pollution for which no available body of scientific knowledge was adequate. The great statesman of nuclear engineering in America, Alvin Weinberg, exposed the problem with his paper on 'trans-science' (1972). For this his paradigm case was the determination of the number of mice necessary for the assurance of the safety of environmental radiation at federal standards: some eight billion (8×10^9) would be required. Other problems, such as those called 'zero-infinity risks', and (again from Weinberg) 'Faustian bargains' in which future generations are to cope with our pollutants, have emphasized the radical insufficiency of the scientific inputs to urgent policy issues. The contradictions are both cognitive and social. On risks questions, the official task of scientific reassurance is either to prove the impossibility of the undesired event, which is logically impossible; or to prove its 'acceptability' to a suspicious public, which is practically impossible. Worse, the awareness of technologies that are 'unforgiving' or 'brittle' spread more quickly among protestors and critical scientists than among designers and expert-apologists. Finally, the prevalence of very ordinary weaknesses of morale and discipline among managers and operatives in extraordinarily sensitive and dangerous installations deprived such enterprises of all credibility among their critically concerned publics.

Environmental politics also punctured another element of the old faith of science, that of its *openness*. For in such struggles, only a part of the relevant information is 'public knowledge', produced by academic scientists whose rewards are derived through the conventions of citation by others. Crucial information will be 'corporate know-how': data on processes or pollutions which are the property of institutions, private or state. In this sort of contested science, the art is to provide non-information, dis-information, mis-information, anything but the real thing, to those standing in the way of this particular manifestation of progress. Even within the traditional university research sector, the 'open society' of science is in retreat, as more funding for research comes in contracts rather than in grants and (as in fields like biotechnology) scientists become inventors and entrepreneurs as well as discoverers. Other aspects of the traditional openness of science have also failed the test of critical scrutiny. Entry or advancement has been no more immune to the effects of prejudices based on class, race or sex than in other fields of human endeavour. Even if such regrettable practices are now less tolerated than in the past, their becoming known represents a change in the public image, the self-image and the ideology of science. These are themselves as real, and as important for the activity, as the social practices that they reflect.

Reality itself came up for effective questioning in the 1960s, for the first time in several centuries. This was not then in the form of a competing research programme, or paradigm, for mainstream science itself. Rather, altered states of consciousness, made possible on a mass scale by the achievements of modern chemical science, were invoked in a challenge to the billiard-ball universe that constitutes the metaphysical orthodoxy of science. This formed the basis for a wide-ranging critique of the supposed inhumanity and corruption of the modern scientific enterprise, in the name of Roszak's 'counter-culture' (1969). In such an intellectual environment, venerable pseudo-sciences moved in from the margins of respectability, to capture the interest and commitment of even the best-educated young people.

Thus, in that decade of the 1960s, many aspects of science that were previously unquestionable were subjected to criticism, on a large scale, in public, and to some extent from within the community that supplies science with its recruits and with its principal audience and social support. One decade of convulsions in the realm of ideas is far from sufficient to effect a rapid radical change in the large-scale social enterprise to which they relate. But in spite of the subsiding of the ferment of the 1960s, many of the ideas that achieved plausibility and power then have survived, maintaining a stable existence on the margins, some remote but some quite close, to the mainstream of the contemporary scientific—technical enterprise.

Some Effective 'Alternative' Approaches

Even during the 1960s, there was a variety of positive, practical initiatives devoted to resolving particular problems revealed in the general critique. These took permanent shape during the following decade, along with critical movements that appeared quite suddenly at the end of the decade of ferment (such as radical feminism); and now there is a goodly spread of stable, partly institutionalized activities that in one way or another can be called 'alternative'.

The least impact on science has been made by the more traditional socialist, or Marxist, critique. To see how the 'development of the means of production' can be systematically evil (as in warfare and pollution) requires a perspective not to be found in the Marxist canon; and the continued failure of the established socialist societies to provide an example of success in science could not but weaken the force of the Marxist critique of capitalist science. The quaintly named 'British Society for Social Responsibility in Science', which quite rapidly transformed itself from a club of left-of-centre academics to a ginger-group of young radicals, settled down to providing a valuable service in the field of occupational hazards, and also in providing a base for young professionals protesting the incompetence and corruption of their established state-welfare institutions. But there never appeared a mass base, or even an effective organized constituency, in any of the groups to which such a movement necessarily appeals. The contradiction of a movement *for* the workers which was not *by* the workers was never resolved. The movement for 'alternative technology' did not fare much better in terms of recruits and successful designs. Windmills and methane digesters could not fit in with modern industrial systems; and industrial process that were small-scale, non-polluting, humane *and* profitable have been elusive in practice.

By contrast, the issue of 'the environment' has found a broad and stable constituency, though not as yet a single mass institutional base. The issue is well expressed by American acronyms: NIMBY (Not In My Back Yard) groups opposing LULUs (Locally Unwanted Land Uses). These have all the strengths, and weaknesses, of special-interest activist movements. For them, the beneficence and openness of science are in discredit; as well as the innocence and integrity of the corporate 'experts', where their local interests are affected. They derive much of their strength from ideologically committed national pressure groups, such as Friends of the Earth, or (in the USA) the Citizens' Clearinghouse for Hazardous Wastes, Inc. An essential element in their struggles is a new sort of 'scientific discovery': that of investigative journalism, usually TV, that exposes the callous inhumanity of selected corporate offenders and the impotence or complicity of state regulatory agencies.

308

Local 'environmental' campaigns are symbiotic with a militant 'ecological' movement, which interprets high-technology catastrophes (recently, Bhopal, Challenger, Chernobyl, the Rhine poisoning) as symptoms of a deep sickness in the style and values of modern science-based civilization. Through magazines (such as *The Ecologist*) and activist groups (such as Greenpeace) they drive home the message of the corruption of established science, be it on the whales, civil nuclear power, or the tropical rainforests. Their positive programme calls for a transformation of life-styles and values, along the lines of mystical—communitarian prophets such as Gandhi and Schumacher. As yet they have an effective political base only in West Germany; but unless the problems they address are either resolved or are overwhelmed by much worse ones, they will not go away.

In response to the ecologists' political challenge, a cynical analysis is that there are no votes in sewage. But there are votes in the home, where children, growing or as yet unborn, are exposed to insidious hazards. Through such issues, women's movements escape the contradictions inherent in their standard complaints about science: is it bad because it discriminates against women, or is it the sort of sexist, soulless grind that no sensitive person would want to go into anyway? 'Housewives' epidemiology' uses disciplined methods, sometimes quite inventive, to supplement and expose official statistics that show 'no evidence of harm' from suspected pollutants. Although on a relatively small scale as yet (after the first flush of enthusiasm in the 1970s) women's 'self-health' groups constitute a radical alternative to prevailing medical ideas about what is significant, and what is 'normal', in the functions and problems of women's bodies. In that sense, they are unavoidably political; and to the extent that they make the subjective feeling of being a woman into a self-aware and shared experience, they plant the seeds for a demystification of male-dominated knowledge and ways of knowing, of which modern science is the paradigm case.

The success of 'alternative' approaches is perhaps best seen in medicine. Largely through the triumphs of bacteriological medicine (perhaps owing more than is generally admitted to soap, sewers and window-screens), the classic infectious diseases of temperate climates have been brought under control. Now health hazards are known to relate as much to life-style as to 'germs'. The legendary ancient Chinese principle of paying a doctor to keep one healthy is reflected in the American Health Maintenance Organizations. Psychogenic disease, forgotten for some centuries, has become respectable again. Different approaches to healing, until very recently dismissed and denounced as the province of charlatans and quacks, are now given grudging respect for their accomplishments if not for their theories; such are homeopathy, herbalism, chiropractic and acupuncture. This last, involving the manipulation of *chi* energy, may be a meeting-point for orthodox and alternatives, as for East and West. Practitioners and researchers, in China and elsewhere, apply a scientific approach to the study of *chi*, and let the two styles complement each other in a single course of therapy.

All such developments are still on the margins of regular medical practice; and as marginal activities they are conducted in a very different social style. They are more 'open' not only in the sense of presenting fewer barriers in the form of lengthy training, but also in exhibiting none of the exclusiveness that the 'medical sects' of earlier times employed to maintain their shreds of prestige. The openness extends to varieties of the healing art that are 'alternative' in the extreme; indeed some which in England had been classed as witchcraft until the 1950s. Healing by laying on of hands, with or without contact, and with or without theories of orthodox religion or of unorthodox spirituality, is now regularly administered by some thousands of persons. It is of course possible that their achievements will follow on those of *chi* energy in being explained within a slightly enriched scientific world-picture. But in the meantime, such a practice constitutes a challenge to the reality defined by the prophets of the scientific revolution, and accepted unquestioningly in the world of science ever since. It is all the more effective for being quiet, non-antagonistic, and outwardly consistent with any life-style or medical treatment. Its practitioners and clients need not think of themselves as metaphysical revolutionaries; individually, they believe themselves simply to be giving and receiving help. It is thereby less vulnerable to being outlawed on the one hand, or to being commercialized or co-opted on the other. But given its cultural context it is likely that its adherents will need to learn all over again that even 'spirituality' can be as materialistic as any other attachment.

With this last activity we have come a long way from what is currently accepted as 'science' in any sense of the term. But the challenge raised by the 'alternative' approaches is that the prevalent idea of science is itself a product of history. In that history, coinciding with the course of modern European civilization, the original contradictions, so long latent under all the successes, have now matured and become manifest. What sorts of interactions eventually develop between orthodox science, its critics, and its alternative approaches, will be for future historians to study. But we can be sure that any new orthodoxy will never be the same as in its triumphalist centuries up to the middle of our own.

This essay is to be published in *A Companion to the History of Science* (eds G. Cantor *et al.*), Routledge, London, in 1989. I am grateful to them for permission to publish it here also.

References

Brush, S.G. 1974 'Should history of science be X-rated?', *Science* 183, 164–72.
Carson, R. 1963 *Silent Spring* (Hamilton, London).
Commoner, B. 1966 *Science and Survival* (Gollancz, London).
Ehrlich, P.R. 1968 *Population Bomb* (Ballantyne, London).
Feyerabend, P. 1975 *Against Method* (New Left Books, London).
Greenberg, D.S. 1969 *The Politics of American Science* (Penguin, London).

Illich, I.D. 1971 *De-Schooling Society*; 1974 *Energy and Equity*; 1975 *Medical Nemesis* (Calder and Boyars, London).

Kuhn, T.S. 1962 *The Structure of Scientific Revolutions* (University of Chicago Press).

Lakatos, I. and Musgrave A. (eds) 1970 *Criticism and the Growth of Knowledge* (Cambridge University Press).

Latour, B. and Woolgar S. 1977 *Laboratory Life: The Social Construction of Scientific Facts* (Sage, Beverly Hills and London).

Mach, E. 1883 *The Science of Mechanics* (Open Court, Chicago).

Popper, K.R. 1963 *Conjectures and Refutations* (Routledge, London).

Ravetz, J.R. 1971 *Scientific Knowledge and Its Social Problems* (Oxford University Press, London and New York).

Roszak, T. 1969 *The Making of a Counter-Culture* (Doubleday, New York).

Schumacher, E.F. 1973 *Small Is Beautiful* (Blond and Briggs, London).

Watson, J.D. 1968 *The Double Helix* (Weidenfeld and Nicolson, London).

Weinberg, A. 1972 'Science and trans-science', *Minerva* 10, 209–22.

Towards a Critical Science

We can now permit ourselves some final speculations on possible trends in the future of the natural sciences. The process of industrialization is irreversible; and the innocence of academic science cannot be regained. The resolution of the social problems of science created by its industrialization will depend very strongly on the particular circumstances and traditions of each field in each nation. Where morale and effective leadership can be maintained under the new conditions, we may see entire fields adjusting successfully to them, and producing work which is both worthwhile as science and useful as a contribution to technology. Recruits to this sort of science will see it as a career only marginally different from any other open to them; and it is not impossible for men of ability and integrity to rise to leadership in such an environment. This thoroughly industrialized science will necessarily become the major part of the scientific enterprise, sharing resources with a few high-prestige fields of 'undirected' research, and allowing some crumbs for the remnants of small-scale individual research. A frank recognition of this situation will help in the solution of the problems of decision and control. Since the criteria of assessment of quality will be heavily biased towards possible technical functions of results, they will thereby be more easily applied, and less subject to abuse, than those which are based on the imponderable 'internal' components of value.

Thus, provided that the crises in recruitment and morale do not lead to the degeneration and corruption of whole fields, we can expect the emergence of a stable, thoroughly industrialized natural science, responsible to society at large through its contribution to the solution of the technical problems set by industry and the state. Scientists, and their leaders and institutions, will be 'tame': accepting their dependence and their responsibilities, they will be unlikely to engage in, or encourage, public criticisms of the policies of those institutions that support their research and employ their graduates. Such a policy of prudence is not necessarily corruption; whether it becomes so will depend on many subtle factors in the self-consciousness of this new sort of science, and the claims made to its audiences. But not all the members of any

312

group are easily tamed, and the emergence of a 'critical science', as a self-conscious and coherent force, is one of the most significant and hopeful developments of the present period.

There have always been natural scientists concerned with the sufferings of humanity; but with very few exceptions they have faced the alternatives of doing irrelevant academic research to gain the leisure and freedom for their social campaigns, or doing applied research which could benefit humanity only if it first produced profits for their industrial employer. The results of pharmaceutical research must pass through the cash nexus of that industry before being applied, and that process may on occasion be an unsavoury one. Only in the fields related to 'social medicine' could genuine scientific research make a direct contribution to the solution of practical problems, of protecting the health and welfare of an otherwise defenceless public. Now, however, the threats to human welfare and survival made by the runaway technology of the present provide opportunities for such beneficial research in a wide range of fields; and the problems there are at least as difficult and challenging as any in academic science. These new problems do more than provide opportunities for scientific research with humanitarian functions. The response to this peril is rapidly creating a new sort of science: critical science. Instead of isolated individuals sacrificing their leisure and interrupting their regular research for engagement in practical problems, we now see the emergence of scientific schools of a new sort. In them, collaborative research of the highest quality is done, as part of practical projects involving the discovery, analysis and criticism of the different sorts of damage inflicted on man and nature by runaway technology, followed by their public exposure and campaigns for their abolition. The honour of creating the first school of 'critical science' belongs to Professor Barry Commoner and his colleagues at Washington University, St Louis, together with the Committee for Environmental Information, which publishes *Environment*.

The problem-situations which critical science investigates are not necessarily the result of deliberate attempts to poison the environment. But they result from practices whose correction will involve inconvenience and money cost; and the interests involved may be those of powerful groups of firms, or agencies of the state itself. The work of scientific enquiry is largely futile unless it is followed up by exposure and campaigning; and hence critical science is inevitably and essentially political. Its style of politics is not that of the modern mass movements or even that of 'pressure groups' representing a particular constituency with a distinct set of interests; it is more like the politics of the Enlightenment, where a small minority uses reason, argument, and a mixture of political tactics to arouse a public concern on matters of human welfare. The opponents of critical science will usually be bureaucratic institutions which try to remain faceless, pushing their tame experts, and hired advocates and image-projectors, into the line of battle; although occasionally a very distinguished man is exposed as more irresponsible than he would care to admit.

In the struggles for the exposure and correction of practices damaging to humanity and the environment, the role of the state is ambiguous. On the one hand, every modern government is committed in principle to the protection of the health of its people and the conservation of its natural resources. But many of the agencies committing the worst outrages are state institutions, especially the military; and in any event the powerful interests which derive profit or convenience from polluting and degrading the environment have more political and economic power than a scattering of 'conservationists'. It sometimes occurs that two state agencies will be on opposite sides of an environmental struggle; but the natural tendency of regulatory agencies to come under the control of those they are supposed to regulate can make such a struggle a one-sided affair.

The presence of an effective critical science is naturally an embarrassment to the leadership of the responsible, industrialized, tame scientific establishment. Their natural (and sincere) reaction is to accuse the critics of being negative and irresponsible; and their defensive slogan is along the lines of 'technology creates problems, which technology can solve'. This is not strictly true in all cases, since nothing will solve the problems of the children already killed or deformed by radioactive fall-out or by the drug thalidomide. Moreover, this claim carries the implication that 'technology' is an autonomous and self-correcting process. This is patent nonsense. We have already seen that a new device is produced and diffused only if it performs certain functions whereby human purposes can be served; and if the intended beneficiaries do not appreciate its use, or if those injured by its working can stop it, the device will be stillborn. The distortions of technological development arise when the only effective 'purposes' in the situation are those of the people who believe themselves to derive pure benefit from the innovation. On the self-correcting tendency of technology, one might argue that no large and responsible institution would continue harmful practices once they had been recognized; but this generalization is analogous to the traditional denial of the cruelty of slavery, along the lines that no sensible man would maltreat such valuable pieces of property. And the history of the struggles for public health and against pollution, from their inception to the present, shows that the guilty institutions and groups of people will usually fight by every means available to prevent their immediate interests being sacrificed to some unproven public benefit. If the campaigns waged by critical science come to touch on some issue central to the convenience of the state or other very powerful institutions, we may yet experience a polarization of the community of natural science, along the same lines as occurred on the Vietnam issue in some of the human sciences in America. In such a situation, it will not be possible for a leader of science to be both honest and tame; and if an establishment within science chooses to serve its paymasters rather than truth, it will be recognizably corrupt.

Such extreme situations may be a long time in developing, if for nothing else than that critical science is still in its infancy. As it develops, it will be at risk of encountering many pitfalls, partly those characteristic of immature sciences applied to practical problems, and partly those of radical and reforming political movements. Perhaps the most obvious will be an accretion of cranks and congenital rebels, whose reforming zeal is not matched by their scientific skill. But there are others, arising from the contradictory relations between critical science and the relevant established institutions of society. As true intellectuals rather than a technical intelligentsia, individual members may find some sinecures within the interstices of bureaucratized intellectual systems; but there will need to be some institutions providing a home for the nucleus of each school, and external sources of funds for research. Hence, especially as critical science grows in size and influence and society becomes more sophisticated about the problems of runaway technology, some accommodation between the critics and the criticized will inevitably develop. We can even expect to see critical research being supported, critical slogans being echoed, and leaders of critical science being rewarded by institutions whose basic destructive policies still are unchanged. Such phenomena have already occurred in the USA, in the politics of race; and on this issue, where the interests concerned are mainly major institutions which can hire talented and enlightened experts at will, it is even more likely. The movement of critical science would then face the pitfalls of corruption as soon as, or even before, it had skirted those of impotence. But this is only a natural process, characteristic of all radical movements. It is easy to maintain one's integrity when one's words and actions are ineffective; but a long period of this can produce a sectarian or a crank. If one begins to achieve power, and one's policies affect the interests of many others, one must decide where one's responsibility lies. If it is to the ideal alone, then one is set on a course towards tyranny, until overthrown by the host of enemies one has raised up. And if one accepts responsibility for the maintenance of a general welfare, including that of one's opponents, one is on the path to corruption and impotence. This may seem a gloomy prognosis: but a society which does not present such hazards to radical movements of every sort is not likely to retain its stability; and a radical movement which cannot resolve such contradictions does not deserve to succeed. I see no reason why critical science should be less exposed to them than to any other reforming movement.

A cautionary tale that should be read by all who are embarking on political activism based on 'critical science' is the play by Ibsen, *The Enemy of the People*. Superficially, it is about an honest doctor who is hated by the corrupt forces of his town for his determination to expose the scandal of polluted waters being used in the town's profitable baths, as a result of economies in their construction. But on closer reading, it can be seen that Dr Stockmann's misfortunes were also due to his own naivety and egoism. I found it significant that in his own version of the play (Viking Press, New York, 1951) Arthur Miller strengthened its 'progressive' message by transposing the passage where the town meeting declares Dr Stockmann to be 'an enemy of the people'. In Miller's version it comes at the very beginning of the meeting, before he has spoken; in the original it comes after the Doctor's harangue, concluding with

'Let the whole country perish, let all these people be exterminated'. It is true that he had been goaded by implacable enemies and false friends until he reached this extreme position; but the reaction of the town in the original version is then not a simple case of McCarthyism. After studying the play with a class at Harvard, where this modification was discovered, I was struck by the idea that a worthwhile sequel could be written, entitled 'The People's Friend', in which the entrenched forces, if only a bit less stupid and venal than in the original, could corrupt the good Doctor without difficulty. I recall being told later that scientific tests of the sort that convinced Dr Stockmann of the pollution of the baths are themselves far from conclusive.

We can expect, then, that the future political history of critical science will be as complex and perhaps as tortured as that of any successful radical and reforming movement. But if it does survive the pitfalls of maturation, and so contributes to the survival of our species, it can also make a very important contribution to the development of science itself. For if the style of critical science, imposed by the very nature of its problems, becomes incorporated into a coherent philosophy of science, it will provide the basis for a transformation of scientific inquiry as deep as that which occurred in early modern Europe. The problems, the methods and the objects of inquiry of a matured and coherent critical science will be very different from those of academic science or technology as they have developed up to now; and together they can provide a practical foundation for a new conception of humanity in its relations with itself and the rest of nature.

The work of inquiry in critical science involves an awareness of craft skills at all levels, and the conscious effort of mastering new skills. The data are obtained in a great variety of ways, from the laboratory, from the field, and from searching through a varied literature, not all of it in the public domain. Much of it lacks soundness, and all of it requires sophisticated and imaginative treatment before it can function as information. Indeed, since the problem-situations are presented in the environment, and much of the crucial data must be produced under controlled conditions in the laboratory, work in critical science may overcome the dichotomy between field-work and lab-work which has developed in science, even in the biological fields, over the past century. In the later phases of investigations of problems, the same challenges of variety and novelty will always be present. The establishment of the strength and fit of each particular piece of evidence is a problem in itself; and the objects of inquiry (including the measures of various effects and processes, as well as conventional standards of acceptability in practice) are so patently artificial that there should be little danger of critical scientists' being encased in them as a world of common sense. The establishment of effective criteria of adequacy for solved problems is possible, for the work will frequently be an extension and combination of established fields to new problems, and so critical science can hopefully escape the worst perils of immaturity. Also, any critical publication is bound to be scrutinized severely by experts on the other side, so high standards of quality are required because of the political context of the work. Indeed, a completely solved problem in critical science is more demanding than in either pure science or technology. In the former, it is usually sufficient to obtain a conclusion about those properties of the artificial objects of inquiry which can be derived from data obtained in the controlled conditions of experiment; in the latter it is sufficient for an artificial device to perform its functions without undue disturbance by its natural environment; while here the complex webs of causation between and within the artificial and natural systems must be understood sufficiently so that their harmony can be maintained.

The social aspects of inquiry in critical science are also conducive to the maintenance of its health and vitality, at least until such times as the response to its challenge becomes over-sophisticated. The ultimate purpose which governs the work is the protection of the welfare of humanity as a part of nature; and this is neither remote, nor vulgar. Critical science cannot be a permanent home for careerists and entrepreneurs of the ordinary sort; although it may well use the services of bright young people intending eventually to serve as enlightened experts. Those who want safe, routine work for the achievement of eminence by accumulation will not find its atmosphere congenial; its inquiries are set by a succession of problem-situations, each presenting new challenges and difficulties. Hence although critical science will doubtless experience its periods of turbulence, both political and scientific, it is well protected from stagnation and from the sort of creeping corruption that can easily come to afflict industrialized science.

Finally, the objects of inquiry of critical science will inevitably become different from those of traditional pure science or technology, for here the relation of the scientist to the external world is so fundamentally different. In traditional pure mathematical—experimental natural science, the external world is a passive object to be analysed, and only the more simple and abstract properties of the things and events are capable of study. In technology, the reactions of the uncontrolled real world on a constructed device must be taken into account, but only as perturbations of an ideal system; the task is to manipulate it or to shield the device from its effects. But when the problem is to achieve a harmonious interaction between man and nature, the real world must be treated with respect: both as a complex and subtle system in its own right, and as a heritage of which we are temporary stewards for future generations. Hence, even though studies of our interaction with the environment will necessarily use all the intellectually constructed apparatus of disciplined inquiry, their status and their content will inevitably be modified. They will be more easily recognized as imperfect tools, with which we attempt to live in harmony with the real world around us; and although this attitude may seem conducive to scepticism, it will be the healthy one which recognizes that genuine knowledge arises from lengthy social experience, and that such knowledge depends for its existence on the continued survival of our civilization. The objects of enquiry themselves will include final causes among their essential attributes, not merely the limited functions appropriate to

317

technology, but also the judgements of fitness and success already developed in classical biology and ecology. All this is work for the future; but if it is successful, the opposition between scientific knowledge and human concerns, characteristic of the sciences derived from the dehumanized natural philosophy of the seventeenth century, will be overcome.

Postscript, nearly two decades on: When I first wrote the above section, I knew and said that critical science was in its infancy; and the institutions where it was fostered were, and would be, scattered and vulnerable. There is still no settled institutional form, nor a large organization, created around this concept. Whether the eventual transformation of science, should it occur, explicitly takes this form, is of little concern to me. In my more recent essays I have concentrated on various aspects of what needs to be done, rather than calling for a particular form of campaign. This is because I believe that what will come cannot be hurried, and I would rather devote my energies to understanding what is to come, than spending them on a special-interest advocacy.

If I were to revise the above text significantly, it would be in connection with a remark about industrialized science, near the beginning of the section. There I mentioned crises in recruitment and morale as a contingency that was outside my analysis; and now I believe that these will need to be confronted quite directly by anyone who is concerned for the health and indeed the survival of industrialized science in our part of the world. I sense that over the next two decades the triumphalist ideology of science, with which I grew up and which in its philosophical and political expressions provided me with a great intellectual challenge, may pass into oblivion. What will happen to technology, to education, to the conduct of research in other disciplines, and other learned activities that have taken science for their model is far beyond the scope of this comment. But we may expect that then the blanketing scientific orthodoxy of the present will have become enfeebled and confused; and for a generation who have grown up with Greenpeace as we grew up with the Bomb, the world-view of critical science may become a commonplace. Its own divergent and contradictory tendencies will then have full play; and the challenges presented by critical science to the established order will be presented explicitly and reacted to as such; until eventually a new equilibrium, with its new latent contradictions, may be achieved. All this is speculation, which may yet mock me when I read it later; but my account would be incomplete without this personal glimpse into an unknowable future.

Adapted from the Conclusion of *Scientific Knowledge and Its Social Problems*, Oxford University Press, 1971.

Epilogue:
Science and Charity

In the study of the history of science, we are no longer embarrassed by the presence of styles of work that are very different from the one defined by the 'disenchantment and dehumanization' of Nature, which has been dominant since the Scientific Revolution of the seventeenth century. Among all the varied currents in the endeavour to understand and control the natural world, we can identify an alternative philosophy that has provided a vehicle for a politically radical folk-science that challenges the dominant, bureaucratized science of its time. In this tradition, the study of nature is explicitly seen as a social and also spiritual act; one dialogues rather than analyses; and there is no protective cover of belief in the 'neutrality' or 'objectivity' of one's work. Such a philosophy of nature becomes articulated and advanced, as part of a general reaction against the formal, dry style that pervades the official version of the activity. There is an analogous tendency in religion, and indeed the two sometimes interact. Looking back into history, we can find an affinity of doctrine or style, and sometimes a linking tradition, as far back as the Taoists of ancient China, through St Francis of Assisi, to Paracelsus, William Blake and the 'counter-culture' prophets of the 1960s.

Not every one of these figures would claim to be a natural scientist of any description; but as philosophers, poets or prophets they must be recognized as participating in and shaping a tradition of a certain perception of nature and its relation to man. Granted all the variety of their messages and styles, certain themes recur. One is the 'romantic' striving for immediacy, of contact with the living things themselves rather than with book-learned descriptions. Another is 'philanthropy'; the quest is not for a private realization, but for the benefit of all men and nature. And related to these is a radical criticism of existing institutions, their rules and their personel. Looked at from the outside, each upward thrust of the romantic philosophy of nature is doomed to failure. Mankind will not be transfigured overnight; and the romantic style has its own destructive contradictions. Whereas the 'classic' style degenerates gradually into an ossified form and a sterile content, the 'romantic' style goes off much more quickly, through chaos of form and corruption of content. But even in disciplined scientific inquiry, the categories of 'success' and 'failure' are neither so absolutely opposed, nor so assuredly assignable in particular cases, as the traditional ideology of science assumed. And the failure to achieve Utopian dreams, in science as well as in social reform, is not at all the same thing as futility.

The dreams of the romantic, philanthropic philosopher-prophets cannot move towards realization by the accumulation of facts or of battalions. Rather, they exist through a discontinuous, perhaps erratic, series of crises and responses. Sometimes they have the good fortune of producing a creative tension in a man brave enough to attempt the synthesis of a prophet's vision with a world managed by priests. He too will fail, almost certainly; some problems are insoluble. But this message, perhaps in a particular science or walk of life, perhaps of a generalized wisdom, will speak to men in later ages, coming alive whenever it has insights to offer. In this present period, we may find Francis Bacon speaking to us more than Descartes the metaphysician-geometer or Galileo the engineer-cosmologist. As deeply as any of his pietistic, alchemical forerunners, he felt the love of God's creation, the pity for the sufferings of man, and the striving for innocence, humility, and charity; and he recognized vanity as the deadliest of sins. To this last he ascribed the evil state of the arts and sciences.

> For we copy the sin of our first parents while we suffer for it. They wished to be like God, but their posterity wish to be even greater. For we create worlds, we direct and dominere over nature, we will have it that all things *are* as in our folly we think they should be, not as seems fittest to the Divine wisdom, or as they are found to be in fact.

The punishment for all this, as Bacon saw it, was ignorance and impotence. It might seem that the problem is different now, for we have so much scientific knowledge and merely face the task of applying it for good rather than evil. But Bacon assumed his readers to believe themselves in possession of great knowledge; and much of his writing was devoted to disabusing them of this illusion. Perhaps the daily reports of 'insufficient knowledge' of the effects of this or that aspect of the rape of the earth, and our sense of insufficient under-standing of what our social and spiritual crises are all about, indicate that in spite of the magnificent edifice of genuine scientific knowledge bequeathed to us, we are only at the beginning of learning the things, and the ways, necessary for the human life.

Bacon was a shrewd man, fully sensitive to the weaknesses of the human intellect and spirit. He was aware of the superficiality of ordinary thought and discourse, at whatever educational level; and he also distrusted the extraordi-nary enthusiast, in religion or politics, for the damage he could cause. His life's endeavour was to overcome this contradiction somehow, and to bring about a true and effective reformation in the arts and sciences of nature. For him, this was a holy work, a work of practical charity inseparable from spiritual

320

redemption. His audience was inevitably among the literate; and so he tried, by scattering hints and half-concealed invitations, to call together his brothers, who would gently and silently show by their example that a good and pure way into Nature is also the practically effective way. Of course he failed, in his philosophical reform as in his political career. There was no English audience for his particular message during his lifetime, and at his death he was alone and neglected.

Shortly after his death, however, there was a stirring; and Bacon's message of 'philanthropic' science began a career of its own. For a while, his followers knew what he was about; but with the passage of decades and disillusion, this was forgotten, and only the vulgar fact-finding Bacon survived. Yet when we now come back to read Bacon, perplexed and worried as we are by the sudden transformation that science has wrought upon itself as well as upon the world, we can find relevance in passages like the following:

> Lastly, I would address one general admonition to all; that they consider what are the true ends of knowledge, and that they seek it not either for pleasure of mind, or for contention, or for superiority to others, or for profit, or fame, or power, or any of these inferior things; but for the benefit and use of life; and that they perfect and govern it in charity. For it was from lust of power that the angels fell, from lust of knowledge that men fell; but of charity there can be no excess, neither did angel or man ever come in danger by it.

Adapted from the concluding pages of *Scientific Knowledge and Its Social Problems*, Oxford University Press, 1971; full references will be found there.

Index

Compiled by Sara Firman.

absolutism 292, 299
academic science 10, 270
activism 62, 70, 115, 234, 294–8
  environmental 28–9, 40, 70, 297,
    306, 308–9
  NIMBY campaigns 28, 49, 71, 89,
    295, 308
  special-issue campaigns 28, 295, 308
Adler, A. 184
agriculture 18, 99
alchemy 105, 114, 117, 130, 140
alternative medicine 29, 220, 222, 234,
  294–5, 296, 297, 309–10
alternative science 234, 294–8, 301,
  308–10
alternative technology 28, 305, 308
Andromeda strain, see recombinant
  DNA research
applied science 26, 293
appropriate technology, see alternative
  technology
Aristophanes 98, 137–8
Aristotelian philosophy 102, 105, 107,
  108, 110, 113, 140, 188–9
astrology 105, 114, 184
astronomy 102, 108, 113, 185
atomic science 264–6
atomism 106–7, 140, 219, 222

Bacon, F. 97–8, 101–7 passim, 113,
  116–36, 139, 140, 160, 161, 260,
  301–2, 320–1
basic science 26, 289
Berg, P., and DNA debate 67, 69, 70,
  71
Bernal, J.D. 98, 142, 153–73, 282

'big' science 145, 163, 267
biology 63, 108, 141, 169, 285
Brenner, S., and DNA debate 70, 77
British Society for Social Responsibility
  in Science 143, 308
bureaucracies 16, 28, 45–7, 85–7,
  146–7, 162, 164, 289, 313

capitalism 111, 112, 120, 161, 168, 169;
  see also consumerism; materialism
charisma-industry 201–2, 205–6, 209
charity 23, 98, 131, 132, 320; see also
  human welfare; philanthropic
  science
chemistry 110, 143, 171
China,
  feng shui 22
  social system 28, 207–9, 299
choice 146, 223, 267–8, 270
Clark, B. 277, 281
commercial science 10, 16, 83, 85, 157,
  285, 287
Commoner, B. 305, 313
complementarity 243, 244, 258
complementary medicine, see alternative
  medicine
consumerism 178, 199–210, 304, 305;
  see also capitalism; materialism
contradiction, see dialectics
Copernican theory 101–2, 107, 108,
  116, 213, 264
corpuscular philosophy 105, 108, 111,
  170
corruption 89, 91–2, 145, 155, 203, 315
cosmology 12, 13, 17, 20–2

counter-culture 22, 118, 141, 143, 194, 304, 307, 319
craftsmanship ix, 80, 103, 117, 145, 226, 286, 291, 306, 316
creationism 98, 144
critical science ix, 62, 306, 312–18
criticisms 14, 80, 98, 137–51, 144
cultural differences 18–22, 114–15, 200–2, 211–12

Darwinism 17, 107, 141, 144, 213, 303
data,
    for critical science 316
    lack of 38, 45, 148
decision-making 48, 51, 238–9, 272, 272–4, 279
dehumanization 97, 103, 104–5, 112, 115
democracy 16, 155, 291
Descartes, R. 101–9 passim, 113, 114, 119, 139, 242, 244, 264, 301–2, 320
dialectics x, 13
    and history 20–1
    and materialism 172
    and poverty 18, 19
    and society 23
    of success 280–1
    and truth 23
    see also complementarity
disenchantment 97, 103, 104–5, 106, 112, 115, 168, 169
DNA helix controversy 71
dogmatism 140, 157, 158, 181, 184, 185

ecology 2, 118, 159–60; see also Gaia hypothesis
education 1, 2, 15, 17, 27, 46, 52, 140, 234, 271, 293, 298
Einstein, A. 184, 185, 253–4, 285, 303–4
élitism 16, 40, 64, 98, 103, 112, 113, 114, 140, 146, 293, 298
empirical research 116, 117
engineering 53–4, 265, 279, 293
Enlightenment 101, 109, 118, 140–1, 157, 166, 181, 186, 196
entrepreneurial science 147
environmental activism 28–9, 40, 70, 297, 306, 308–9
environmental assessment, total 273–4, 275
environmental politics 307
environmental (biospheric) problems 1, 10, 12, 15, 39, 82, 94, 97, 115, 159–60, 237, 238, 260–83 passim, 287, 314; see also Gaia hypothesis
epistemology, see knowledge
errors 22, 148, 271; see also human errors; scientists, fallibility
ethics (morality) ix, 16, 104, 119, 146, 226–7, 287
    and consumerism 206–9
    and DNA debate 73
    F. Bacon's views 121, 124, 133
    J.D. Bernal's views 160–2
    and nuclear weaponry 81, 155
    and risk 55, 58
European civilization 7, 18–30, 100, 112, 260–1
European science 18–30
experimental science 110
experimental–mathematical science 107, 113, 317

facts 1, 25, 32, 98, 156, 177, 267, 271, 274
false beliefs 15
falsifiability 148, 183, 185
fault trees 37, 38
Faustian view of science 14, 69, 142, 306
feasibility 268
feminist movements 89, 110, 308, 309
Feyerabend, P. 178, 187, 192–5, 196, 243, 304–5, 306
fraud 226, 305
Freud, S. 184, 185, 213
Funtowicz, S.O. 233

Gaia hypothesis 178, 211–21
Galileo 101–7 passim, 111–14 passim, 116–19 passim, 139, 166, 168, 193, 236, 242, 264, 301, 302, 320
games theory 93, 228
Gemeinschaft 18, 141, 210
genetic manipulation, see recombinant DNA research
Genetic Manipulation Advisory Group x, 63, 75–8
Gesellschaft 18
GIGO science 196
GMAG, see Genetic Manipulation Advisory Group

heuristics 191, 196, 223
hierarchy 54, 292, 299

holism 141
human behaviour and safety control
    55−7, 60−1
human errors 35, 37, 46, 55, 60; *see
    also* morale; scientists, fallibility
human judgements 45, 236
human values 13, 223, 271, 274
human welfare 12, 13, 14−15, 23, 163,
    223, 313; *see also* charity;
    philanthropic science
Huxley, A. 143

Ibn Khaldun 178, 199−210
ideology 102−9, 180−98, 301−2
ignorance 1, 22, 37, 215−18, 225, 233,
    245, 260−83, 306
Illich, I. 19, 21, 194, 305
individualism 21, 23−4, 207
inductive philosophy 119
industrialized science ix, 1, 7, 10, 74,
    143, 146, 147, 286−7, 303, 306,
    312
institutions, of science 162, 163, 172,
    178, 318
interdisciplinary collaboration 233,
    262−3, 266
international science 74, 162, 233, 280

knowledge (epistemology) 112, 128, 196,
    215−18, 222, 236, 245, 260−83,
    286−7, 306
Kuhn, T.S. 178, 186−9, 192, 218, 234,
    243, 265, 292, 304, 306

Lakatos, I. 144, 177, 178, 180, 186,
    187, 189−92, 196
logic ix, 22, 93, 94, 178, 182
logical positivism 178, 183, 196, 244,
    304
LULU plans 49, 71, 308

Mach, E. 183, 303
magic 22, 103, 105, 106, 110, 113−15,
    117, 138−9, 140, 201
management 156, 287; *see also* risk
    management
Marxism 98, 103, 110−11, 120, 142−3,
    145−6, 153−73, 184−5, 299, 303,
    308
Mason, S.F. 167, 170
material prosperity 14−15, 24, 25, 100
materialism 94, 172, 182; *see also*
    capitalism; consumerism

materialistic scientism 141, 142
mathematics 21, 52, 103−4, 106, 108,
    109, 111, 113, 117, 118, 139, 180,
    186, 190, 191, 196, 303; *see also*
    quantitative information
mechanical science 108, 120, 121, 140,
    169
media 218−19, 237, 275, 289, 297, 308
    and DNA debate 72, 78, 79, 80
    and poverty 19
    and risk 61−2
medicine 17, 158−9, 169, 194, 264, 265,
    313; *see also* alternative medicine
Merton, R.K. 144, 146, 161, 306
metaphysics 20, 21, 22, 29, 30, 105,
    110, 117, 119, 181, 219−20, 229,
    242
microbiological hazards 65−80
military science 10, 16, 81−94, 287; *see
    also* nuclear weaponry
mission-orientated science 26
morale 55, 203−6, 210, 307, 312, 318
morality, *see* ethics
mysticism 117, 118, 142, 172, 201

Needham, J. 164−5, 171
neutrality of science 146, 319
NIMBY campaigns 28, 49, 71, 89, 295,
    308
'normal' science 187, 218, 234, 265, 292
novelty 104
nuclear power 164, 225, 306
    and risk 31−58 *passim*
nuclear wastes 217
nuclear weaponry 8−9, 63, 81−94, 106,
    155, 162, 228−9, 305
numerical analysis 239
NUSAP notational system 235−9

objectivity 17, 25−6, 28, 64, 172, 224,
    319
occult sciences 13, 14
ontology, *see* reality

Paracelsian philosophy 130, 132, 140
philanthropic science 15, 23, 319−21;
    see also charity; human welfare
philosophy 81, 177, 180−98, 236
    Aristotelian 101, 105, 107, 108, 110,
        113, 140, 188−9
    corpuscular 105, 108, 111, 170
    and counter-culture 304
    English movement 24

and F. Bacon 116−36
and Gaia hypothesis 211−12
inductive 119
organismic 142
Paracelsian 130, 132, 140
and risks debates 64
physics 52, 63, 81, 142, 167, 180, 243,
    244, 254, 285
plagiarism 178, 226, 305
Polanyi, M. 144, 162, 292, 306
policy decisions, and risk 32, 34, 36, 37
policy-science 12, 26−7, 144−7, 151,
    236−9, 267, 269−76, 296
politics 16, 24, 28−9, 144−7, 293
    and critical science 313, 315, 316
    and risk 33, 41, 43, 46, 48, 57−9, 64
Popper, K. 148, 178, 181, 183−6,
    187−92 passim, 196, 219, 292,
    303−4
poverty 18−20, 223
power 24, 102, 103, 105, 146, 158, 168,
    172, 222, 286−7, 292
practical science 296, 297
probability, in risk 33, 34−5, 36, 42−3
propaganda 118, 144−7, 271, 303, 306
pseudo-sciences 103, 184, 185, 196
public information 2, 26, 80, 219, 307
    on risk 52, 65, 67
    see also propaganda
public interest representation 76, 78
public perceptions 1, 13, 99, 177, 275,
    288−90, 294−8, 312−13
    and DNA debate 71
    of nuclear weapons systems 84−5
    of risk 40−53
pure science 25, 27, 111, 145, 146, 223,
    270, 286−7, 289, 293
puzzle-solving 187−8, 234, 304

quality assessment 145−6, 233, 276−7,
    281, 312
quality control ix, x, 8, 162, 178,
    203−6, 219, 226, 233, 266−7, 305
    and nuclear weapons systems 85−9
    and risk 32, 62
quantitative information 180, 235−9
    on uncertainties 31

rationality 13, 169, 170, 182−3, 184,
    195
reality (ontology) 17, 22, 82, 94,
    219−20, 302
recombinant DNA research 8, 51, 61,
    63−80, 147

reductionism 17, 29, 141, 236
regulatory science 26, 197
religion 13, 20, 21, 106, 111, 182,
    195−6, 201, 319
    and DNA debate 72
    and F. Bacon 98, 121, 124, 130, 132
    and J.D. Bernal 153, 157, 167
research 2, 25, 116, 117, 156−7,
    162−3, 218, 262, 267, 291−2, 313
research funding 27, 146, 163, 285, 307
research monitoring 66
research projects 137
Rifkin, J., and DNA debate 72−3, 75
risk assessment 8, 32−40, 70
risk management 8, 33, 39, 47, 48, 51
    failure 49
    as social process 59−62
    US v. British styles 65, 75−8
risk monitoring 278−80
risk regulation 8, 51, 60, 70, 78, 80
risk research 31, 32−3, 76
risk triangle 32, 59−62
risks 8, 235, 238−9
    imposition of 32, 48, 57−8
    in recombinant DNA research 64, 66
Romanticism 140−2, 143, 319−20
Rose, H. 146, 172
Rose, S. 146, 172
Rosicrucianism 119, 139
Royal Society (London) 105, 116, 289

safety 34, 44
    control systems 53−7, 75−8
    standards 67, 70, 77
Schumacher, E.F. 20, 143, 305, 309
science,
    basic v. applied 26−7, 261, 270, 293
    basic v. pure 289
    as civilizing process 16
    limitations of 1, 10−11, 12, 15, 53,
        284−5
'science for the people' 28, 293, 299
scientific community 133, 150, 161,
    162, 163, 237, 292
scientific discovery 297
scientific inquiry 10, 11, 319
scientific method 104, 109, 116, 148,
    158
scientific revolution 97, 100−15
    and European culture 21−2
scientists 97, 146, 148, 307, 312,
    312−13
    as businessmen 74
    conflicting roles 1, 150

scientists – *contd*
  fallibility 16, 27, 39, 45–6, 47, 51,
    66, 91–2, 148–9, 178, 226–7, 296,
    305; *see also* human errors
  as politicians 144
  recruitment 16, 307, 312, 318
  social roles 145
secrecy 75, 78, 227
social contract, for science 284–300
social oppression 168, 169
society and science ix, 1–2, 9, 10–11,
    23–8, 43, 146–7, 209
Soviet science 142–3, 205
statistics 224–5, 236, 238, 241
superstition 21, 157, 185, 201
Swift, J. 108, 140, 158, 302
Szilard, L. 69, 145, 147

technological errors 225–6
technological risks 44–7
technology 112, 113, 117, 201; *see also*
    alternative technology
techno-positivism 146
theology, *see* religion
Third World,
  and nuclear power 37, 57

and scientific–cultural imperialism
    19, 169
trade unions 61, 76, 78
'trans-science' 16, 34, 45, 47, 52, 196,
    263, 306
truth ix, 15–16, 18–19, 22–3, 104, 189

uncertainties 1, 8, 31, 36–7, 233,
    237–9
universities 26, 71, 140, 296

verificationism 149, 184
Vienna Circle 181–4, 244, 304
vitalism 108, 141

war 25, 112–13, 157, 171; *see also*
    nuclear weaponry
waste disposal 50, 56, 215–18
Weinberg, A. 145; *see also*
    'trans-science'
Western science, *see* European science

Zuckerman, Sir S. (Lord Zuckerman),
    and nuclear weapons systems 89,
    155, 162, 228